THE NUCLEAR FUEL CYCLE

THE NUCLEAR FUEL CYCLE

Nicholas Tsoulfanidis, Ph.D.

American Nuclear Society
La Grange Park, Illinois USA

Library of Congress Cataloging-in-Publication Data

Tsoulfanidis, Nicholas, 1938–
  The nuclear fuel cycle / Nicholas Tsoulfanidis, Ph.D.
  pages cm
  Includes bibliographical references and index.
  ISBN 978-0-89448-460-5
  1. Nuclear fuels. 2. Nuclear fuels—Management. 3. Nuclear fuels—Generation of
electricity. I. Title.
  TK9360.C53 2013
  621.48'335—dc23

2012035082

ISBN: 978-0-89448-460-5
Library of Congress Catalogue Card Number: 2012035082
ANS Order Number: 350024

© 2013 American Nuclear Society
555 North Kensington Avenue
La Grange Park, Illinois 60526 USA

Editorial and production: Quantum Publishing Services, Inc.,
Bellingham, WA, USA
Typography: Beljan Ltd., Dexter, MI, USA
Printed in the United States of America

CONTENTS

Chapter 3   Conversion and Enrichment

Chapter 4   Fuel Design and Fabrication

Chapter 5   Reactor Physics Calculations

Chapter 8   Electric Utility and Nuclear Power Economics

Chapter 9   High-Level Waste Management

Chapter 10   LLW Management and Decommissioning of Nuclear Facilities

Chapter 11   Nuclear Nonproliferation and Safeguards

Chapter 12   Environmental Effects from the Generation of Electricity

PREFACE

A book titled *The Nuclear Fuel Cycle: Analysis and Management* was first published in 1990. It was co-authored by me and the late Dr. Robert G. Cochran. A second edition appeared in 1999. During these 20-plus years, many aspects of the nuclear fuel cycle have changed, hence this present attempt to look again at the topic and make changes, additions, and corrections as needed. I am sure Dr. Cochran would wholeheartedly agree with this new approach.

This book is intended primarily as a college text for a one-semester course offered at the senior or first-year graduate school level. Secondarily, the book serves as a reference for practicing engineers in the nuclear field. The assumption is that the reader has a background in college physics, chemistry, and mathematics as well as basic nuclear engineering concepts.

All of the processes involved in the nuclear fuel cycle—from "cradle to grave"—are discussed in detail. Chapter 1 presents an introduction and overview of this enterprise. Chapter 2 provides information about nuclear fuel resources and methods of extracting them from the ground and transforming them into chemical compounds ready for the next step. Chapter 3 discusses the topics of conversion and enrichment, two processes necessary for the current fuel cycle used by the nuclear industry. Chapter 4 deals with materials used to make nuclear fuel, types of nuclear fuels, and manufacturing of those fuels.

Chapter 5 provides a general review of reactor physics; the objective is to provide information about basic principles and approximations of the computer codes used by engineers involved in nuclear fuel management. In-core fuel management is presented in Chapter 6. Topics discussed include core loading patterns, length and extension of fuel cycles, and refueling activities. Although the title of this book includes the words *fuel cycle*, the current practices of the nuclear industry, called the "once-through fuel cycle," do not complete the cycle; how the fuel cycle can be closed is described in Chapter 7 in which reprocessing and recycling are treated.

Basic economic principles, as they pertain to electric utilities are presented in Chapter 8. Only general principles are given, since a detailed calculation of electricity costs depends on the accounting practices of the particular utility.

Nuclear fuel does not disappear after it is used, unfortunately. It remains radioactive for a long period of time. In addition, radioactive materials are produced during all steps of the fuel cycle. Radioactive materials must be stored or disposed properly—isolated from the biosphere. Chapters 9 and 10 deal with the proper management of radioactive wastes.

Chapter 11 about nuclear safeguards is new to this book. We live in a world in which nuclear weapons are owned by just a few countries, and the possibility exists that rogue nations or groups may misuse nuclear materials to make additional weapons. It is in the interest of all people on our planet to make sure that nuclear materials are used for peaceful purposes only. The international policies having to do with safeguarding nuclear materials are the topic of Chapter 11.

The final chapter, Chapter 12, describes the pros and cons of the various methods of generating electricity. There is no "free lunch" in terms of providing for society's energy needs; that is, any method of producing electricity has some effects that are detrimental to people and the environment. The task of a civilized society is to select the most environmentally benign methods such that the total environmental effect on the earth can be minimized.

Writing a book on this topic presents a unique challenge because parts of the fuel cycle stay essentially the same (mining, conversion, enrichment, fuel manufacturing), whereas others keep changing (materials used for fuel, management of used fuel and of radioactive wastes, economics, government policies, etc.). My objective was to provide to the reader the latest data, techniques, computing methods, and policies and regulations as they existed in 2012.

I am grateful to Larry Foulke, Larry Miller, and Jim Tulenko who served as the American Nuclear Society's technical review committee for this book.

Nicholas Tsoulfanidis
November 2012

ONE

REVIEW OF THE NUCLEAR FUEL CYCLE

1.1 General Comments

Nuclear energy is used throughout the world. The nuclear industry is international, perhaps more so than most of the other "traditional" industries. The international status of nuclear energy stems not so much from the fact that as of this writing (2012), there are 441 operating power reactors and 66 under construction in many different countries (104 are operating in the United States, with two under construction), but from the fact that governments are heavily involved in the management and operations of the nuclear industry. Government involvement manifests itself in regulations, in political decisions regarding the exploration or importation of nuclear facilities or of nuclear fuels, and in the form of international agreements to safeguard nuclear materials to stop the proliferation of nuclear weapons.

An international agency has been created for the sole purpose of regulating and controlling the international nuclear activities of its membership—the International Atomic Energy Agency (IAEA), headquartered in Vienna, Austria. Established in 1957, the agency assists its members with the formation of international agreements such as the Nuclear Non-Proliferation Treaty (NPT). The IAEA has played a role in the policy decisions of many countries. Two examples are (1) Australia's policy regarding uranium exports and (2) the U.S. restrictions on the export of fuels to countries that have not signed the NPT.

This international flavor of the nuclear industry is the result of two factors. The first is the similarity of peaceful nuclear activities to those used for the production of nuclear weapons. The second is the realization that in the event of an accident, released radiation will probably cross international borders, as demonstrated by the 1986 accident at Chernobyl in the Ukraine. Of course, chemical spills that disperse into the atmosphere will do the same, but the reaction of people and governments to radiation is always different from that for any other potential pollutant.

1

The nuclear fuel cycle, as we understand it today, refers to all of the activities related to the use of fissile materials as the fuel in fission reactors. Fission reactors, constructed and operated for the first time in the 1940s, are being used today for the generation of electricity (primarily), for the propulsion of naval ships, for research, and for the production of radioisotopes for medical and other uses. All of the reactors operating today, with the exception of a very few research reactors, use uranium as the nuclear fuel. In addition to uranium, one could use thorium and its breeding product ^{233}U, or plutonium, the breeding product of ^{238}U. In this book, the reserves of both uranium and thorium are addressed; however, only the detailed uses of uranium are discussed, most of which would apply to thorium as well.

One special characteristic of nuclear fuel that makes it quite different from fossil fuels is that nuclear fuel is on the books of a utility for a long period of time. Coal, oil, and gas are purchased, stored for a relatively short period (e.g., there may be a supply of coal on hand for 3 months of operation at the plant site), burned, and removed from the books. Of course, the inventory of coal at a fossil plant is continuous in order to take care of shipment irregularities caused by weather, mining, shipping, and labor strikes. State utility commissions usually limit coal supply costs in the rate base to about 90 days. Nuclear fuel, by contrast, has a much longer book life. Typically, a fuel manager will start working on the purchase of new fuel about 2 years before refueling is scheduled. The newly fabricated fuel arrives on site about 2 months before it is needed. It is then burned in the reactor and produces energy for 3 to 5 years. After the fuel is discharged from the core, the current practice is to store it on site for many years prior to disposal off site. Throughout this period, the company is responsible for the fuel and, obviously, carries it on the books. This extremely lengthy accounting period for a commodity is quite different from any other "burnable" material that a utility, or any other industry, had to handle before nuclear power came into the picture. As a result of this nuclear fuel longevity, some special accounting methods had to be developed. Not only have the accounting methods been modified, but ownership of the fuel can belong to some entity other than the utility, such as banks and subsidiaries (see Chapter 8). Another feature of nuclear fuel is that after producing the power it was designed for, it does not disappear; it is physically in the same shape as when it was fresh and still has about the same weight. This used nuclear fuel (UNF) is radioactive and will have to be isolated from the biological environment for many years.

The nuclear fuel cycle starts with the extraction of uranium ore from the ground and terminates with the disposal of radioactive wastes. The objective of Chapter 1 is to provide a "bird's-eye view" of the fuel cycle by describing the various reactor types, discussing the nuclear fuel cycle itself, and presenting general definitions of concepts involved and terms used to describe nuclear fuel activities. In addition, a few comments are provided about costs and regulations.

1.2 Nuclear Fission Reactor Types

Nuclear reactors are classified in many different ways, according either to the predominant energy of the neutron that causes fission or to the coolant and moderator used. First, based on neutron energy, we have fast and thermal reactors. In fast reactors the average neutron energy is about 100 keV; in thermal reactors, it is <1 eV.

In terms of coolant and moderator, thermal reactors either use water as a moderator and coolant (they are designated as light water reactors, LWRs) or they use graphite as a moderator and either water or a gas (He or CO_2) as a coolant. A thermal reactor designed by Canada, called CANDU, uses heavy water as moderator and light water as coolant. The fast reactors do not employ a moderator; those that have been constructed and operated as of 2012 use liquid sodium or lead as a coolant.

The LWRs are either boiling water reactors (BWRs) or pressurized water reactors (PWRs). The difference is the phase of the coolant (water) in the reactor core: The BWR coolant exits the core as steam that goes directly to the turbine, whereas in a PWR the coolant exits the core as hot liquid water that goes through a steam generator that is part of a second coolant loop, with steam from the steam generator driving the turbine.

All nuclear reactors are "converters" to some degree; that is, they have the ability to generate new fissile material in the course of the normal operation that burns the original fuel by fission. For example, a thermal reactor that uses uranium at the approximate $^{235}U/^{238}U$ mass ratio of $4/96$ converts some of the ^{238}U to plutonium, a perfectly good fissile material, while at the same time burning the ^{235}U. The plutonium thus generated is consumed continuously and is responsible for a fraction of the reactor power, sometimes as much as 20%. If a nuclear reactor produces more new fuel than it consumes, it is called a *breeder*. The ability to convert and breed has been demonstrated convincingly, using research reactors as well as power reactors.

1.3 Generations of Fission Reactors

Since the deployment of the first nuclear plants in the late 1950s, their designs have evolved continuously to meet the objectives of ever increasing safety, increasing power, and generally improving operations. The various designs are classified today using the word *generation* (see also the Bibliography, p. 28, in particular the book by Gail Marcus):

GEN-I: These early prototype reactors were designed in the 1950s and were constructed by the mid-1960s. Examples are Shippingport (the first nuclear plant to operate in the United States, 1957, a PWR), the Dresden BWRs, Fermi-1, and the U.K. MAGNOX reactors (see p. 26 for a list of reactor names).

GEN-II: These are commercial power reactors designed and built before 2000 and constitute more than 90% of the power reactors operating today in the world. They are PWRs, BWRs, and CANDU reactors.

GEN-III: The lessons learned and experience obtained from the operation of GEN-II reactors have guided the design of GEN-III reactors, expected to be deployed in the period 2012–2030. GEN-III reactors incorporate many evolutionary improvements over GEN-II designs. Examples are the ABWR, System 80+, and AP600; later designs are the EPR, AP1000, ESBWR, ACR-700, ACR-1000, GT-MHR, and PBMR. Some of these later designs have been referred to as GEN-III+. Because there are no big differences in design philosophy between GEN-III and GEN-III+ and also because the designs keep changing—some are dropped, and new ones are proposed—the distinction GEN-III+ will not be used in this book.

The GEN-III designs were stimulated by the U.S. Energy Policy Act of 1992 that aimed to facilitate licensing, simplify construction, and improve operation of nuclear power plants by using designs that would be certified by the U.S. Nuclear Regulatory Commission (NRC). Certification of reactor designs was meant to enhance safety and reliability of a plant through standardization. The other important step in the construction of new nuclear power plants is the decision by the NRC to introduce a one-step licensing process.

The NRC issued a first rule[a] to create a one-step licensing in 1989, with an update in 2006. The rule added alternative licensing processes for early permits, standard design certifications, and combined licenses. The combined construction-operation license (COL) will allow resolution of safety and environmental issues early in the licensing proceedings, even before construction begins, in most cases. With the COL, the NRC gives permission to the licensee to construct and operate (under specified conditions) a nuclear power plant at a specific site, subject to applicable laws and regulations.

Approval of the site is not, necessarily, included in the COL. The COL is valid for 40 years from the date the NRC issues it, in accordance with 10 CFR 52.103(g). Thus, as long as an electric utility orders a certified plant design and constructs it without changes, it is expected that the licensing process will be expedited.

The success of the one-step license approach will depend to a large extent on design standardization. To understand standardization, consider how the airlines buy new airplane designs. The government certifies a plane design (e.g., a Boeing 747) and the airline buying the plane does not have to go through a "safety licensing" process for each plane. All the 747s have exactly the same safety features and the only items the airline may change are the

---

[a] NRC rules and guidelines regarding the nuclear industry are found in Title 10 of the *Code of Federal Regulations* (10 CFR); Part 20 (10 CFR 20) deals with standards for protection against radiation, and Part 52 deals with licensing.

color of the fuselage and the fabric of the seats. Nuclear power plant certification is visualized to work in the same way. Several designs have been submitted and some have been certified as licensable by the NRC. Because there is a continuous flow of certifications, new applications for certification, and amendments, it is not useful to describe here the designs that have been certified (design certification is a moving target!). A certification is valid for 15 years from the day it is issued (10 CFR 52.55).

A common characteristic of these advanced designs is their enhanced safety. Most of the safety features of GEN-I and GEN-II reactors designed in the past 40 years are "active," in the sense that an operator's action and/or electric power are necessary to activate some safety features (a switch needs to be turned, a key to be pressed, etc.). In contrast, for most of the GEN-III reactor designs, the safety measures are passive or inherent because they rely on phenomena that automatically occur because of natural laws such as gravity, thermal expansion, density change, and natural convection and thus will always work without operator action and even with loss of electric power. In addition to their excellent safety features, these new reactors are expected to be easier to construct, easier to license (due to design certification), and simpler to operate. Advanced design elements have been introduced in the nuclear steam supply system (NSSS), instrumentation and control, radiation protection, containment, and the balance of plant systems.

GEN-IV reactor designs are expected to be deployed in 2030 and beyond. They will operate at higher temperatures than earlier generation reactors (operating temperatures will be 510°C to 1000°C, as opposed to GEN-II and III reactors that operate at about 330°C); GEN-IV designs are expected to (1) have reduced capital cost, (2) exhibit enhanced safety using passive safety systems, (3) use a nuclear fuel cycle that minimizes generation of radioactive wastes, and (4) operate in such a way that nonproliferation of nuclear materials for weapons is enhanced. In terms of power output, they have a range from 150 to 1500 MWe.

An international forum selected six designs for GEN-IV reactors for further consideration; these designs were still under consideration as of 2012:

- *Very High Temperature Reactor (VHTR):* graphite moderated, He cooled

- *Supercritical Water-cooled Reactor (SCWR):* high temperature, high pressure, water cooled, operating above the thermodynamic critical point of water

- *Gas-cooled Fast Reactor (GFR):* He cooled

- *Lead-cooled Fast Reactor (LFR):* Pb-Bi eutectic mixture as coolant

- *Sodium-cooled Fast Reactor (SFR):* may be used to burn actinides

- *Molten Salt Reactor (MSR):* epithermal neutron spectrum, circulating liquid mixture of uranium and a molten salt as fuel.

A brief description of the main features of reactors in Generations II to IV is presented in the next three sections.

1.4 GEN-II Reactors

The main GEN-II reactor designs are BWR, PWR, VVER, CANDU, HTGR (thermal), and LMFBR (fast), described in this section. A nice description of GEN-II reactors may also be found in a book by Gail Marcus (see the Bibliography).

BWR. Boiling water reactors (BWRs) manufactured by General Electric Company (now Hitachi-GE) have the general layout shown in Fig. 1.1. Water is pumped into the core from the bottom. The energy released by fission in the reactor core heats up the water and causes it to boil and become steam before it leaves the core. The steam from the core goes directly to the turbine that turns the generator to produce electricity, after which it is condensed to water and returns to the core. Because the steam from the core goes directly to the turbine, the whole coolant loop is somewhat radioactive,

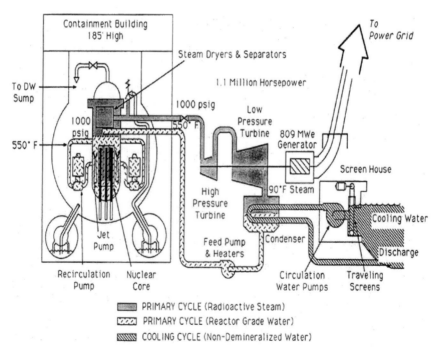

FIGURE 1.1 Schematic of a BWR. The BWR is fueled with slightly enriched uranium, in the form of UO_2 pellets, which are held inside zirconium alloy tubes in the core. Water is pumped through the core, boils, and exits as steam. The steam is piped into the turbine, which in turn rotates the generator.

including the turbine. However, due to the water flashing to steam, the carry-over in radioactivity is relatively small. Numerical data about the size of the core, the fuel, and the general performance of a BWR are given in Table 1.1.

PWR. Pressurized water reactors (PWRs) have been designed by many companies: Westinghouse (now Toshiba-Westinghouse), Combustion Engineering (CE) (purchased by Westinghouse), and Babcock & Wilcox (B&W) (purchased by Framatome). Reactors designed by CE and B&W are still operating in the United States. The French PWRs were originally purchased from Westinghouse, but they have since been modified and now AREVA, a French company, markets them as their own. As Fig. 1.2 shows, a PWR has two coolant loops: the primary, in which pressurized liquid water circulates, and the secondary, in which steam circulates and drives the turbine. The primary loop is radioactive because the hot pressurized water circulating in it goes through the core. The secondary loop is not radioactive. The connecting link between the two loops is the steam generator, in which the energy of the water from the primary loop is transferred to the secondary and transforms that water into steam. Numerical data are given in Table 1.1.

VVER. The VVER is a Russian PWR design. In terms of power, there are two designs: 440 and 1000 MWe. A schematic of a VVER is shown in Fig. 1.3. One major difference between the VVER and Western-designed PWRs is that the steam generator in the VVER is placed horizontally. Other than that, the method of circulation of water and steam is the same in a VVER and Western PWRs.

TABLE 1.1
Numerical Data for the Major Operating Reactor Types (GEN-II)

	BWR	PWR	CANDU	LMFBR
MWe	1100	1100	508	1200
Efficiency (%)	33	33	30	40
Assembly geometry	8 × 8	17 × 17	Cylindrical	Hexagonal
	9 × 9			array
Assembly length (m)	3.8	3.70	0.50	1
Number of assemblies	590	180	4680	360
			(12 per channel)	
Core height (m)	3.8	3.7	5.95	1
Mass of fuel/assembly (kg)	270	600	37	80
Total mass of fuel in core (kg)	138,000	90,000 to 100,000	105,000	29,000
Burnup (MWd/t)	45,000	45,000	8,000	100,000
Fuel replaced per year	1/4	1/3	Continuous	Varied
Enrichment (%)	2.5	3.5	0.711	
Power density (kW/ft)	54	100	12	280
Linear heat rate (kW/m)	19	17	26	29

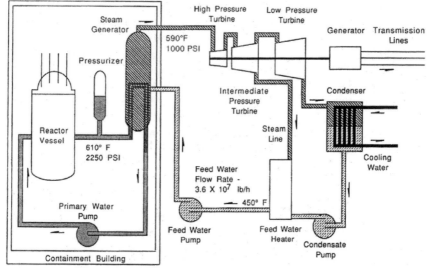

NOTE: 3 or 4 Steam Generator Loops are used in a 1000 MW Plant at 100% Power.

FIGURE 1.2 Schematic of a PWR. The PWR is fueled with slightly enriched uranium, in the form of UO_2 pellets, which are held inside zirconium alloy tubes in the core. Water under pressure is heated as it passes through the reactor core; it leaves the reactor vessel and enters a steam generator, where it gives up its heat to a separate water loop, turning the water into steam. The steam drives the turbine, which in turn rotates the generator.

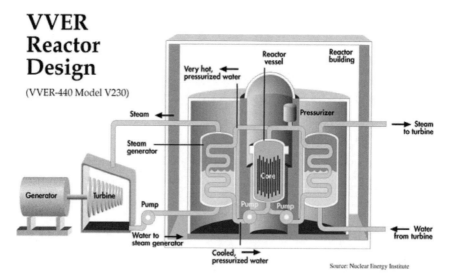

FIGURE 1.3 Schematic of a VVER reactor.

CANDU. Canada Deuterium Uranium (CANDU) reactors are designed in Canada. Most of them have been built and are operating in Canada, but they have been sold and operate in other countries as well (India, Pakistan, China, South Korea). CANDU reactors use heavy water (^2H_2O) as moderator and light water (^1H_2O) as coolant (see Fig. 1.4). Because of this combination of moderator–coolant, the CANDU can operate with natural uranium as fuel (see Table 1.1). Another unique characteristic of the CANDU is that it is refueled online, that is, without shutting down the reactor.

HTGR. High-temperature gas reactors (HTGRs) are designed in the United States by the General Atomics Company (now GA Technologies). They use

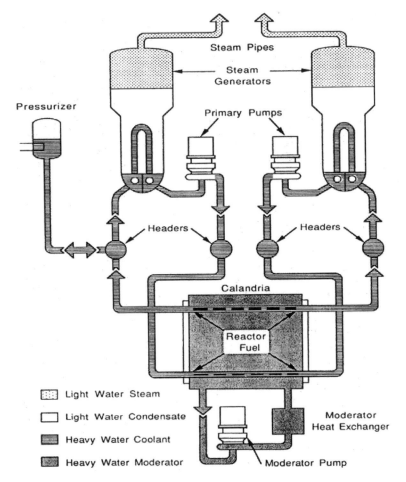

FIGURE 1.4 Schematic of a CANDU reactor. The CANDU uses natural uranium as fuel, heavy water as moderator, and light water as coolant in the primary loop going through the core. The steam loop is essentially the same as that for a PWR.

graphite as moderator and helium as coolant. The HTGR design has the core, steam generators, and pumps enclosed inside a prestressed concrete reactor vessel (PCRV) instead of a steel reactor vessel. The only GA HTGR ever operated was the Fort St. Vrain plant in Colorado, with a design power of 330 MWe (842 MWth). The Fort St. Vrain plant operated from 1976 to 1989. After the final shutdown, decommissioning started and was completed in 1992.

LMFBR. Liquid metal fast breeder reactors (LMFBRs) that were constructed and operated or are operating today have used one of the two designs shown in Fig. 1.5. Since these reactors rely on fast neutrons for their fissions, there is no moderator. The coolant is a liquid metal; sodium has been used in all the designs to date. The main advantage of the LMFBR is its excellent utilization of nuclear fuel. Whereas thermal reactors use the ^{235}U isotope, which is only 0.711% of the natural uranium, breeder reactors utilize the ^{238}U isotope. The use of ^{238}U multiplies the possible energy that can be extracted from nuclear fuels by about 70 times relative to that extracted by thermal reactors. LMFBRs do not require enrichment of the fuel except for the first startup. They do require, however, reprocessing of the irradiated fuel to obtain the plutonium (see Section 1.7) that fuels them.

In the United States, Experimental Breeder Reactors I and II (EBR-I and II) and the Fast Flux Test Facility (FFTF) operated for many years, but they were shut down after their mission, as perceived by the government, ended. In France, two power-producing LMFBRs, the PHENIX and the SUPER-PHENIX, were constructed and operated; both have been shut down. Small experimental LMFBRs have been built in Russia, Germany, China, India, Great Britain, and Japan.

1.5 GEN-III Reactors

ABWR. Designed by General Electric, the Advanced Boiling Water Reactor (ABWR) obtained NRC design certification in 1997. Two ABWRs have been constructed in Japan, in less than 50 months and without delays, and were operating in 2011 without any problems. Figure 1.6 shows the main features of an ABWR. The design complies with the industry-developed criteria for advanced reactors and contains many fail-safe features. Internal pumps are used to circulate the coolant through the core, thus eliminating external recirculation piping and large vessel nozzles below the core. In the unlikely case of an accident, the high temperature inside the drywell located directly below the reactor vessel would automatically initiate flooding, using the water in the large suppression pool that surrounds the vessel. Water in the suppression pool would also serve to trap most fission products, thus stopping them from reaching the environment. There is practically no chance for the core to be uncovered, and there is no need of operator action for 72 h after a hypothesized loss-of-coolant accident. The calculated probability for a core damage accident is reported as 1×10^{-6}.

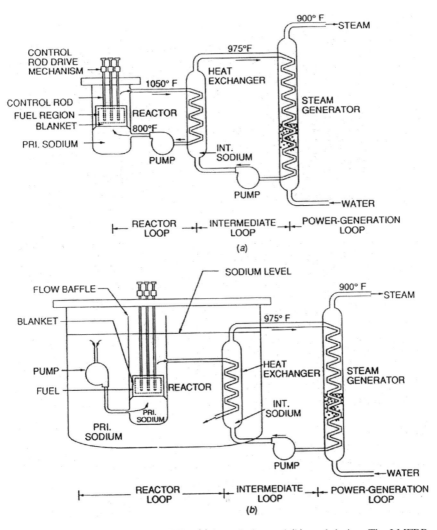

FIGURE 1.5 Schematics of LMFBRs: (a) loop design and (b) pool design. The LMFBR is fueled with natural or depleted uranium and plutonium. It is cooled with a liquid metal, usually sodium. The liquid metal heats up as it passes through the core, then gives up its heat to a second sodium loop through an intermediate heat exchanger. This second loop, which is not radioactive, transfers its heat to water and produces steam in a steam generator.

System 80+. Designed by CE (now Westinghouse-Toshiba), the System 80+ is a 1400-MWe pressurized water reactor that received NRC design certification in 1997. The design includes a spherical steel dual containment (Fig. 1.7) that allows for a simpler yet stronger overall design, requires a reduced amount of materials, and provides more space for workers than a

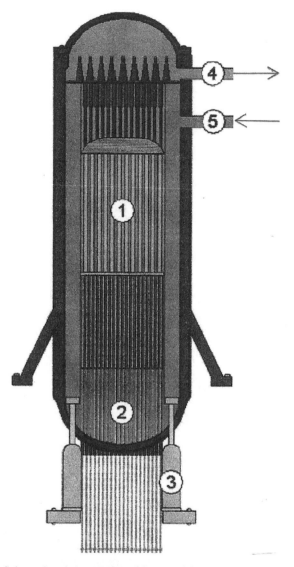

FIGURE 1.6 Schematic of the ABWR: (1) core, (2) control rods, (3) internal water pump, (4) steam line to turbine-generator, and (5) cooling water flow to the core. (Courtesy of GE-Hitachi.)

typical cylindrical containment of the same volume. The dual containment eliminates the possibility of radioactivity releases to the environment, since in the unlikely event that the primary containment is breached, the secondary will contain the potential fission products and thus prevent releases to the environment. The spherical shape offers increased volume that will absorb

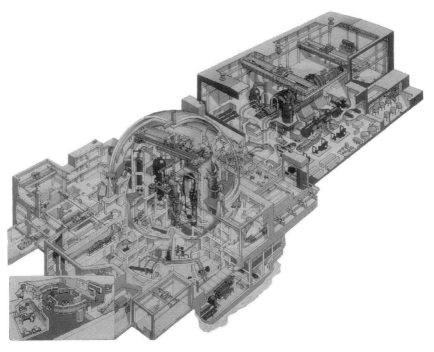

FIGURE 1.7 Schematic of the System 80+ advanced LWR. (Courtesy of ABB-CE, now Westinghouse.)

energy and dilute hydrogen concentration in the event of an accident. Advanced design elements include dedicated safety features that specifically address and mitigate severe accidents; strict separation of instrumentation and control equipment to improve safety, accessibility, operability, and maintainability; and simplicity in the nuclear island layout by eliminating the need for a separate safety-grade auxiliary building. All the safety systems are protected by placing them in the subsphere of containment.

Westinghouse abandoned this design in favor of the AP1000, discussed next.

AP1000. Designed by Westinghouse, the AP1000 is a 1000-MWe PWR. The passive safety features of the AP1000 (Fig. 1.8) rely on gravity, natural circulation, and cooling by natural convection and evaporation to keep the reactor core cool in the event of an accident. Systems for residual heat removal and containment cooling are actuated automatically, if they are needed, without operator action or an external power source. Large tanks of cooling water located above the reactor vessel inside the containment provide for adequate emergency core cooling. If needed, fail-safe valves automatically open, allowing the water to flow from the tank into the core below and keep it adequately cooled indefinitely through natural circulation; the heat is carried

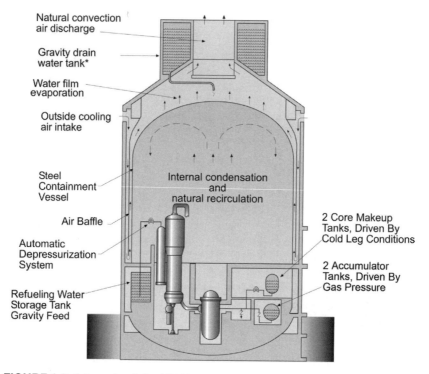

Natural convection air discharge

Gravity drain water tank*

Water film evaporation

Outside cooling air intake

Steel Containment Vessel

Air Baffle

Automatic Depressurization System

Refueling Water Storage Tank Gravity Feed

Internal condensation and natural recirculation

2 Core Makeup Tanks, Driven By Cold Leg Conditions

2 Accumulator Tanks, Driven By Gas Pressure

FIGURE 1.8 Schematic of the AP1000, a PWR designed by Westinghouse, showing its passive safety features. (Courtesy of Westinghouse Electric Company, LLC.)

from the core to the steel containment vessel. A concrete shield building surrounds the steel containment vessel with a space between the two that creates a chimney-like effect, allowing air flow that removes heat by a natural draft. Cooling is accelerated by spraying gravity-fed water, stored in other tanks at the inside top of the concrete building. According to Westinghouse, the estimated core frequency damage probability is 10^{-5} per reactor-year; the probability of fission product release to the environment is estimated to be 10^{-7} per year.

Construction of two AP1000 reactors started in the United States in 2011; construction of two more is planned to start in 2012. Four AP1000 reactors are under construction in China.

EPR. The European Passive Reactor (EPR) was designed by AREVA. The internationalized name of this reactor is the Evolutionary Power Reactor, but it is now simply named EPR by AREVA. EPR is supposed to be a nuclear power plant that satisfies the European utilities' requirements; its rated power is ~1650 MWe. Safety is based on simplification of systems, elimination of common-mode failures through physical separation and diverse backup of safety functions, reduction of sensitivity to human errors by using an optimized man/machine interface with digital instrumentation and control systems, and a modern operator information system supplying status-oriented data. The objective is for EPR to have less than 10^{-5} core melt probability per reactor-year.

GT-MHR. The Gas Turbine Modular Helium Reactor (GT-MHR) was designed primarily by General Atomics. It is a He-cooled, graphite-moderated reactor operating on the Brayton cycle (He gas drives the turbine without the production of steam). The core and the turbine will be placed below grade level (Fig. 1.9). Each module is designed with a 600-MWth power, 286-MWe (i.e., about 48%) thermal efficiency. The increased thermal efficiency is due to the higher temperatures (relative to LWRs) at which the GT-MHR design can operate. The uranium fuel, enriched to ~19.5% in ^{235}U, will be in the form of small coated microspheres that, according to the designers, will contain essentially all the fission products up to the maximum design temperature of 1600°C (see also Chapter 4). In the event of loss of power,

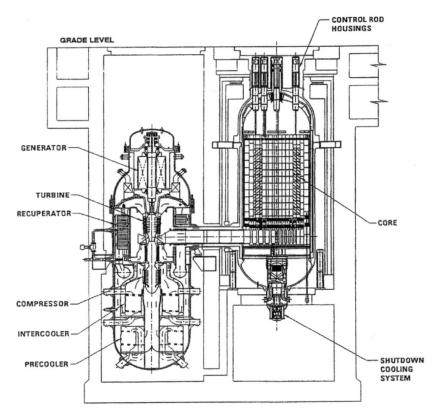

FIGURE 1.9 A schematic of the GT-MHR designed by General Atomics. (Courtesy of General Atomics.)

even if control rods and pumps are incapacitated, the large negative temperature coefficient of the fuel will shut the reactor down. The low–power density core will be adequately cooled by conduction of the decay heat to the reactor vessel, and from there, the heat will be transferred to the surrounding earth via radiation and natural circulation/conduction; computations show that the fuel temperature will be kept below 1600°C. The GT-MHR can use either ^{235}U or Pu as fuel.

PBMR. The Pebble Bed Modular Reactor (PBMR) was designed by the South African company ESKOM. It is called "modular" because a complete plant will consist of eight reactor modules, each producing 165 MWe; thus, the total power output of the plant will be 1320 MWe. Each module is a high-temperature gas-cooled reactor. The PBMR core is based on a German design that was built and operated there for some time. The unique characteristic of the PBMR is its fuel. The uranium fuel, enriched to ~19% in ^{235}U, is encapsulated in 60-mm-diameter graphite spheres. About 400,000 spheres are placed in a steel vessel. Helium gas is percolated through the spheres and keeps the core at the right temperature. The hot He goes directly to the turbine (i.e., the Brayton cycle is used). Refueling will be done online, that is, without shutting down. The spheres are cycled through the reactor; at each pass they are evaluated for burnup and are either recycled or are passed to a storage tank located at the base of the plant. The tank is designed with enough storage capacity to store all the spent fuel for the life of the plant. Design and development of this reactor has been halted by the South African government because of the current global financial condition.

ESBWR. The Economic Simplified BWR (ESBWR) designed by GE-Hitachi represents an evolution of the ABWR. According to the designers, ESBWR utilizes complete passive safety features for heat removal and has many simplification design features that will result in a 42-month construction schedule.

1.6 Small Modular Reactors (SMRs)

The definition of a small reactor is one with electrical output of 300 MWe or less (research reactors are not considered SMRs and are not discussed here). The word "modular" refers to the fact that a power plant may consist of many small reactors, many modules, on one site. For example, if one SMR, one module, produces 150 MWe and the plant consists of 10 SMRs, the total electric output is 1500 MWe.

SMR designs are being pursued by many companies in the United States and other countries. The advertised advantages are as follows:

1. Because of the small size, the capital cost of a single SMR is much smaller than that of a large reactor with a power output of 1000 MWe or more.

2. The components of an SMR may be manufactured in a factory assembly line and then transported to the site for assembly, thus reducing construction time. In some designs the SMR comes to the site as a complete package ready for operation.

3. Because the power is relatively low (thermal power is about 1000 MWth or less), passive safety features can be easily implemented.

4. Some SMRs are designed to undergo no refueling during a 30-year designed operational life. Thus, the utility that operates such a reactor does not have to plan for refueling or spent fuel storage. It is contemplated that the vendor may sign a contract with the obligation to remove the whole plant after its final shutdown. With such a contract, the utility company would not have to plan for decommissioning. Finally, the possibility of clandestine removal of nuclear material is minimized (i.e., nonproliferation is improved) since the nuclear material will be in the core for the life of the plant.

5. Although not necessary, SMRs can be easily placed underground, thus minimizing the possibility of a terrorist attack either from the air or from the ground.

6. For small utility companies (there are many such companies in small or developing countries), an SMR may be considered for purchase and operation, whereas a large reactor ($\sim$1000 MWe or more) is impractical if it represents (a) a large fraction of the generating capacity of the company and (b) a large fraction of the company assets in a single plant.

As of this writing, many SMR designs have been put forward. Clearly, not all of them will survive the forces of the marketplace. What follows is a brief description of the most promising designs.

Hyperion Power Module (HPM). The HPM is based on a Los Alamos National Laboratory project. Each module will produce $\sim$25 MWe ($\sim$75 MWth) power using uranium fuel enriched to less than 20% in ^{235}U. The reactor will be a sealed vessel about 1.5 m across, weighing about 50 tons. It will be transported to the site by truck, train, or barge, and will be set up underground and ready to operate quickly. It will have enough fuel to last for 5 years; at the end of 5 years, it will be returned to the manufacturer for refueling. The HPM has no moving parts; it is a liquid metal–cooled reactor (LMR), cooled with Pb-Bi eutectic mixture. The designers claim that the HPM, due to its unique core physics design, cannot go supercritical or melt down. After the HPM is placed on the site underground and starts operating, it will deliver the 25 MWe continuously for the duration of its fuel (5 years) without the need for operational personnel.

Traveling Wave Reactor (TWR). The TWR, designed by TerraPower, is probably the most innovative SMR design. A thin layer of uranium enriched to ~10% ^{235}U will be loaded into the core to start the fission chain reaction. The rest of the fuel will be depleted uranium (i.e., ^{238}U, essentially). Neutrons absorbed by ^{238}U will breed ^{239}Pu. The fission reaction and the breeding of new fuel will be moving through the core like a wave. The designers claim that this "wave" will traverse the core in about 50 to 100 years, without the need to stop it, as long as there is an adequate amount of fertile ^{238}U in the core.

mPower. The mPower, designed by B&W, will have a nuclear steam supply system (NSSS) that will arrive at the site already assembled, thus requiring relatively little construction. Each reactor module is designed to produce around 125 MWe; the individual modules could be linked together to form the equivalent of one large nuclear power plant.

Super Safe, Small, and Simple (4S). Designed by the Central Research Institute of Electric Power Industry (CRIEPI) of Japan, the 4S is a Na-cooled reactor using U-Zr or U-Pu-Zr as fuel. Each module, designed to produce 10 MWe, will be fabricated in a factory and will be shipped to the site as a sealed unit, thus requiring very little construction on-site. To maintain a steady-state power for a period of 10 to 30 years, the reactor uses a movable neutron reflector. Electromagnetic pumps are used to circulate the liquid Na coolant; in emergencies, natural circulation removes the heat from the core, a design that offers a passive safety feature. Proliferation issues disappear, essentially, since the reactor stays sealed for the duration of its life.

NuScale. The NuScale SMR, offered by NuScale Power, is an LWR fueled with uranium enriched to less than 5% in ^{235}U. Each module, weighing about 500 tons, will have a power output of 45 MWe. A complete NuScale power plant could have up to 24 modules. Refueling would take place every 2 years.

PRISM. The PRISM (Power Reactor Innovative Small Module) designed by GE-Hitachi Nuclear Energy is a Na-cooled fast reactor with a power output of ~311 MWe. The core, fueled with metallic fuel, is placed in a pool of liquid Na. It is inherently safe due to its negative power reactivity coefficient and the large in-vessel coolant inventory that provides a passive heat removal capability. Additional safety is provided by operation at atmospheric pressure and below-grade siting. According to the designers, the PRISM can burn reprocessed used LWR as well as weapons-grade nuclear materials.

IRIS (International Reactor Innovative and Secure). IRIS was designed by Westinghouse with the cooperation of organizations from 10 countries, but Westinghouse is no longer pursuing this design. It was a PWR, with rated power of 335 MWe. In addition to the core and control rods, the IRIS pressure vessel was designed to house all major reactor coolant components (pumps, steam generators, pressurizer). Because of this design, the pressure vessel of IRIS would have been larger than that of a traditional PWR, but the containment building would have been much smaller than that of a traditional PWR.

1.7 Nuclear Fuel Activities

The nuclear fuel cycle activities start with the extraction of uranium ore and terminate with the disposal of radioactive wastes generated during the routine operation of a reactor. It is customary to discuss the "nuclear fuel cycle," even though, in the United States at least, a closed-loop fuel cycle is not practiced as of this writing. Let us first discuss briefly all of the activities necessary for a complete cycle so as to present all the concepts involved. Then we will proceed to examine specific fuel cycles in greater detail. Figure 1.10 shows all of the activities that could be encountered when dealing with nuclear fuels.

Uranium ore is mined and is transferred to a mill, from which it comes out as U_3O_8, a compound usually referred to as *yellow cake*. At this stage, the yellow cake has the isotopic composition of natural uranium:

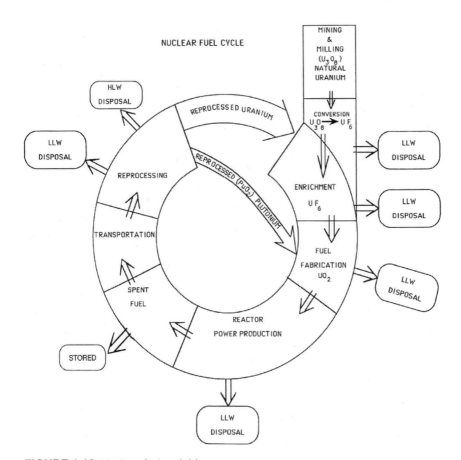

FIGURE 1.10 Nuclear fuel activities.

^{238}U   99.28%

^{235}U   0.711%

^{234}U   0.006%

The above values are in weight percent, and this convention will be followed throughout this book. Most of the power reactors in use are designed in such a way that they need uranium fuel slightly enriched in the isotope ^{235}U. There are many ways to enrich uranium to a desired isotopic content. The predominant methods used for uranium enrichment are the gaseous diffusion and the gas centrifuge processes; both methods employ a uranium compound, UF_6, as a starting material. UF_6 becomes a gas at a temperature slightly higher than room temperature; it is the only uranium compound with this property. Since UF_6 is necessary for the enrichment operation, the second step of the nuclear fuel cycle is the conversion of the U_3O_8 into UF_6. The conversion process is a chemical engineering operation.

The enrichment process starts with natural uranium (0.711% ^{235}U) and produces uranium enriched in the isotope ^{235}U. For LWRs the enriched fuel contains from 3% to 4.5% ^{235}U. What is left behind at the other end of the enrichment operation is depleted uranium, containing between 0.2% and 0.3% ^{235}U, also referred to as *uranium tails*. The depleted uranium currently stored in steel drums is not useful in thermal reactors but is an excellent fuel for fast breeder reactors.

A considerable amount of energy is needed for the enrichment process. The consumption of energy, in turn, determines the price of the enriched product, a price that increases with enrichment and also depends on the value of the uranium tails (see Section 3.5). The price of enrichment is expressed in terms of the work necessary to achieve a certain level of enrichment. The work, in turn, is expressed in terms of a unit called the *separative work unit* (SWU). A detailed explanation of the meaning of SWUs is given in Chapter 3.

The enriched uranium is sent to the fuel fabrication plant, where the UF_6 is converted to UO_2 and made into the fuel assemblies that will be placed into the reactor core. The fuel leaving the fabrication plant is mildly radioactive and is kept almost surgically clean, because any impurities, either inside or on the surface of the fuel, may absorb neutrons (thus removing neutrons that might cause fission) and may also become radioactive materials that must be properly disposed.

At the appropriate time, the new fabricated fuel is placed in the core and starts producing energy. Power reactors are refueled at intervals of 12 to 24 months. During refueling only a fraction, usually a third, of the fuel is removed and replaced with fresh fuel. In fuel management jargon, the number of fuel assemblies that are treated as a group (placed and removed from the core at the same time) is called a *batch*. It can be shown (see Chapter 6) that by replacing only a fraction of the core at refueling, the energy extracted from each batch of assemblies increases.

The energy generated by the nuclear fuel is expressed by the term *burn-up*, given in units of MWd/t (megawatt days thermal per metric ton of uranium fuel). For the first 30 years of the nuclear industry, a typical value of burnup was 33,000 MWd/t. New fuel designs implemented in the 1980s and beyond achieved burnups of 45,000 to 50,000 MWd/t. Obviously, a higher burnup, other things being equal, means more energy per unit mass of fuel and therefore less expensive energy.

The fuel that is removed from the core, called *used nuclear fuel* (UNF; formerly *spent nuclear fuel*), is normally stored on-site under water or, a few years after discharge, in air-cooled vaults also emplaced on-site. The UNF is highly radioactive and eventually has to be removed from the plant site and be disposed or reprocessed. The disposal method depends on the regulatory requirements for the fuel. If the fuel is thought to have no value, it is treated as high-level waste (HLW) and will probably be placed in an interim storage facility or in a geologic repository that will isolate it from the biosphere for as long as necessary (see Chapter 9). If the decision is made to extract the useful isotopes from the spent fuel, then the next step is reprocessing (see Chapter 7).

The main useful isotopes of the irradiated fuel are those of uranium and plutonium, although others, such as ^{137}Cs, may have useful applications in industry and medicine. The UNF still contains most of the original ^{238}U and about 0.6% to 0.8% of the ^{235}U. The ^{238}U has bred plutonium (^{239}Pu, ^{240}Pu, ^{241}Pu, and ^{242}Pu), typically about 6 to 10 g/kg of UNF. With reprocessing, the uranium and plutonium isotopes can be recovered and may be used again as fuel for either thermal or fast reactors. If the recovered material is going to be used in thermal reactors, the reprocessed plutonium is sent directly to the fuel fabrication plant. The reprocessed uranium, depending on its intended use and needs, may (1) be sent to the fuel fabrication plant, (2) be sent to the enrichment plant for reenrichment, or (3) simply be stored.

The leftovers of the reprocessing operation are liquid radioactive wastes and are considered HLW. Just as with non-reprocessed UNF, this HLW must also be isolated from the biosphere.

Radioactive materials are produced during routine operation of any nuclear power plant (and any installation using radioisotopes, e.g., research laboratories, medical facilities, and industrial operations). Examples of such materials are contaminated clothes, tools, papers, liquids, old radioactive sources, etc. These are classified as low-level waste (LLW) and they also must be appropriately disposed of (see Chapter 10).

In the United States two congressional acts deal with the disposal of radioactive wastes. One is the Low Level Radioactive Waste Policy Act (LLRWPA) of 1980, amended in December 1985. The LLRWPA directs the states to find ways for the safe disposal of LLW generated within their boundaries, either individually or by forming compacts with other states. The second is the Nuclear Waste Policy Act (NWPA) of 1982, amended in 1987.

The NWPA directs the U.S. Department of Energy (DOE) to develop a geologic repository for the safe disposal of HLW. The financial resources necessary for the implementation of the NWPA are provided in the form of $0.001/kWh of nuclear-generated electricity, paid to the federal government by every nuclear utility. Collection of this charge started on April 7, 1983. In return for this $0.001/kWh, the government promises to take care of all the used fuel produced by the utilities. Used nuclear fuel generated before April 7, 1983, was charged separately but in such a manner that the cost to the utility is again approximately $0.001/kWh.

1.8 Nuclear Fuel Cycles

There are a large number of variations of nuclear fuel cycles. However, in practice there are only a handful of different cycles that best fit the needs of the particular enterprises and governments involved. For example, the United States has developed reactors that use enriched uranium, because the enrichment plants were available after the war as a result of the Manhattan project (see the book by Ramsey and Modarres, listed in the Bibliography). Also, the U.S. nuclear industry uses light water as coolant since this technology was originally developed for nuclear-powered submarines (i.e., for nuclear-type power plants). Canada, on the other hand, chose the CANDU reactor, which does not require enrichment of the natural uranium. As a result, the Canadian nuclear industry is self-sufficient without going through the considerable expense of developing enrichment facilities. The use of natural uranium as fuel was made possible by the well-developed heavy water (D_2O) technology. The rest of this section gives a brief description of the major fuel cycles.

Once-Through Cycle. This cycle is shown in Fig. 1.11 and represents the LWR fuel activities as practiced by the U.S. nuclear industry today. Comparing Figs. 1.10 and 1.11, one notices that the once-through cycle is not a cycle at all but stops at the UNF stage. In the once-through cycle, the UNF is considered a waste product that will be disposed of as prescribed by the NWPA (see Chapter 9).

Uranium and Plutonium Recycled in LWRs. In this case the UNF is reprocessed and the U and Pu are recovered. The reprocessed U is stored; the Pu, in the form of PuO_2, is mixed with depleted uranium, in the form of UO_2, and fabricated into fuel known as MOX (mixed oxide). The MOX fuel is placed in the core of an LWR, where it fissions and produces power. With the signing of nuclear weapons reduction treaties and the dismantling of a large number of such weapons, a considerable amount of U and Pu has been and will become available and may be used as fuel in LWRs. The main advantages of recycling U and Pu are a decrease in the needed U ore and also a reduction in enrichment services (see Chapter 7). The civilian U.S. nuclear industry does not find it economical to reprocess its UNF and use

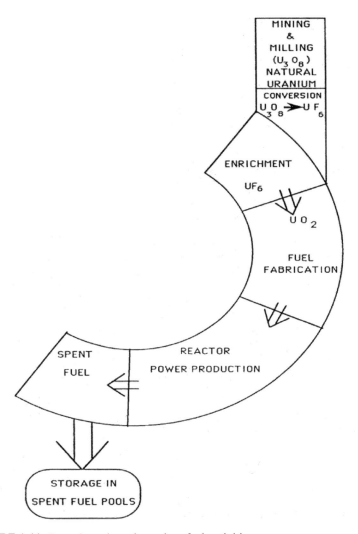

FIGURE 1.11 Once-through cycle nuclear fuel activities.

the recovered Pu as MOX fuel. Other countries, however, are practicing reprocessing and recycling of Pu, with France being the prime example.

Breeder Reactor Fuel Cycle. This cycle is, essentially, the one shown in
Fig. 1.12. In a breeder reactor cycle, reprocessing and recycling are necessary; thus, a breeder reactor must utilize a closed fuel cycle. When a breeder
reactor starts operating, it requires initial fuel to operate that may be ^{235}U or
Pu and ^{238}U. Or, in principle, it may start operating with ^{233}U and ^{232}Th.
After a few cycles, a true breeder produces enough new fuel (Pu or ^{233}U) to
be self-sufficient. It should be noted that whereas a breeder using Pu as a

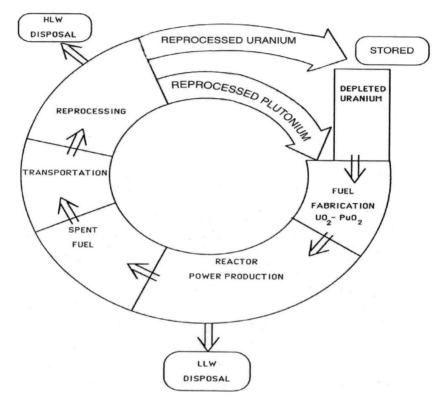

FIGURE 1.12 Nuclear fuel cycle activities taking into account reprocessing of Pu and U.

fuel operates as a fast neutron reactor, a breeder using the Th-^{233}U cycle may operate as a thermal reactor, as was demonstrated by the operation of the Light Water Breeder Reactor in the Shippingport PWR.

1.9 Glossary of Nuclear Fuel Terms

Listed here are some of the terms used in Chapter 1 and throughout the book. These terms are rather unique to nuclear engineering and may be called part of the jargon of our field.

batch: a group of assemblies entering and leaving the reactor core at the same time. This will be a minimum of one assembly per batch. The batch is composed of the same fuel type and enrichment.

book life: the time that a utility must keep track of a batch of fuel from the purchase of the uranium through fuel fabrication, burnup, and cooling. When the DOE takes ownership of the fuel batch from the utility, the utility removes the fuel batch from its books.

burnup (BU): the energy produced by the fuel, expressed in megawatt days per metric ton of uranium (MWd/t) (see *t* below)

capacity factor (CF): determined by the equation (*energy produced during time T*)/($P_o * T$), where P_o represents design power; T is normally 1 year

conversion: the transformation of U_3O_8 to UF_6 (the UF_6 is necessary for the enrichment process)

decommissioning: the processes by which a nuclear site, after activities are terminated, is returned to unrestricted use

enrichment: the process of increasing the ratio of the ^{235}U isotope to that of the ^{238}U isotope

fertile: isotopes that can be converted to fissile material by the capture of a neutron and subsequent one or more decays; for example, ^{238}U and ^{232}Th lead to production of Pu isotopes and ^{233}U, respectively

fissile: isotopes that fission with thermal (slow) neutrons, for example, ^{235}U, ^{233}U, ^{239}Pu, and ^{241}Pu

fissionable: isotopes that fission only with fast neutrons ($E > 1$ MeV), for example, ^{238}U, ^{232}Th, ^{240}Pu, and ^{242}Pu

loop: used to describe both the primary and secondary systems of a nuclear power plant. A BWR has only one loop (Fig. 1.1), which includes the reactor core, piping, pumps, turbine, and condenser. A PWR (Fig. 1.2) has primary and secondary loops; the primary consists of the core, piping, pumps, and primary side of the steam generators, and the secondary consists of the secondary side of the steam generators, the turbine, condenser, and associated pumps.

reactivity (ρ): related to the neutron multiplication factor k by $\rho = (k - 1)/k$; the reactivity indicates the condition of the reactor core relative to criticality

reprocessing: the chemical processes of recovering plutonium, ^{233}U, and unused uranium from spent or irradiated fuel

separative work unit (SWU): a unit of measure indicating the physical effort needed for a certain degree of enrichment; cost of enrichment is proportional to the physical effort

spent nuclear fuel (SNF): see *used nuclear fuel (UNF)*.

t = 1000 kg

used nuclear fuel (UNF): the nuclear fuel that is discharged from the core after it has produced the energy it was designed for.

Reactor Name Abbreviations

ABWR	Advanced Boiling Water Reactor
ACR-700, ACR-1000	Advanced CANDU Reactors
AP1000	Advanced PWR
BWR	boiling water reactor
CANDU	Canada Deuterium Uranium
EPR	European Pressurized Reactor
GT-MHR	Gas Turbine Modular He Reactor
MAGNOX	gas-cooled reactors designed and operated in the United Kingdom
PBMR	Pebble Bed Modular Reactor
PWR	pressurized water reactor
VVER	PWR designed by Russia

Bibliography

The material presented in Chapter 1 comes from the experiences of the author in the nuclear engineering field. Some of the information included is from reports and conversations with other professionals in the field. In addition, the following general references and websites may be useful to the reader.

Code of Federal Regulations, Title 10, "Energy," Parts 1–199, U.S. Nuclear Regulatory Commission.

"The Future of the Nuclear Fuel Cycle," Massachusetts Institute of Technology (2010).

Knief, Ronald Allen, *Nuclear Engineering: Theory and Technology of Commercial Nuclear Power*, 2nd ed., American Nuclear Society (2008).

Lamarsh, J.R., and Baratta, A.J., *Introduction to Nuclear Engineering*, 3rd ed., Prentice Hall (2001).

Marcus, Gail H., *Nuclear Firsts: Milestones on the Road to Nuclear Power Development*, American Nuclear Society (2010).

Murray, Raymond L., *Nuclear Energy*, 6th ed., Elsevier Press (2009).

Ramsey, C.B., and Modarres, M., *Commercial Nuclear Power: Assuring Safety for the Future*, John Wiley and Sons (1998).

Shultis, J.K., and Faw, R.E., *Fundamentals of Nuclear Science and Engineering*, 2nd ed., CRC Press, Taylor-Francis Group (2008).

General Websites

General Atomics (GT-MHR): http://gt-mhr.ga.com

International Atomic Energy Agency: www.iaea.org

Nuclear Energy Agency, Organisation for Economic Co-operation and Development: www.oecd-nea.org

Nuclear Energy Institute: www.nei.org

U.S. Department of Energy: www.energy.gov

U.S. Environmental Protection Agency: www.epa.gov

U.S. Nuclear Regulatory Commission: www.nrc.gov

World Nuclear Association: www.world-nuclear.org/info/inf104.html

Also refer to the websites of the reactor designer companies.

TWO

NUCLEAR FUEL RESOURCES, MINING, AND MILLING

2.1 Introduction

The element uranium (U) was discovered in 1789 by Klaporthe, who named it *uranium* after the then newest planet Uranus. It has been found to be distributed over the entire crust of the earth, with a crustal abundance of 2.8 g/t. It is more abundant than gold and silver but less abundant than lead and copper (Table 2.1). The concentration of uranium with depth is expressed by the function[1]

$$U(z) = U(0)\exp(-z/6300) \tag{2.1}$$

with z in meters and $U(0)$ being the concentration on the surface ($\sim$2.8 ppm).

TABLE 2.1
Crustal Abundance of Selected Elements

Element	Abundance (g/t)
Gold	0.004
Silver	0.07
Tungsten	1.5
Molybdenum	1.5
Uranium	2.8
Thorium	7
Lead	13
Copper	55
Zinc	70
Iron	50,000
Aluminum	81,300

From B. Mason, *Principles of Geochemistry*, 3rd ed., John Wiley and Sons, New York (1966).

The availability of uranium, as with any other metal, is a function of technology and cost; that is, the technology for locating uranium deposits must be in place and mining them must be cost-effective. Currently known ore deposits vary in grade from 0.05% to more than 20%, but there are known deposits with much lower percentages that are not economical to mine at this time.

In this chapter, first presented are the different methods used for uranium exploration, the principal minerals involved, uranium mining methods, and the milling operations. Next, uranium reserves and resources for the United States and the world are discussed along with some comments about economic considerations relative to uranium production. Finally, thorium (Th) characteristics, reserves, and prices are discussed.

2.2 Uranium Exploration Techniques

2.2.1 Geological Studies

The general method of exploring for uranium amounts to conducting a geological evaluation of a large area, which involves both fieldwork and accumulated geological knowledge. In exploring for minerals, prospecting targets are commonly selected on the basis of a geologist's subjective interpretation of a combination of diverse geological data.

For example, the geologist may seek moderate to large volumes of favorable rocks, such as batholith and sedimentary rocks of Tertiary age in Idaho. These are the rock types and formations where uranium has been found in this area of the United States.

In the topical geological studies, special attention is given to those types of nonsandstone environments found throughout the world that might lead to the discovery of new uranium districts, such as in the United States, Australia, southern West Africa, Canada, Greenland, Mexico, and Brazil.

Other favorable geological formations include uranium in Precambrian quartz-pebble conglomerates. Such formations are found in the Wyoming area of the United States. Also, Cretaceous limestone and Tertiary volcanic rocks containing uranium have been found in southwestern New Mexico. The Proterozoic unconformity area near Van Horn, Texas, has also been found to have uranium deposits.

The geological evaluation of Precambrian metasedimentary rocks located in Utah and Colorado indicates uranium deposits. Outcroppings of this type of rock have been found in the Raft River and Grouse Creek mountains of Utah. Also, the Precambrian plutonic rocks of northwestern Arizona contain Proterozoic quartz monzonites and are being studied for uranium and thorium.

In 1973, the U.S. government, through the Energy Research and Development Administration (ERDA), predecessor to the Department of Energy (DOE), initiated the most comprehensive study to date for uranium exploration;

it was called the National Uranium Resource Evaluation[2] (NURE). NURE employed the quadrangle evaluation, which calls for the division of the area to be explored into basic geographic units equal to the 2-deg (scale 1:250,000) National Topographic Map Series quadrangle. The United States was thus divided into 612 areas for geological evaluation.

NURE consisted of two phases:

1. Development of preliminary estimates with the aid of fieldwork, but primarily drawing on accumulated geologic knowledge (this phase was completed in 1976)

2. Development of revised estimates using geologic knowledge to be obtained from an extensive research and development effort (second phase completed in 1983).

NURE had two objectives relative to technology development:

1. Improve existing uranium surveying and exploration instrumentation methods.

2. Design and implement new techniques for geophysical and geochemical surveying and explorations and for data collection and analysis, and new methods of exploitation of uranium ores.

2.2.2 Airborne Surveys

In general, there are two types of airborne surveys. One uses satellites and is preliminary in nature; the other uses aircraft or helicopters and constitutes a more detailed investigation of an area that was examined by satellite or was studied based on geologic knowledge and, in both cases, looks promising.

In 1972, the Earth Resources Technology Satellite, known as Landsat-I, was launched by the National Aeronautics and Space Administration (NASA). By beaming electromagnetic waves onto the surface of the earth and receiving the reflected signal, Landsat can, with the help of sophisticated computerized analyses, provide information about minerals on earth. If the minerals are similar to those encountered in areas where uranium has been found, a more detailed investigation follows.

Airborne surveys using a small aircraft or a helicopter are also called *radiometric surveys*. They are generally conducted after a suitable geological study, and they are very useful since a large area can be covered rather quickly.

The basis of the airborne survey is the detection of the gamma rays that are present in uranium-bearing ores. The detectors used are usually large NaI thallium-activated, gamma-ray detectors of various sizes, up to 5000 cm^3. The detector is normally used as a spectrometer. There are cases, however, when it is used as a total count device. The aircraft flies 1150 m above the ground, if the terrain permits, on lines 1000 m apart. This method permits rapid identification of broad source regions having the highest uranium content, thus helping focus later exploration efforts. To ensure that each airborne system and associated data reduction meet survey specifications, a system qualification or calibration program was developed for use by DOE in the NURE program. This qualification program consisted of evaluating data obtained on the Walker Field calibration pads in Grand Junction, Colorado, and other similar calibration pads.

The items evaluated were system background, resolution, linearity, and sensitivity. In addition, data correction coefficients for stripping, altitude corrections, and airborne radon corrections were obtained. Figure 2.1 shows a helicopter in calibration position on a pad at the Walker Field Airport.

In radiometric surveys, the gamma-ray counters detect the photons emitted by uranium daughters, notably radon (Rn) and bismuth (^{214}Bi). However, other gamma rays detected come from ^{40}K, ^{208}Tl, ^{85}Kr, ^{133}Xe, and ^{232}Th.

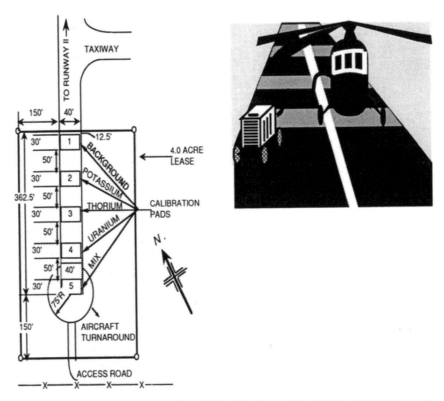

FIGURE 2.1 Diagram showing the DOE calibration pads at Walker Field Airport in Grand Junction, Colorado. An aircraft with its radiometric survey instruments on board parks on each of the different pads to take appropriate calibration measurements. The helicopter uses a separate generator to run its instruments while parked on the pad.

The radiometric procedures can detect uranium ore in areas as small as 50 m^2, with ore grades of 0.2% U_3O_8. Sometimes radiometric surveys can be erroneous, for example, if geochemical processes removed either the uranium or some members of the decay chain from the rock mass under investigation. However, radiometric methods, when properly interpreted, can detect reliably the presence of uranium ore, although they do not give information about the quantity or quality of uranium present. For this reason, radiometry constitutes only the first phase of uranium prospecting. If the radiometric measurements look promising, the analysis of ground samples and groundwater and the drilling of sample wells follows.

2.2.3 Surface Surveys

Surface surveys are made by carrying a radiation counter on foot, on horseback, or on some other rough terrain–traveling vehicle (Figs. 2.2 and 2.3). The radiation detector used may be a simple Geiger-Mueller (G-M) counter or some version of a gamma-ray scintillation counter (NaI) similar to the airborne radiation detectors. Currently, germanium detector probes are being increasingly used because of their excellent energy resolution for gamma-ray spectra relative to that of NaI scintillation counters.

Initial radiation measurements are made to detect radon gas originating from uranium or thorium deposits and percolating through the ground. The distribution and amount of radon at a particular location gives information

FIGURE 2.2 A 35-yard^3 ore-hauling truck coming out of the ore pit.

FIGURE 2.3 A front-end loader picking up uranium ore as directed by a radiological technician. The technician uses a G-M detector to locate the uranium ore.

about the presence of uranium or thorium. Since the uranium in the ore is essentially ^{238}U, the 1001-keV gamma ray from ^{234}Th, the first daughter, can be detected down to 50-ppm levels. The sensitivity improves if one measures the 63.3-keV X-ray from ^{234}Th (which is good down to $\sim$1 ppm). In addition, the prospector may look for gamma rays from fission products such as ^{85}Kr and ^{133}Xe coming from spontaneous fission. Surveys also include a search for photons emitted from other uranium daughters, notably ^{214}Bi and ^{219}Rn. Other gamma rays may come from ^{40}K, ^{208}Tl, ^{85}Kr, and ^{234}Th.

2.2.4 Hydrochemical Methods

The radioactive analysis of water samples taken from streams, wells, and other sources can indicate whether the water has flowed through uranium ore. In this method, one looks for uranium, radium, and radon. The presence of concentrations of radon greater than 10^3 pCi/L or of radium greater than 5 pCi/L indicates that the water has passed through a uranium ore deposit. The chemical analysis of lead isotopes in groundwater is another technique. In this technique the U/Pb ratio is measured, since variations in and around known mineralization will frequently detect a geochemical "halo." These halos, or *roll fronts*, explain how ores are moved and leach out of volcanic ash. Geo-chemical halos also contain various metals (such as selenium, vanadium, and arsenic). Thus, the detection of the above heavy metals by chemical or spec-troscopic methods gives a good indication of the presence of uranium. To detect heavy metals, water samples are usually collected and taken to a laboratory for analysis on a mass spectrometer or flame spectrometer. Another survey method sometimes used is neutron activation analysis of the surface and well water samples. This method will detect uranium in water down to 1 ppm.

2.2.5 Well Logging

Well logging is based on the drilling of wells to explore surface discoveries in more detail. In fact, this method is used to locate and evaluate ore depos-its precisely (Fig. 2.4). After wells are drilled a few hundred feet in depth, detectors are lowered down the hole to measure the radioactivity. Germa-nium detector probes are frequently used for this purpose. The delayed neutron

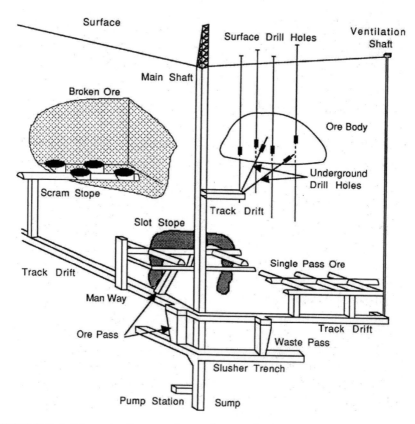

FIGURE 2.4 Schematic diagram of an underground mine.

logging system (similar to the system used for oil well logging) is also utilized. This method usually employs a photoneutron source and detects the delayed fission neutrons produced by the uranium in the ore.

The measurement of helium from a borehole is still another method. The helium method is based on the fact that uranium and thorium and most of their daughters are alpha-particle emitters; therefore, they both produce helium. Being a gas, helium diffuses through the rock and soil and reaches the surface of a borehole. Actually, instead of measuring pure helium, the variations of the $^4He/^{36}Ar$ ratio are measured. Since ^{36}Ar is a stable isotope and in abundance throughout the earth, it provides a very stable comparison.

2.2.6 Botanical Methods

Botanical methods (or uranium botanical prospecting) is based on the fact that many deep-rooted plants (e.g., junipers and pinyons) absorb and accumulate uranium compounds from the ground. The uranium is absorbed through the roots and then transferred, in detectable amounts, to the branches and leaves. This method of exploring for uranium has been made practical by the development of extremely sensitive methods for uranium detection. To detect the uranium, parts of the plant are ground, dried, and ashed; uranium in the ashes is reported as parts per million (http://pubs.usgs.gov/tei/605/report.pdf).

In addition to uranium, certain other elements (e.g., selenium and sulfur) are found in the vicinity of uranium ores. Thus, the presence of such elements is again an indication of the presence of uranium in that ore.

2.3 Principal Uranium-Bearing Minerals

Uranium is usually, but not always, found in some mineral form. Nearly 100 species of uranium-bearing minerals have been identified. A very nice description of uranium minerals is given in Ref. 3; the most important ones are shown in Table 2.2. The minerals listed all have characteristic colors; for example, the oxides are black or brown, the common uranium phosphates (autunite) are yellow, and torbernite is green. In each mineral listed in Table 2.2, the actual amount of U_3O_8 will vary with the deposit.

Another large source of uranium is the Chattanooga shale in the central United States. Measurements show that there is uranium in the shale with a concentration of 60 ppm. Since large quantities of the shale would have to be extracted to provide useful quantities of uranium, it is not economically or environmentally sound to mine this source at present.

2.4 Uranium Mining Methods

The method used to mine uranium depends on the size and location of the ore. There are three methods employed today: open-pit mining, underground

TABLE 2.2

Uranium-Bearing Minerals

Mineral	Chemical Composition
Autunite	$Ca(UO_2)_2(PO_4)_{2x}8-12H_2O$
Brannerite	$(U, Ca, Fe, Th, Y)_3Ti_5O_{16}$
Davidite	$(Fe, Ce, La, Y, U, Ca, Zr, Th)(Ti, Fe, Cr, V)_3(O, OH)$
Carnotite	$K(UO_2)_2(VO)_2 \cdot 3H_2O$
Coffinite	$U(SiO_4)_{1-x}(OH)_{4x}$
Torbernite	$Cu(UO_2)_2(PO_4)_2 \cdot 8-12H_2O$
Tyuyaminite	$Ca(UO_2)(VO_4)_{2x} \cdot 5-8H_2O$
Uraninite	UO_2
Uranocircite	$Ba(UO_2)_2(PO_4)_{2x}8-10H_2O$
Uranophane	$Ca(UO_2)_2SiO_3(OH)_2 \cdot 5H_2O$
Zeunerite	$Cu(UO_2)_2(AsO_4)_{2x}8-10H_2O$

mining, and *in situ* leaching (solution mining). A smaller fraction of uranium is obtained as a by-product material (see Section 2.4.4). In terms of magnitude of effort in each method, open-pit and underground mining constitute ~62%, *in situ* leaching ~29%, and by-product ~9%.

2.4.1 Open-Pit Mining

Careful planning and the use of versatile equipment are needed to handle the wide range of conditions encountered in this type of mining. Final mine design and pit layout depend on closely spaced delineation drilling to augment earlier exploration drilling. Depending on the nature of the ore body, drilling holes at 50-ft centers may be needed to define the ore bed. At this time, the gamma-ray logs made in the ore bed–defining wells are read at 1-ft intervals. From the drilling information, the optimum economic pit limits are found. Generally, pits are planned with 0.75 to 1 net slopes with a shallow surface berm to eliminate surface slides. When opening a pit, topsoil is generally stockpiled separately so that it can be used later to spread over backfilled pits and be seeded, thus reducing the environmental impact of the operation. If waste rock or other overburden contains some U_3O_8, it is placed on a specially prepared pad to allow recovery of the uranium by other methods. The overburden is usually removed by large scrapers and hauled by large trucks (23 yard^3) to the stockpile. Trucks as large as 35 tons and more are sometimes used. Surface mines may generate 40 tons of waste rock for every ton of ore.

When the uranium ore bed is reached, closer excavating is needed. The ore is then dug with small front-end loaders and loaded into ore-hauling trucks. In many cases, the ore is hauled to the surface and stockpiled. Later, it is hauled to the mill by suitable over-the-road trucks. Figure 2.2 shows an ore-hauling truck coming out of the pit and Fig. 2.3 shows a front-end loader picking up uranium ore located by technicians with a G-M probe.

After the uranium ore has been removed from the pit, the overburden is pushed back into the hole and the topsoil is replaced and seeded. However, some pits are so large that converting them to man-made lakes is more desirable than trying to restore them to the original landscape.

2.4.2 Underground Mining

Underground mining is conducted much like coal mining or mining for other minerals. The opening to the mine may go down nearly a mile. Side tunnels are cut into the ore deposits and the ore is removed, raised to the surface in mining carts, and hauled by trucks to the mill. Figure 2.4 shows a schematic diagram of an underground mine.

Mine waste is piled in empty tunnels and mine water is pumped to the surface from underground sumps. In this type of mining, part of the ore cannot be extracted because it has to be left behind to support the roof of the mine. An advantage of underground mining is that very little of the surface area over the mine is disturbed. Underground mines may generate less than 1 ton of waste rock for every ton of ore. However, because of the tunneling, subsidence problems may eventually develop.

There are several human hazards in underground mining. It is well known that mine cave-ins occasionally take place, killing or trapping miners. Another hazard is radon gas (^{222}Rn). To keep radon gas concentrations down to acceptable levels, a considerable amount of ventilation is necessary. A tentative average radon emission via the ventilation air is 15.9 Ci/t of U_3O_8 mined. The miners are required to wear masks while in the ore-producing region of the mine, and in addition, each miner is required to wear a suitable radon detector to measure his cumulative radiation dose because radon is dangerous to the human lung. It enters the lung as a gas but decays into alpha-emitting isotopes that will deposit considerable energy in the lungs, resulting in a considerable radiation dose.

2.4.3 *In Situ* Leaching (Solution Mining)

Solution mining is still in the experimental stage because of potential environmental problems, but it appears to be an economically attractive alternative to open-pit and underground mining because of two main potential advantages. First, *in situ* leaching eliminates stripping, mining, and milling of the ore and depositing of waste tailings on the surface of the mining area. This is a big advantage since uranium tailings have to be covered with about 6 to 8 in. of clean soil. Second, *in situ* leaching offers the possibility of recovering uranium from ore grades lower than those achieved by either of the other two mining methods. *In situ* mining is the only mining method regulated by the NRC because it is viewed as a process, as a result of which it comes under NRC regulation.

Most often in solution mining, five holes are drilled 50 ft apart. The hole in the middle is used to inject the solution down to the ore (Figs. 2.5 and 2.6). The solution used is designed to mobilize and dissolve the uranium. It is usually a combination of water, oxidants, and an ionic complex agent. The four corner holes are used to pump the solution up to the surface facilities where, by using the appropriate chemical processes, the U_3O_8 is removed. For full recovery and cleanup, the injection-production holes may be reversed.

Summarizing, the advantages of *in situ* leaching are (1) elimination of stockpiling and hauling of ore; (2) elimination of the crushing, grinding, and other milling operations; (3) elimination of large-scale excavations; (4) reduction of risks to the miners because they don't have to work underground; and (5) a very small fraction (5%) of the radioactivity of the ore reaches the surface. The disadvantages are (1) a potential for contamination of groundwater and (2) a lower recovery rate; 50% is considered optimum at present.

2.4.4 Recovery of Uranium as By-Product from Mining Other Materials

At various times different companies and nations have studied the possibility of recovering uranium from by-products such as (1) phosphates, (2) copper dump and leach liquor, and (3) coal and lignite. Of all these substances, the

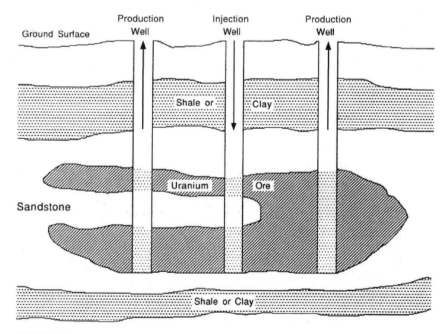

FIGURE 2.5 *In situ* leach mining of a hypothetical vertical section of a roll front uranium deposit.

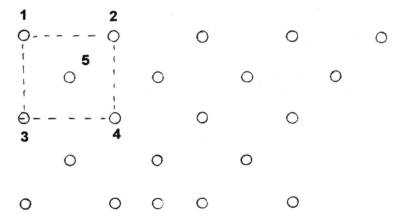

FIGURE 2.6 The pattern of holes used for *in situ* uranium mining, viewed on the horizontal plane. Hole 5 is the injection well; holes 1 through 4 are production (uranium retrieval) wells.

recovery of uranium from phosphates has reached the commercial stage. Late in 1975, the Uranium Recovery Corporation (URC), an affiliate of United Nuclear Corporation, began recovering uranium from wet-process phosphoric acid in the phosphate plant at Barlow, Florida. The first stage of recovery took place at the phosphate plant and the final stage of recovery takes place at URC's central finishing plant in Mulberry, Florida. The first shipment of uranium was made in 1980. Other companies have also demonstrated processes for the recovery of uranium from phosphate.

In the period 2000–2010, the U.S. Bureau of Mines, the Kennecott Copper Corporation, and Wyoming Mineral Corporation, a Westinghouse subsidiary, have done extensive testing on the recovery of uranium from copper dump leach liquor. Leach liquor from western copper frequently contains 2 to 20 parts U_3O_8 per million parts of solution.

Lignite usually contains 1 to 10 ppm U_3O_8. The recovery of uranium from lignite ash is not economical under current uranium prices.

2.4.5 Recovery of Uranium from Seawater

The estimated average concentration of uranium in seawater is about 3.3 ppb, which gives about 4.5×10^9 t of the metal in all of the earth's oceans. Uranium may be extracted from seawater using various chemical engineering processes. The first such reported method used hydrogen titanium oxide (HTiO) to absorb the uranium from seawater, and then a solution of $NH_4CO_3H_2O$ (ammonium carbonate) was used to separate it. When the price of uranium seemed to skyrocket in the early 1970s, Japan started a pilot plant to recover uranium from seawater. The plant produced the meager amount of 5.3 kg of uranium in 1986, the first year of its operation, and 7.5 kg in 1987. Because the cost at this rate of production amounted to about $1940/kgU, whereas the uranium market price at the time was $44/kgU, the process was obviously uneconomical and the plant was shut down.

Methods of extraction developed recently are based on biochemical principles.[4] In Japan, an adsorbent was developed by irradiating a polymer fiber that selectively removes heavy metals from seawater. France and India are also collaborating in the development of uranium extraction methods based on synthetic adsorbents and on magnetic separation.

There are no reliable numbers for the price of uranium extracted from seawater. Since the methods to extract the metal are still under development, any quoted price is speculative. However, all published reports indicate that uranium from seawater is definitely, at present (2012), more expensive than mined uranium, which can be purchased for ~$150 to $180/kgU.

2.5 Uranium Exploration and Mine Activities

Uranium exploration activities were low and about constant worldwide from 1996 to 2004. In 2004, expenditures started increasing at a rapid rate[5] (Fig. 2.7). It should not be surprising that most of the exploration expenditures were concentrated in areas considered the most promising for discovery of economically minable deposits. In 2008, the bulk of expenditures (>90%) were reported in only six countries: Australia, Canada, Kazakhstan, Niger, the Russian

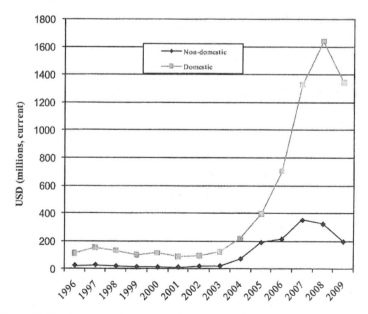

FIGURE 2.7 Trends in uranium exploration and development expenditures.[5]

FIGURE 2.8 The location of the most significant uranium reserves and production centers in the United States as of the end of 1997. [*Source:* Based on U.S. DOE Grand Junction Project Office (GJPO), *National Uranium Resources Evaluation, Interim Report,* June 1979, Fig. 3.2, and GJPO data files.]

Federation, and the United States. In 2010, the major uranium-producing countries in order of production were Kazakhstan, Canada, and Australia.

The major uranium-producing areas in the United States are shown in Fig. 2.8. They have bedded sandstone sediment deposits in the Triassic, Jurassic, and Tertiary basins of the Western United States (Tertiary basins, Wyoming; sandstones, Colorado plateau; sandstones of coastal plain, Texas). For a typical U.S. mine, the capital cost is 38%; the rest, 62%, is the operating cost. Mining expenditures in the United States during the period 2004–2009 are shown in Table 2.3. The U.S. mine production is shown in Fig. 2.9.

TABLE 2.3
Mining Expenditures in the United States, 2004 to 2009*

Year	Land Exploration and Reclamation	Production	Drilling	Total
2004	48.4	27.8	10.6	86.8
2005	59.7	58.2	18.1	136.0
2006	115.2	65.9	40.1	221.2
2007	178.2	90.4	67.5	336.1
2008	164.4	221.2	51.9	467.5
2009	104.0	141.0	35.4	280.4

*Values are in $ $\times 10^6$.

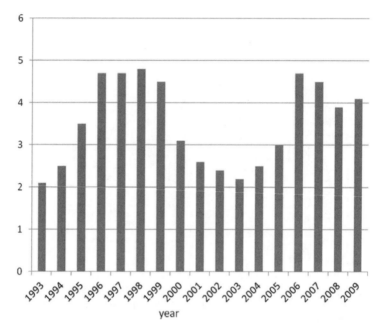

FIGURE 2.9 U.S. mine production for the period 1993–2009.

2.6 The Milling of Uranium Ore

After the uranium has been mined, it must be concentrated into U_3O_8, the substance commonly known as yellow cake. This process takes place in a uranium mill. Figure 2.10 shows the flow chart for a typical 2000 ton/day mill. Figure 2.11 shows the major operations and a typical layout of a uranium mill.

The ore is first crushed and ground into powder, which is then roasted to remove most of the organic material. This procedure is followed by either leaching, ion exchange, or solvent extraction. After solvent extraction, the uranium is precipitated out and washed. The resultant U_3O_8 is then centrifuged, dried, and finally packaged into 55-gal steel drums (Figs. 2.12 and 2.13).

2.7 The Mill Tailings

As indicated in Fig. 2.11, waste material from a uranium mill is released to a tailings pond. Tailings ponds receive nearly all of the radium and the other decay products of the original ore. As a result, such tailings require control, essentially in perpetuity, to safeguard the surrounding environment from radioactive contamination or the exposure of people to unwarranted radiation. The alternative to control of the tailings on-site is to remove the radioactive

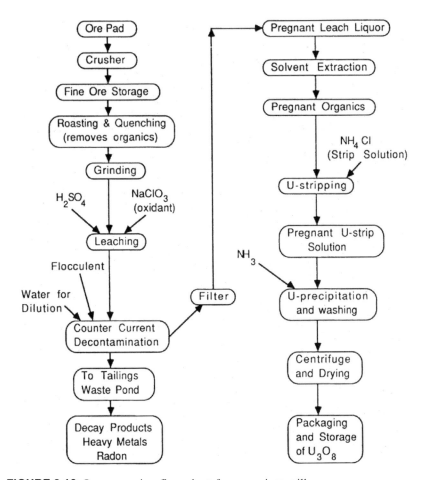

FIGURE 2.10 Ore processing flow chart for a uranium mill.

materials when processing the ore. So far, removal of the radioactive materials has not been successful.

Since the tailings ponds also receive used acids and slime from the milling process, in addition to the radioactivity, the pond must be constructed to hold its contents under all conditions. Thus, these tailings ponds are constructed so that runoff water will not flood them.

Because the mill tailings constitute a source of radioactivity, in 1978 Congress passed the Uranium Mill Tailings Radiation Control Act, which has two principal features. First, it directs the federal government to undertake the elimination of the hazards associated with more than a score of inactive tailings piles left from past uranium-milling operations. The affected states are asked to pay 10% of the total cost involved. Second, the act clarifies and

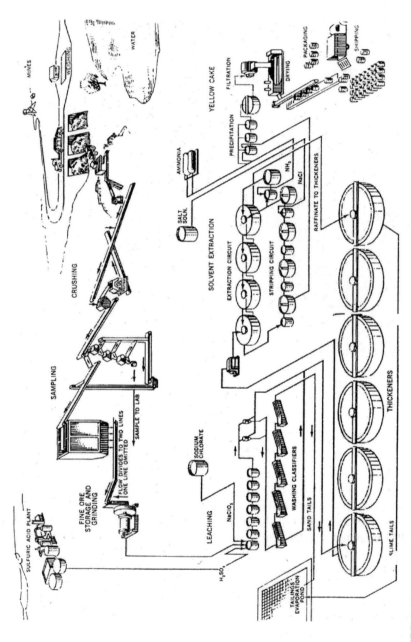

FIGURE 2.11 The major operations and typical layout of a uranium mill.

FIGURE 2.12 A technician at a uranium ore mill weighing a 55-gal drum of yellow cake.

strengthens the authority of the NRC to insist on proper tailings management by its uranium mill licensees. Equally important, it requires those states that have chosen to license such milling operations to abide by substantive standards at least as stringent as the NRC's. Procedural standards for public hearings and environmental studies also are prescribed.

In late 1982 and in 1983, the U.S. Environmental Protection Agency (EPA) proposed standards relative to uranium mill tailings cleanup and their disposal. EPA standards are contained in 40 CFR 192, "Health and Environmental Protection Standards for Uranium and Thorium Mill Tailings." The standards are divided into two parts; one deals with the management of tails during the operation of the mill and also during the period following the cessation of operations but before final disposal, and the other deals with the final disposal of the tails.

The standards regarding operations limit particulate emissions, radon emissions, and contamination of surface and groundwater. For contaminated land,

FIGURE 2.13 Uranium yellow cake storage area.

the standards require a surface concentration of ^{226}Ra of <5 pCi/g of soil within the top 15 cm of soil and <15 pCi/g below that level.

The protection standards relative to the air quality in mines and buildings are expressed in terms of a quantity called the *working level* (WL), which is defined on the basis of energy released by radon (Rn) and its daughters. Any combination of Rn and its daughters that releases in 1 L of air 1.30×10^5 MeV of energy from alpha particles amounts to 1 WL; calculations show that 100 pCi/L will release that amount of alpha energy. The exposure is defined in terms of working level month (WLM), where

$$WLM = WL * (\text{hours of work in a month}/170) \tag{2.2}$$

As an example, consider a case where the Rn concentration amounts to 0.8 WL and a miner worked for 100 h in that environment during that month. The exposure is then 0.8(100/170) = 0.47 WLM. The relationship between WLM and units of dose (Sv or rems) is given by different groups as 25 to 160 mSv/WLM (2.5 to 16 rems/WLM). The NRC uses the number 25 mSv/WLM (2.5 rems/WLM). For uranium mines, the limit is 4 WLMs in any 12-month period. If we accept the equivalence of 5 rems/WLM, then 4 WLMs amount to 20 rems/year. As in all other activities involving radiation, exposure from mill tailings is subject to the "as low as reasonably achievable" (ALARA) principle.

Disposal of tailings requires control of any potential hazards, in most cases for 1000 years and in no case for less than 200 years. Radon emission would be limited to 20 $pCi \cdot m^{-2} \cdot s^{-1}$ averaged over the surface of the piles. Other measures would be required to avoid releases of any other hazardous substance.

The EPA's 1983 estimate of the cost to comply with the standards for uranium mill tailings generated by the year 2000 was between $400 and $700 million. The government will pay for 90% of the cost except on Indian reservations, where it will pay 100%.

2.8 Uranium Reserves and Resources

The DOE's Energy Information Administration (EIA) defines *reserves* as follows: "Reserves are estimated quantities of uranium in known mineral deposits of such grade, quantity, and configuration that the uranium can be recovered at or below a stated production cost with currently proven mining and processing technology and current law and regulation." Estimation of the amount of reserves is based on direct radiometric and chemical measurements of drill holes and other types of sampling of the ore.

Resources are uranium quantities that are estimated; the amount of resources reported carries an uncertainty greater than that for reserves. Until 1982, the DOE used the following three resource classifications:

1. *"Probable" potential resources:* those that occur in known production uranium districts in extension of known deposits or in undiscovered deposits within known geological trends

2. *"Possible" potential resources:* those estimated to occur in undiscovered or partly defined deposits in formations or geologic settings productive elsewhere within the same geologic province

3. *"Speculative" potential resources:* those estimated to occur in undiscovered or partly discovered deposits in formations or geologic settings not previously productive.

Although this classification has been abandoned and has been replaced by a two-group structure, it is presented here because it describes the inherent uncertainties in the resource estimates. Today (2012), the DOE/EIA classifies resources as estimated additional resources (EAR) and speculative resources (SR).

A slightly different classification of resources is used by the Organisation for Economic Co-operation and Development (OECD). Uranium reserves are called *reasonably assured resources* (RAR) by the OECD; the resources are classified as inferred resources (IR) and undiscovered resources (UR). Further, OECD calls the sum of RAR and IR *identified resources*. The correspondence between the two sets of definitions is, roughly, as follows:

DOE/EIA Definition	OECD Definition
Reserves	Reasonably assured resources (RAR)
Estimated additional resources	Inferred resources (IR)
Speculative resources	Undiscovered resources (UR)

Reporting amounts of reserves or resources must be accompanied by the production cost for the category being reported. The production cost, always in U.S. dollars, represents what is called the *forward cost*. (The definitions of the various uranium costs/prices used by the industry are given in Section 2.10.) Reserves and resources for the major uranium producers in the world are shown in Tables 2.4 and 2.5, with corresponding production costs.

Total identified resources (RAR + IR) as of January 2009 are reported to be 5,404,000 tU in the <$130/kgU category and 6,306,300 t uranium in the <$260/kgU; total undiscovered resources are estimated to be 10,400,000 tU. The reader should keep in mind that these numbers represent a "snapshot" of the estimates for uranium to be found on earth. The numbers are dynamic and keep changing as demand and prices change.

The U.S. resources (RAR + IR) (Refs. 5 and 6) are estimated to be 207,400 tU in the <$130/kgU cost category and 472,100 tU in the <$260/kgU cost. U.S. reserves by state are given in Table 2.6. Based on current needs by the nuclear power plants, the U.S. uranium reserves in the <$260/kgU category represent approximately 23 years' worth of demand; the <$130/kgU reserves represent about 10 years of demand (assuming that all fuel needs are satisfied by domestically produced uranium).

TABLE 2.4
Reasonably Assured Resources (RAR), as of January 1, 2009*

Country	Production Cost			
	<$40/kgU	<$80/kgU	<$130/kgU	<$260/kgU
Australia	—	1,612,000	1,673,000	1,679,000
Brazil	139,900	157,700	157,700	157,700
Canada	267,100	336,800	361,100	387,400
China	52,000	100,900	115,900	115,900
Kazakhstan	14,600	233,900	336,200	414,200
Niger	17,000	42,500	242,000	244,600
Russian Federation	—	100,400	181,400	181,400
South Africa	76,800	142,000	195,200	195,200
Ukraine	2,500	38,700	76,000	142,400
United States	—	39,000	207,400	472,100
Uzbekistan	—	55,200	76,000	76,000

From *Uranium 2009: Resources, Production, and Demand*, OECD Nuclear Energy Agency and International Atomic Energy Agency (2010).
* Values are in tons of U, rounded to the nearest 100 tons.

TABLE 2.5
Identified Resources (RAR + IR), as of January 1, 2009*

Country	Production Cost			
	<$40/kgU	<$80/kgU	<$130/kgU	<$260/kgU
Australia	—	1,163,000	1,176,000	1,179,000
Brazil	139,900	231,300	278,700	278,700
Canada	366,700	447,400	485,300	544,700
China	67,400	150,000	171,400	171,400
Kazakhstan	44,400	475,500	651,800	832,000
Niger	17,000	73,400	272,900	275,500
Russian Federation	—	158,100	480,300	566,300
South Africa	153,900	232,900	295,600	295,600
Ukraine	5,700	53,500	105,000	233,600
United States	—	39,000	207,400	472,100
Uzbekistan	—	86,200	114,600	114,600

From *Uranium 2009: Resources, Production, and Demand*, OECD Nuclear Energy Agency and International Atomic Energy Agency (2010).
*Values are in tons of U, rounded to the nearest 100 tons.

2.9 Uranium Production

Uranium production through the past four decades followed, as one might expect, the trends of the nuclear power industry. With many orders for nuclear power plants being announced, production increased sharply in the mid 1970s. It reached a peak in 1980, then declined, and now, after 2000, is on the rise again.

TABLE 2.6
Uranium Reserves in the United States by State, End of 2008

State	$50/lbU$_3O_8$			$100/lbU$_3O_8$		
	Ore (10^6 tons)	Grade (% U_3O_8)	U_3O_8 (10^6 lb)	Ore (10^6 tons)	Grade (% U_3O_8)	U_3O_8 (10^6 lb)
Wyoming	145	0.076	220	398	0.056	446
New Mexico	64	0.14	179	186	0.105	390
Arizona + Colorado + Utah	22	0.145	63	117	0.084	198
Texas	15	0.089	27	32	0.062	40
Others	28	0.09	50	95	0.081	154
Total	274		539[a]	828		1228[a]

From the U.S. Department of Energy, Energy Information Administration, http://www.eia.gov/nuclear.
[a] Divide by 2.6×10^3 to obtain tons of uranium; then the numbers are consistent with those of Table 2.4.

World uranium production in 2008 was 43,880 tU (41,244 tU in 2007 and 39,617 tU in 2006). In 2008, the 438 operating power reactors in the world, with a total generating capacity of 373 GWe, required 59,065 tU. The difference between the demand (59,065) and production (43,880) was covered with supplies of uranium already mined. By the year 2035, it is projected that the nuclear generating capacity will be 511 to 782 GWe; the corresponding uranium demand will be 87,370 to 138,165 tU.

In 2010, the major uranium producers were Kazakhstan (33%), Canada (18%), Australia (11%), Namibia (8%), Niger (8%), Russian Federation (7%), Uzbekistan (4%), and United States (3%).

The U.S. mine production is shown in Fig. 2.9.

2.10 Economic Considerations of Uranium Production Methods

After economic deposits of uranium have been identified and evaluated, still more detailed engineering and economic feasibility studies are required before it can be said with some certainty that a given deposit will make money if it is extracted. Every deposit has to be studied individually to determine whether a given reserve may be economical to mine. In addition, a deposit that is economical at a uranium price of, for example, $100/kgU may not be so at $50/kgU. The objective of any mining company is to maximize the product recovered and minimize the production costs. Uranium mining and milling are capital-intensive enterprises.

Regarding uranium price, it has had its ups and downs following the expansion and contraction of the nuclear industry. Prices for the period 1980–2011 are shown in Figs. 2.14 and 2.15.

It should be mentioned here that the price of this commodity depends on many factors, such as type of contract (long or short time interval), quantity, "spot" market purchase, etc. In the uranium industry, a certain terminology has developed with regard to cost and prices:

- *Forward cost:* includes operating and capital costs yet to be incurred at the time the estimate of the reserves is made. Profit, production costs, labor costs, taxes and insurance, and sunk costs, such as past expenditures to acquire the property, exploration, and mine development, are not included. Thus, forward cost is independent of the market price at which the uranium to be produced from these reserves will be sold.

- *Contract price:* price determined at the time the contract is signed, with escalating factors.

- *Market price:* price not determined at the time the contract is signed; it is based, instead, on the prevailing market price at the time of delivery. The market price is ~1.5 times the forward cost.

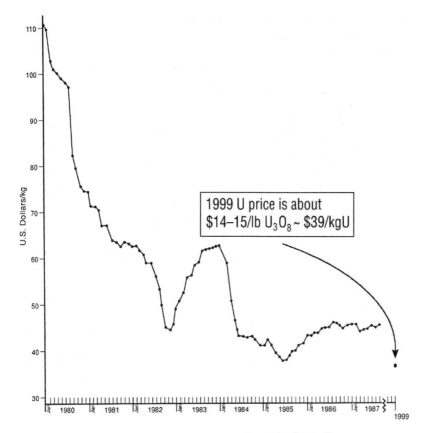

FIGURE 2.14 Uranium prices for the period 1980–1987 (Ref. 6).

- *Spot price:* price for one-time transaction and prompt delivery, typically within a year, for limited quantities up to 500,000 lbs U_3O_8 (192,308 kgU).

2.11 Thorium Minerals and Estimated Reserves

Thorium has an atomic number of 90 and only one isotope of thorium found in nature, ^{232}Th, with a half-life of 1.4×10^{10} years. The average concentration of thorium in the earth's crust is about 7.2 ppm, which makes it about three times more abundant than uranium, and its deposits are usually associated with uranium or rare earth elements. Thorium, like uranium, occurs in a large number of minerals; however, only two, monazite and thorite, are of commercial or potential commercial importance.[8] Monazite, the most important commercial source of thorium, is a rare earth phosphate generally containing 1% to 10% ThO_2. It occurs characteristically as a minor accessory

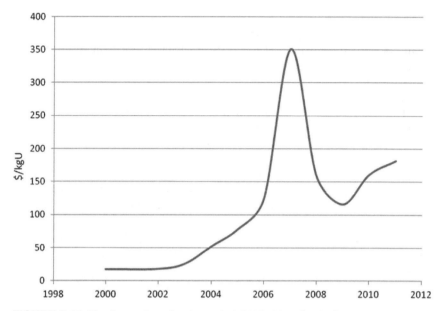

FIGURE 2.15 Uranium prices for the period 2000–2011 (Ref. 7).

mineral to igneous rocks and is concentrated by the natural processes of weathering and erosion in streams and beach placers. The minerals are readily recovered by dredging, followed by gravity, magnetic, and electrostatic concentration. The principal reserves of monazite are in the beach sands of India, Australia, and Brazil. In the United States, monazite is found in many areas, but the only commercial production has been from stream placers in Idaho and western North and South Carolina.

Thorite is a thorium silicate ($ThSiO_4$). Pure thorium silicate, however, is unknown in nature, and thorite is usually found in hydrated form with uranium. Thorite is less abundant than monazite, with only traces present in most placers. In the United States, placer thorite is found in California, Idaho, and Montana. The so-called Lemhi Pass district on the Montana-Idaho border is believed to have the largest concentration of thorium resources in the United States.

Since there is no large demand for thorium today, it and its compounds are produced, primarily, as a by-product from the recovery of Ti, Zr, Sn, and rare earths from monazite. Today, the principal applications of thorium utilize the high melting point of ThO_2 (3300°C) and the emission of electrons when alloyed with tungsten for use in filaments for high-powered magnetrons for radar applications.

Thorium is also part of certain magnesium alloys called Mag-Thor, which are used in aircraft engines to impart high strength and creep resistance at elevated temperatures. Thorium dioxide (ThO_2) and thorium nitrate ($Th(NO_3)_4$) are used in mantles of portable gas lights (e.g., camping lights). Excess thorium not needed for industrial use is either disposed of as radioactive waste or stored for potential future use as nuclear fuel.

Current (2012) consumption of thorium in the United States is about 5.3 t, a decrease from the 11.4 t used in 1997.

Estimated reserves of thorium are given in Table 2.7; these data are taken from an OECD report.[8] The U.S. Geological Survey[9] (USGS) gives a slightly different total estimate of 1,300,000 t thorium. In view of the uncertainties in estimating reserves for any mineral, the two numbers are remarkably close. The OECD report gives the amount of estimated additional resources as 2,086,000 to 2,557,000 tTh, without assigning price to them. There is no doubt that if demand for thorium increases, the amount of reserves (and resources) will increase.

The isotope ^{232}Th, the only thorium isotope found in nature, is fissionable (i.e., it fissions with the absorption of a fast neutron, $E > 1$ MeV), but more important than that, ^{232}Th is a fertile isotope that can breed ^{233}U, a fine fissile isotope:

$$^{232}Th + n \rightarrow {}^{233}Th \rightarrow \beta^- \rightarrow {}^{233}Pa \rightarrow \beta^- \rightarrow {}^{233}U$$

Uranium-233 is a remarkable isotope; it is the only known isotope that can fuel either a thermal or a fast neutron reactor. When it is used in reactors, it produces a smaller amount of transuranics than uranium and, more important, does not produce weapons-grade materials such as Pu isotopes (^{233}U

TABLE 2.7
Thorium Reserves, 2006 Estimate*

Country	Reserves <$80/kgTh
Australia	13
Brazil	171
Greenland	54
India	319
Russian Federation	75
South Africa	18
Turkey	344
United States	122
Others	23
Total	1139

From "Forty Years of Uranium Resources, Production and Demand in Perspective," OECD Nuclear Energy Agency (2006).
* Values are in thousands of tons.

could be used to make a weapon, but it is more difficult to handle because of its higher specific activity, relative to that of ^{239}Pu). Thorium in a molten salt form may fuel a thermal reactor that uses fuel in liquid form. One such reactor, the Molten Salt Reactor Experiment (MSRE), was designed and operated at the Oak Ridge National Laboratory (ORNL); it went critical in 1965 and operated until 1969. One of the GEN-IV reactor designs is the Molten Salt Reactor (MSR). Among the countries that use nuclear power, India, with 28% of the world's thorium reserves, is very aggressive in pushing thorium as a fuel.

Bibliography

"The Future of the Nuclear Fuel Cycle," Massachusetts Institute of Technology (2010).

Hazen, R.M., Ewing, R.C., and Sverjensky, D.A., "Evolution of Uranium and Thorium Minerals," *American Mineralogist*, **94**, 1293–1311 (2009).

Mason, B., *Principles of Geochemistry*, 3rd ed., John Wiley and Sons, (1966).

Metals and Minerals: Minerals Yearbook, Vols. I, III, and VI, published annually by the U.S. Department of the Interior.

Stavropodis, E.D., *Nuclear Fuels*, Greek Atomic Energy Commission, Athens (1977).

"Uranium: Mineralogy, Geochemistry and the Environment," *Reviews in Mineralogy*, 38, P.C. Burns and R. Finch, Eds., Mineralogical Society of America (1999).

Uranium Mining and Hydrogeology, B.J. Merkel and A. Hasche-Berger, Eds., 5th International Uranium Mining and Hydrogeology Congress, September 2005, Freiberg, Germany, Springer (2008).

van Gosen, B.S., Gillerman, V.S., and Armbustmacher, T.J., "Thorium Deposits of the US: Energy Resources for the Future," Circular 1336, U.S. Department of the Interior, U.S. Geological Survey (2009).

References

1. Herring, Stephen, personal communication.

2. "National Uranium Resource Evaluation (NURE) Program Final Report," GJBX-42(83), U.S. Department of Energy (1983).

3. Elevatorski, E.A., *Uranium Ores and Minerals*, Minobras (Library of Congress 77-72238) (1977).

4. Seko, N., Katakai, A., Hasegawa, S., Tamada, M., Kasai, N., Takeda, H., Sugo, T., and Saito, K., "Aquaculture of Uranium in Seawater by a Fabric-Adsorbent Submerged System," *Nucl. Technol.*, **144**, 274 (2003).

5. *Uranium 2009: Resources, Production, and Demand [The Red Book]*, OECD Nuclear Energy Agency and International Atomic Energy Agency (2010).

6. "NUEXCO Monthly Report," #228, NUEXCO, Denver, Colorado (Aug. 1987).

7. U.S. Department of Energy, Energy Information Administration, http://www.eia.gov/nuclear (2011).

8. "Forty Years of Uranium Resources, Production and Demand in Perspective," OECD Nuclear Energy Agency (2006).

9. "Thorium Statistics and Information: Mineral Commodity Summaries—Thorium," U.S. Geological Survey, http://minerals.usgs.gov/minerals/pubs/commodity/thorium/index.html#mcs.

Problems

2.1. Is the statement "The U.S. has 1,300,000 tons of uranium resources" complete?

2.2. Figure 2.16 shows the discovery rate of U_3O_8, per foot drilled, in a certain price range. Based on these data, estimate the total amount of uranium that can be recovered in this price range.

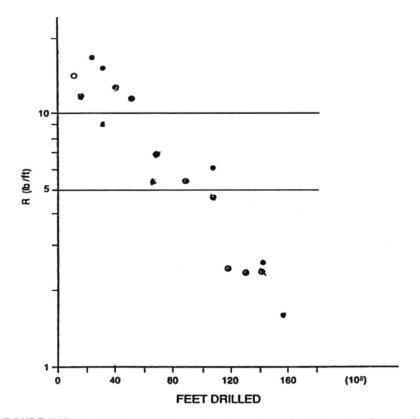

FIGURE 2.16 Feet drilled versus the number of pounds per foot of uranium discovered.

2.3. Assuming Eq. (2.1) is correct, what fraction of the earth's uranium can be found within the first 1000 m of the earth's crust?

2.4. In 1976, the U.S. nuclear industry needed about 10,000 tons of U_3O_8. Assuming that enrichment and tails requirements do not change and the industry increases at a rate of $x\%$ per year, how long would it take for the \$130/kgU reserves to be exhausted? Assume that the reserves are 600,000 tons of U_3O_8. After you develop the equation for the time, obtain numerical results for $x = 2\%$, 4%, and 6%.

2.5. Assume that a decision is made to start ordering reactors at a constant rate per year from 1990 until 2030, at which time orders will stop, so that all known uranium reserves of 2.3 million tons (with price up to \$260/kgU) will be used up. Assume the following:

(a) All plants are identical and need 150 tons of natural uranium per year.
(b) It takes 10 years to build a plant.
(c) Every plant has a 30-year lifetime.
(d) There are 120 plants operating in 1990.
(e) Reactors operating in 1990 start retiring in 2000, at the rate of 10/year. For these reactors, consider their needs only after 1990.

Calculate how many reactors per year could be ordered and the maximum number of reactors operating at any single time.

2.6. How many 1000-MWe LWRs can the world reserves of uranium serve? Consider the price category up to \$80/kgU. Assume that each reactor needs 150 tons of natural uranium per year and has a lifetime of 30 years. Also assume annual refuelings of one-third of the core.

THREE

CONVERSION AND ENRICHMENT

3.1 Introduction

Every country that designed and constructed nuclear power reactors for the generation of electricity relied on available technology, at least in the initial phase of the development of nuclear power. The United States built and operated the first uranium enrichment facilities in the world because they were needed for the atomic bomb program (the Manhattan project). After the end of World War II, the United States developed the water-cooled, uranium-fueled reactors for submarines, which also needed enriched uranium. It is not surprising, therefore, that when the civilian nuclear industry started, the availability of enrichment services influenced the decision toward the light water reactor (LWR). Canada, on the other hand, without enrichment facilities and with plenty of natural uranium resources, opted for the Canada Deuterium Uranium (CANDU) reactor, which does not require enrichment. Currently, most power reactors in the world are LWRs and require uranium slightly enriched in the ^{235}U isotope.

Many processes for isotope enrichment were known in 1941 when the Manhattan Project started in the United States. The two processes seriously considered were enrichment by electromagnetic separation or by gaseous diffusion. Because time was of the essence, the gaseous diffusion method was chosen and implemented for the weapons program.

The first large gaseous diffusion plants were built at the Oak Ridge National Laboratory in Tennessee. Later diffusion plants were built at Paducah, Kentucky, and Portsmouth, Ohio. The principal operating cost of a diffusion plant is the electrical power required to operate the compressors that move the UF_6 through the process equipment. The Oak Ridge area was selected because of the availability of abundant electric energy from the hydroelectric plants of the Tennessee Valley Authority and also because it was far from any coast, and thus more difficult to be discovered by spies.

The gaseous diffusion process utilizes a gaseous uranium compound, uranium hexafluoride (UF_6), which comes from the conversion of U_3O_8 that is the product of the uranium mill. This conversion of U_3O_8 to UF_6, a chemical engineering operation, although small in magnitude relative to the enrichment itself, is a necessary step in the nuclear fuel cycle.

3.2 Purification of U_3O_8

Before U_3O_8 can be converted into UF_6, it must be purified because uranium must be free of impurities to perform satisfactorily as a nuclear reactor fuel. The impurities usually found in natural uranium are boron, cadmium, chlorine, and many of the rare earths. Several purification processes are available in the uranium industry. Fortunately, uranium has two unique properties that make possible a very clean separation from the impurity elements:

1. Uranium forms chemical compounds with ease and is readily extracted by organic solvents immiscible with water.

2. Uranium is capable of forming an organic-soluble, electrically neutral complex compound with solvent or with an added complexing agent.

The two methods normally used in the United States for purification are both solvent extraction processes:

1. The PUREX process. Uranyl nitrate may be extracted selectively from aqueous solutions by certain oxygenated organic solvents, such as diethyl ether, methyl isobutyl ketone, and tributyl phosphate.

2. A method using uranium peroxide, $UO_4 \cdot 2H_2O$, which is precipitated quantitatively from weakly acid solutions of uranyl salts by hydrogen peroxide. After the uranium concentrate is highly purified, it is ready to be converted to UF_6.

3.3 Conversion of U_3O_8 to UF_6

Uranium hexafluoride (UF_6) was selected for the gaseous diffusion process because of its special properties. A phase diagram for UF_6 (shown in Fig. 3.1) makes it readily apparent why UF_6 is a desirable uranium compound for "feed" to a gaseous diffusion plant. The fact that UF_6 is a solid at room temperature makes it easy to handle. At slightly elevated temperatures (above the triple point at 22 psi and 147°F), it becomes a gas, making it ideal for the gaseous diffusion process, which requires the uranium to be in a vapor form for isotopic separation. Furthermore, since the atomic weight of fluorine is relatively low, with a single fluorine isotope, it does not interfere with the diffusion process of uranium molecules. It should be noted that UF_6

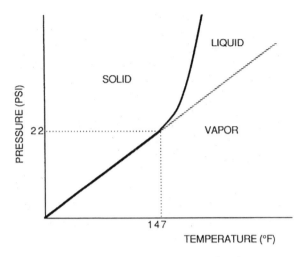

FIGURE 3.1 Phase diagram of uranium hexafluoride (UF_6).

is the only known compound of uranium that is a gas (vapor) at moderate temperatures.

The basic physical properties of UF_6 are as follows: density of solid, 4.68 g/cm^3; density of liquid, 3.63 g/cm^3; melting point, 64.05°C; and boiling point, 56.54°C. To convert U_3O_8 into UF_6, one of the following chemical processes is used: (1) dry hydrofluor process or (2) wet solvent extraction process. Figure 3.2 shows the flow chart for the dry hydrofluor process. The following four steps constitute this operation:

1. The U_3O_8 is ground to a fine powder, so as to make it a suitable feed material for the next step.

2. The ground material then enters a fluidized-bed reactor, where it is maintained at a temperature of 1000° to 1200°F and reduced by hydrogen. The resulting product consists mainly of uranium dioxide (UO_2), a brown oxide.

3. The crude UO_2 is passed on to two successive hydrofluorination fluidized-bed reactors, where interaction occurs with anhydrous hydrogen fluoride (HF) at a temperature of 900° to 1000°F. The chemical reaction that takes place is

$$UO_2 + 4HF \rightarrow 2H_2O + UF_4$$

The uranium tetrafluoride (UF_4), a green salt, is a nonvolatile solid with a high melting point (1700° to 1800°F).

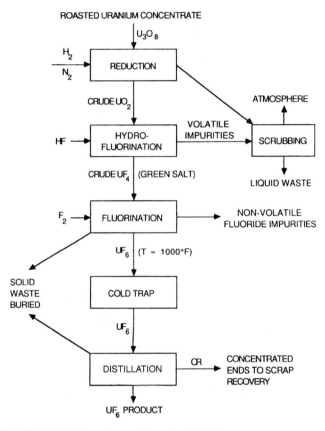

FIGURE 3.2 Simplified flow chart of the dry hydrofluor process to convert U_3O_8 to UF_6.

4. The UF_4 is treated at high temperatures with fluorine gas to form UF_6, according to the reaction

$$UF_4 + F_2 \rightarrow UF_6$$

Since some volatile impurities do follow the UF_6, the UF_6 must be purified by fractional distillation.

The second conversion process, the wet solvent extraction process (Fig. 3.3), also uses the reduction, hydrofluorination, and fluorination steps, but these are preceded by solvent extraction to remove impurities. However, since the UF_6 produced in this process is pure, fractional distillation is not required. The highly pure UF_6 produced at these plants is collected in steel cylinders and shipped to the enrichment plants.

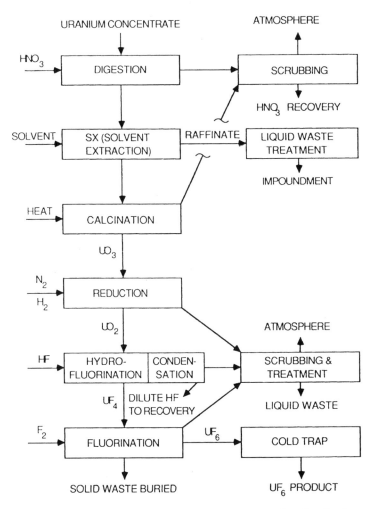

FIGURE 3.3 Simplified flow chart of the wet solvent extraction-fluorination process to convert U_3O_8 to UF_6.

A UF_6 conversion plant consists of two separate chemical plants: the UF_6 conversion facility and a fluorine plant that produces fluorine gas by electrolytic decomposition of hydrofluoric acid. Since the availability of the two plants cannot always be "in phase," the availability of the entire plant is equal to the product of the two individual plant availabilities.

Demand for conversion services is affected by many factors, such as growth of the nuclear industry, the tails assay of the enrichment process (see Section 3.4), the reprocessing and recycling of used fuel, and the availability and use in LWRs of uranium and plutonium from weapons dismantlement.

3.4 Enrichment of Uranium by Gaseous Diffusion

Separation and enrichment of isotopes by the gaseous diffusion process is based on the difference in rates at which the hexafluorides of ^{235}U and ^{238}U effuse through a thin barrier containing many millions of tiny pores. If the UF$_6$ molecules are kept at a temperature T, they have a kinetic energy $kT = \frac{1}{2}MV^2$, where k is the Boltzmann constant, M is molecular mass, and V is the speed of the molecule. Since the ratio of the speeds of two molecules with different masses M_H and M_L is equal to

$$\frac{V_L}{V_H} = \sqrt{\frac{M_H}{M_L}} = \alpha \tag{3.1}$$

the ^{235}UF$_6$ molecules will be slightly faster than the ^{238}UF$_6$ ones. It has been shown that the separation of molecules is due to the fact that the relative frequency with which molecules of different species pass through a small hole of a barrier (see Fig. 3.4) is proportional to the speed of the molecule, or inversely proportional to the square root of the molecular weight. Thus, effusion of the lighter molecules is faster and the gas passing through the barrier is slightly enriched in ^{235}UF$_6$.

A measure of the ability to separate the two isotopes by this method is the value of the separation factor given by Eq. (3.1). For the present case,

$$\alpha = \sqrt{\frac{M_H}{M_L}} = \sqrt{\frac{238 + 6x19}{235 + 6x19}} = 1.004289 \tag{3.1a}$$

The higher the value of α, the easier it is to separate isotopes and thus enrich one stream to one isotope and deplete the other. Equation (3.1a) gives the theoretical value of α. The practical value, in contrast to the ideal one, is given by the Rayleigh distillation calculations as equal to 1.003. The reduction in the value of α is due to downstream backpressure and nonseparable flow through the barrier.

Because the separation factor for UF$_6$ is so small, enrichment of uranium to the isotope ^{235}U to values even as low as 3% to 4% requires repetition of this basic process thousands of times. The basic constituent of the operation is the stage; a stage consists of a compressor, the compressor motor, and a converter through which the compressor directs the UF$_6$. Stages are joined together to form cells; a number of cells forms a unit. The complete setup—stages, cells, and units—constitutes a cascade. The efficiency of the stages can be increased by using "enriching" stages and "stripping" stages as shown in Fig. 3.4. Consider stage B; gas enters from the bottom and about half is allowed to pass through the barrier. The diffusate, which is richer in ^{235}U, thus flows into stage A. In stage A, the diffusate undergoes further

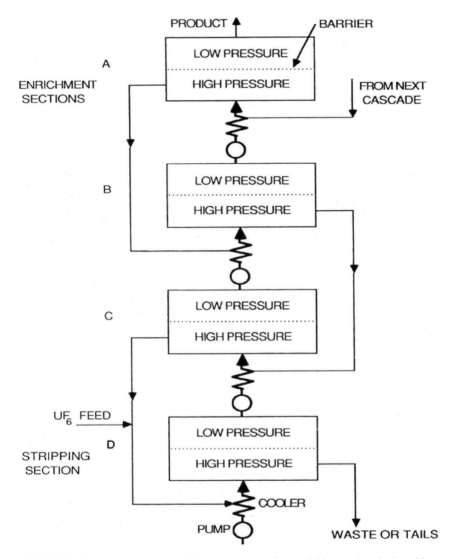

FIGURE 3.4 A typical gaseous diffusion cascade for enriching and stripping. Note that the pressure is less than atmospheric in all stages to increase the mean free path (mfp) of the molecules.

diffusion. Again consider stage B; the gas reduced in ^{235}U is pumped to stage C, where it joins the diffusate from stage D. In stage C, the gas diffuses to stage B and the residual returns to stage D to be recycled. Thus, the gas moving up the cascade is richer in light molecules (^{235}UF$_6$), whereas gas moving down in the cascade is partially depleted of ^{235}U. (Calculations of

FIGURE 3.5 Typical gaseous diffusion equipment.

the above phenomena are similar to those of fractional distillation.[1]) Notice that the stripping stages normally recover some of the uranium from the waste product stream, thus reducing the number of enrichment stages. Figure 3.5 shows typical gaseous diffusion equipment.

The barrier used in the gaseous diffusion process is an extremely important part of the process. An ideal barrier consists of a large number of small holes of nearly uniform diameter. If the diameter of the holes and the thickness of the barrier are smaller than the mean free path (mfp) of UF_6 at the upstream pressure of the barrier, individual molecules of UF_6 will flow through the holes without colliding with other molecules. The rate of flow of molecules can be predicted by the use of Knudsen's law.[2,3] This is known as *molecular flow*. However, an actual barrier has neither straight nor circular holes of uniform diameter; thus, true molecular flow probably does not exist. Because of the security of the diffusion plant data, very little information is available in the open literature concerning the technical data of the U.S. diffusion process.

Following is a summary of the facts concerning the diffusion process barrier, for which the requirements are very stringent:

1. Barrier materials reportedly used are sintered nickel and anodized aluminum, plus others.

2. The barrier must be thin, and thus delicate.

3. Billions of holes per cubic inch are required, with each hole 10^{-7} in. (2.54×10^{-9} m) in diameter.

4. The barrier material is attacked by organic materials—lubricants, vacuum pump oil, etc.

5. There must be methods of preventing or removing uranium compounds that form on the barrier.

6. Leakage of air into the system cannot be tolerated because UF_6 and air or air and water combine to form a solid oxide of uranium (UO_2F_2) and release fluorine gas. This solid would also plug the barrier.

One should note that radioactivity is not a problem in the gaseous diffusion process, since uranium is predominately an alpha emitter. Therefore, no special shielding is needed. However, if material escapes from the system, it may be a health hazard to workers (from inhalation of UF_6).

The settling out of uranium into solid compounds could cause the formation of a critical mass, if the settling out were to take place in higher stages. The possibility of a critical mass of ^{235}U must always be carefully considered in the handling, shipping, and storage of enriched uranium. To summarize, the main operational concerns of an enrichment plant are (1) criticality, (2) UF_6 leaks, and (3) plugging of the diffusion barriers by solids.

Criticality issues (moderator geometry, fissile mass, etc.) must be addressed even at low enrichments.

The small amount of ^{234}U found in natural uranium goes along with the ^{235}U, during enrichment, because of the closeness of the masses of these two isotopes. The presence of this small amount of ^{234}U in the LWR fuel has no consequences for the performance of the fuel. The ^{234}U, however, is the principal isotope of concern for dose received from inhaled uranium. In a conservative approach, the dose delivered from uranium uptake is taken to be 100% due to ^{234}U.

3.5 Quantitative Aspects of Enrichment by Gaseous Diffusion

When enrichment services are needed, it is necessary for the customer requesting such services to know (1) the amount of natural uranium feed needed by the enrichment plant per unit of product enriched to the desired percent in ^{235}U, and (2) the cost of enrichment per unit of product. The quantitative answers to these questions are presented and discussed in this section.

Six external variables are involved in gaseous diffusion, satisfying the following equations:

$$F = P + W \tag{3.2}$$

$$x_f F = x_p P + x_w W \tag{3.3}$$

where

x_f = weight fraction of ^{235}U in the feed material

x_p = weight fraction of ^{235}U in the product (i.e., desired enrichment)

x_w = weight fraction of ^{235}U in the waste stream (depleted uranium); also known as *tails assay*

F = number of kilograms of feed material (per unit time)

P = number of kilograms of product enriched (per unit time)

W = number of kilograms of uranium in the waste stream (per unit time).[a]

Since there are two equations and six variables, it is possible to specify four external variables independently and solve for two ratios in terms of these four variables. In practice, the four variables specified are

- x_f: At present, without recycling of uranium, this is equal to 0.711%, the ^{235}U content of natural uranium.

- x_p: This is the enrichment requested by the customer, that is, the utility that will use the enriched product.

- x_w: Its value is between 0.2% and 0.3%; in principle, the customer sets this variable, but in practice (in the United States at least), the company operating the enrichment plant decides what the x_w value is. The value of x_w has an effect on the cost of enrichment, as will become obvious from the discussion that follows.

- P: Denotes the mass (acually the mass per unit time) of the desired product.

The feed rate F and the waste rate W are then calculated from Eqs. (3.2) and (3.3):

$$F = P \frac{x_p - x_w}{x_f - x_w} \tag{3.4}$$

[a] Although F, P, and W are defined as mass flow rate (kilograms per unit time), these quantities are frequently referred to as the "total" mass, without reference to time. Obviously, no error is introduced if one is consistent.

$$W = P \frac{x_p - x_f}{x_f - x_w} \tag{3.5}$$

Equation (3.4) is most frequently used and is written in the form

$$\frac{F}{P} = \frac{x_p - x_w}{x_f - x_w} \tag{3.6}$$

The quantity given by Eq. (3.6) is known as the *feed factor* because it calculates the number of kilograms of uranium needed as feed for the enrichment process per kilogram of product, for a specified set of values for x_p, x_f, and x_w. Values of the feed factor are usually tabulated as a function of x_p for many values of x_w.

Equation (3.5), written as

$$\frac{W}{P} = \frac{x_p - x_f}{x_f - x_w} \tag{3.7}$$

is known as the *waste factor*. Note that

$$\frac{W}{P} = \frac{F}{P} - 1 \tag{3.8}$$

In addition to the feed factor, one needs to calculate the physical effort needed to reach a certain enrichment. That physical effort, which in turn determines the cost of enrichment, is given by the quantity known as the *separative work unit* (SWU). One should think of the number of SWUs as the quantity directly related to the resources required to perform the enrichment to the desired level of x_p, given the values of x_f and x_w. The resource needed for the isotope separation by the diffusion process is electric energy. Hence, the number of SWUs, a number proportional to the energy consumed, determines the cost of enrichment.

The number of SWUs produced by an enrichment plant during a time period τ is given by[2]

$$\text{SWU} = [P * V(x_p) + W * V(x_w) - F * V(x_f)] * \tau \tag{3.9}$$

where the quantities $V(x_i)$, known as the *separation potentials*, are given by

$$V(x_i) = (2x_i - 1) \ln \left(\frac{x_i}{1 - x_i} \right) \tag{3.10}$$

where x_i stands for x_f, x_p, or x_w.

Since P, W, and F are mass flow rates, the units of SWU in Eq. (3.9) are kilograms or, as more commonly given, kg-SWU. During the time τ, the plant produced $P * \tau$ kg of enriched product. Therefore, the number of SWUs per unit product is

$$SF = \mathrm{SWU}/(P * \tau) = V(x_p) + \frac{W}{P} V(x_w) - \frac{F}{P} V(x_f) \qquad (3.11)$$

The quantity SF, given by Eq. (3.11), is commonly referred to as the *SWU factor*. Values of the SWU factor are usually tabulated along with values of the feed factor (FF) [Eq. (3.6)]. Figure 3.6 shows the values of FF and SF for enrichments up to 5% with $x_w = 0.2\%$. Note that although the SWU factor is, strictly speaking, dimensionless, its "units" are kg-SWU/kg; that is, Eq. (3.11) gives the number of SWUs needed per kilogram of enriched product and not per ton or per gram. Throughout this book, units of kg-SWU/kg are used, unless otherwise specified. For simplicity in writing, however, the kg is dropped and the unit of SF will be indicated as SWU/kg.

If one divides both sides of Eq. (3.9) by the time τ, the result is kg-SWU/time. For enrichment plants, the time τ is normally taken to be a year, and the result is kg-SWU/yr, the customary unit expressing the capacity of an enrichment plant.

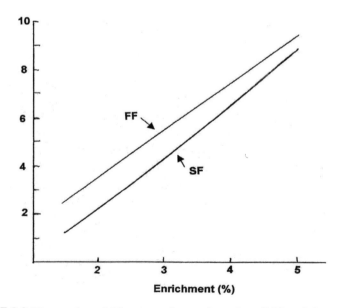

FIGURE 3.6 The number of kilograms of natural uranium (FF) and the number of SWU (SF) per kilogram of enriched product as a function of enrichment, up to 5% $(x_w = 0.2\%)$.

■ *Example 3.1:* (a) What is the number of kilograms of natural uranium that has to be provided as feed in an enrichment plant if one requests 30,000 kg of uranium enriched to 3% in ^{235}U? Assume the tails assay is 0.2%. (b) What is the number of SWUs needed for the separation?

Answer: (a) Use Eq. (3.6) to obtain the feed factor:

$$\frac{F}{P} = \frac{3 - 0.2}{0.711 - 0.2} = 5.479 \text{ kg feed/kg product}$$

The total number of kg needed as feed is

$$F = 30,000 \text{ kg product } (5.479 \text{ kg feed/kg product})$$

$$= 164,370 \text{ kg feed uranium.}$$

(b) Use Eq. (3.10) to obtain the values of the three separation potentials:

$$V(x_f) = (2 * 0.00711 - 1) \ln \left(\frac{0.0071}{1 - 0.00711} \right) = 4.869$$

$$V(x_w) = (2 * 0.002 - 1) \ln \left(\frac{0.002}{1 - 0.002} \right) = 6.188$$

$$V(x_p) = (2 * 0.03 - 1) \ln \left(\frac{0.03}{1 - 0.03} \right) = 3.268$$

The SWU factor, using Eq. (3.11), is

$$SF \, [\text{SWU/kg}] = 3.268 + (5.479 - 1) * 6.188 - 5.479 * 4.869 = 4.307$$

and the total number of SWUs is

$$(30,000 \text{ kg})(4.307 \text{ SWU/kg}) = 129,210 \text{ SWU .} \quad ■$$

■ *Example 3.2:* What are (a) the feed factor and (b) the SWU factor for uranium enriched 4% in ^{235}U? Assume 0.2% tails assay.

Answer: (a) The feed factor is

$$\frac{F}{P} = \frac{4 - 0.2}{0.711 - 0.2} = 7.436$$

(b) For the SWU factor, the $V(x_p)$ must be calculated for 4% enrichment:

$$V(x_p) = (2 * 0.04 - 1)\ln\left(\frac{0.04}{1 - 0.04}\right) = 2.924$$

$$SF = 2.924 + (7.436 - 1) * 6.188 - 7.436 * 4.869 = 6.544$$

Note: With a 1% increase in enrichment, the *FF* increases by $(7.436 - 5.479)/5.479 = 0.357 \sim 36\%$. The *SF* increases by $(6.544 - 4.307)/4.307 = 0.519 \sim 52\%$. ∎

The number of stages needed to obtain a desired enrichment is given by

$$N = \frac{2}{\ln \alpha} \ln\left[\frac{x_p(1 - x_w)}{x_w(1 - x_p)}\right] - 1 \tag{3.12}$$

If $x_p = 0.03$ and $x_w = 0.002$, $N = 1277$, with $\alpha = 1.004289$.

An isotope separation plant has to operate for a rather long time, when first started, before it can produce the product of specified enrichment. This "delay" in production is due to the fact that the amount of desired isotope held in the plant may represent many days of normal production. After start-up, the plant must operate without product withdrawal for enough time to produce a working inventory of the desired isotope. An approximate equation for the equilibrium time t_p is

$$t_p = \frac{8h}{(\alpha - 1)^2}\left\{\frac{x_p - 2x_p x_f + x_f}{x_p - x_f}\ln\left(\frac{x_p(1 - x_f)}{x_f(1 - x_p)}\right) - 2\right\} \tag{3.13}$$

where h is the stage holdup time (of the order of seconds). A typical time is $t_p \sim 20$ to 25 days.

Using principles of thermodynamics, one can calculate the minimum theoretical energy required per SWU, given by

$$\frac{4RT}{M(\alpha - 1)^2} \, [\text{kW/(SWU/yr)}] \tag{3.14}$$

where R is the universal gas constant ($= 8.31441$ J/mol·K) and T is the temperature in degrees kelvin. If the temperature of the gas is taken to be 58°C, $M = 235$, the result is 0.0802 [kW/(SWU/yr)], which amounts to 702 kWh/SWU. However, the actual energy consumed, due to various losses, is close to 3000 kWh/SWU.

3.6 The Management of Uranium Enrichment Tails

As seen in the previous section, a relatively large amount of UF_6 with ^{235}U content between 0.2% and 0.3% is left behind as *tails* (or *waste* or *depleted uranium*). For example, if the desired enrichment is 4% (see Example 3.2), to obtain 1 kg of enriched product, 7.436 kg of natural uranium are needed as feed, which means that 6.436 kg become tails or waste. It is estimated that the United States has in storage (as of 2011) about 700,000 tons of tails as UF_6. Because UF_6 is corrosive and not chemically stable enough for long-term storage, plans are under way for the deconversion of the UF_6 first into UF_4 and finally into UO_2, a stable powdered oxide. The fluorine that becomes available will be utilized for industrial purposes. One deconversion plant started operating in 2010 and two more will start in 2013–2014.

3.7 The United States Enrichment Corporation (USEC)

The Energy Policy Act of 1992 established the United States Enrichment Corporation (USEC) as the organization to provide enrichment services in the United States. As a result of this legislation, Congress transferred the enrichment enterprise from the Department of Energy to USEC. In 1996, Congress passed the USEC Privatization Act with the objective to make USEC a privately owned corporation. In 1998, the final step in the privatization process took place with the announcement of an initial public offering of common stock. USEC is now traded on the New York Stock Exchange. As of 2012 USEC operated the only gaseous diffusion plant in the United States, in Paducah, Kentucky, with a capacity of 11.3×10^6 SWU/yr. This plant is allowed to enrich uranium up to 5% in ^{235}U. (A second gaseous diffusion plant, operated by USEC in Portsmouth, Ohio, stopped operations in 2001.)

3.8 The Use of Weapons Uranium for Civilian Nuclear Fuel

The dismantling of nuclear weapons, as a result of disarmament treaties, made available highly enriched uranium (HEU) that can be used as an LWR fuel, after "blending it down" to the 3% to 5% enrichment required by the currently operating LWRs. When HEU ($\sim$90%) coming from dismantled nuclear weapons is used to produce LWR fuel ($\sim$4%), it is not sent through enrichment (or depletion). Instead, a process called *downblending* is used. In downblending, two streams of UF_6, one with natural U and the other with HEU, are mixed in such a way that the final product of mixing has the desired enrichment. It is like mixing two shades of paint to produce a desired third one.

The use of HEU to make civilian fuel is carried out under a program called Megatons to Megawatts; it is based on an agreement signed in 1993 between Russia and the United States. As a result of this agreement, Russian nuclear warheads are dismantled and their uranium is sold to the United States; this HEU is then downblended, either in Russia or in the United

States, and is converted into fuel that is loaded into nuclear power plants in the United States to generate electricity.

3.9 Enrichment of Uranium by the Centrifuge Method

Early work on the use of the gaseous centrifuge method was done by J. W. Beams[4,5] at the University of Virginia, where he succeeded in separating isotopes of some of the light elements in an ultracentrifuge.

Similar work was carried out in Germany during World War II by G. Zippe. Later, in the 1950s, Groth and coworkers in Germany developed and built a series of progressively larger gas centrifuge units. In the 1960s, gas centrifuge methods began to appear to be competitive for large-scale enrichment. In 1970, the governments of the United Kingdom, the Netherlands, and Germany signed the Treaty of Almelo with the objective of collaborating in the development of centrifuge enrichment technology; as a result of the agreement, the company URENCO was created, jointly owned by the three governments. A uranium enrichment plant, based on centrifuge technology, was built and is still operating at Almelo, a small city in the Netherlands.

The Japanese developed a laboratory-size centrifuge enrichment facility in 1956.

In the United States, there were several pilot plants carrying out research and development work. In 1977, the Carter administration announced that the next enrichment plant would be using this technology. Construction of the Gas Centrifuge Enrichment Plant (GCEP), with a projected capacity of 8.8 million SWUs per year, was started in Portsmouth, Ohio. In 1985, with the GCEP almost finished, the Reagan administration decided to abandon the centrifuge technology in favor of the atomic vapor laser isotope separation (AVLIS) process (see Section 3.11).

The centrifuge operates on the principle that in a rotating drum or cylinder, the centrifugal force tends to compress the gas molecules in the cylinder to the outer wall. However, the velocity due to thermal agitation tends to redistribute the gas molecules throughout the whole volume of the cylinder. The lighter molecules are favored by this effect because of their greater velocity, so a higher concentration of the lighter molecules gathers near the center of the rotating drum.

The rotating drum or bowl has a set of three concentric, nonrotating tubes at the axis (Fig. 3.7) that provide the means to (1) admit the UF_6 gas feed, (2) withdraw the light molecules from the bottom, and (3) withdraw the heavy molecules from the top. The rotating bowl is supported at the bottom by a needle bearing. At the top, it is centered by a magnetic bearing. The bowl rotates inside an outer vacuum case that keeps air out, and if the bowl disintegrates, retains the flying debris.

The centrifuge has a relatively large separation factor compared to gaseous diffusion but a flow rate smaller than a gaseous diffusion stage.

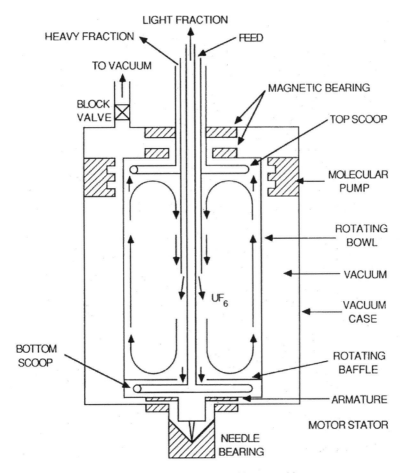

FIGURE 3.7 Schematic showing the Zippe centrifuge machine.

For a gas centrifuge machine, the separation factor can be obtained approximately by

$$\alpha = \exp\left\{\frac{(M_H - M_L)\omega^2 a^2}{2RT}\right\} \tag{3.15}$$

Since α has a value close to 1, the equation for the separation factor may be written, without introducing a significant error, as

$$\alpha = 1 + \frac{(M_H - M_L)\omega^2 a^2}{2RT} \tag{3.16}$$

where

ω = angular speed of the rotating bowls (rad/s)

a = radius of rotor (inside dimension)

M_H = molecular weight of $^{238}U^{19}F_6$

M_L = molecular weight of $^{235}U^{19}F_6$

R = gas constant

T = temperature (K).

The separation factor for a centrifuge with a 1-ft-diam rotor spinning at 350 m/s (2.3×10^3 rad/s) at a temperature of 300 K is $\alpha \sim 1.1$ to 1.2. Compare this to a gaseous diffusion stage, which has 1.004289.

The separative capacity of a single rotating bowl may be written in the form[6]

$$SWU \sim \text{separative capacity} \sim L(\omega a)^4 (M_H - M_L)^2 / T^2 \qquad (3.17)$$

The objective of Eq. (3.17) is not to show the exact form of the separative capacity equation; instead, the intent is just to show the dependence on the important changeable parameters defining the process. Thus, the capacity is (1) proportional to the length L of the bowl, (2) proportional to the fourth power of the peripheral speed, and (3) inversely proportional to the square of the temperature.

Based on the above, one should use a long bowl and rotate it at the highest possible speed, which is usually done. There are constraints, however, for a bowl of a certain size if destruction of the rotating drum is to be prevented when the mechanical strength is exceeded by the forces produced because of the rotation.

The separative capacity of a single centrifuge is relatively small. A plant with a total capacity of about 9 million SWUs per year will require between 90,000 to 100,000 machines. Such a large number of machines necessitates an extremely high degree of reliability. Just consider that if the mean time between failures is 3 years per machine, the plant would have about 90 machine failures per day. Reports from the Almelo demonstration plant in the Netherlands indicate that very high availability (99%) can be achieved.

Since isotope separation in the gas centrifuge is a thermodynamically reversible process, the power consumption is much lower than that for gaseous diffusion. Almost all the power in the centrifuge is consumed in overcoming bearing and gas friction, rather than for the separation process itself. The estimate is that the energy per SWU for a gas centrifuge is about 1/10 of that required by the diffusion process.

Because of this large difference in energy consumption per SWU, almost all enrichment plants under construction today employ the centrifuge method. In the United States, one such enrichment plant started operating in 2010 with a capacity of 5.7×10^6 SWU/yr; it is the URENCO U.S. facility located in Eunice, New Mexico, owned by the Louisiana Enrichment Services (LES) company. Two plants are under construction: One is owned by USEC and is located in Piketon, Ohio; it will have a capacity of 3.5×10^6 SWU/yr. The second, owned by AREVA, is located in Bonneville County, Idaho; it will have a capacity of 3.0×10^6 SWU/yr. These plants will be allowed to enrich uranium up to 10% in ^{235}U. For capacities of enrichment facilities around the world, see Ref. 7.

3.10 Enrichment of Uranium by the Separation Nozzle Method

Another method of enriching uranium is that of the separation nozzle. Although the nozzle principle has evolved through a number of forms, the first experimental proof was achieved by Becker in Germany.[8-10] Further development of the nozzle process was carried on in South Africa, the Netherlands, and Brazil. Figure 3.8 depicts the nozzle principle.

Feed gas, $UF_6 + H_2$, in a ratio of 5% to 95%, is forced into the orifice at pressures from 266 to 2660 Pa (20 to 200 Torr). The nozzle is in a high vacuum, of course. The gas flow mixture experiences large centrifugal

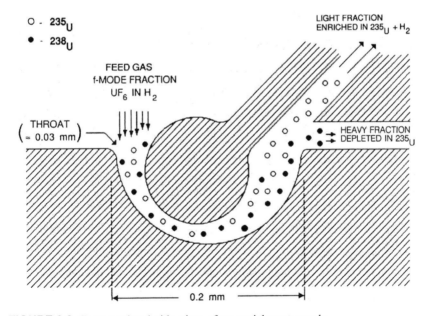

FIGURE 3.8 Cross-sectional side view of an enrichment nozzle.

acceleration as it moves through the curved slit and gas beam scattering. The lighter isotope scatters first, thus causing some separation of ^{235}U and ^{238}U. As shown in Fig. 3.8, two paths are provided, one for the light molecules and one for the heavy molecules. Reported separation factors vary but seem to be about 1.015.

Dilution of the UF_6 with hydrogen is beneficial for two reasons. First, the mixture has a higher sonic velocity than pure UF_6; thus, much higher velocities can be reached. Second, the inert gas increases the separation factor (for reasons not fully understood).

The engineering features of the nozzle must be very precise, since the nozzle is made to extremely small dimensions, and extremely stress resistant materials are required for construction. The engineering analysis of the separation nozzle, which is quite complicated because of the nonequilibrium condition of the $^{238}UF_6$, $^{235}UF_6$, and H_2, is not presented here.

Because the nozzle process has a separation factor higher than that of gaseous diffusion, about 500 nozzle stages would be required to produce 3% enriched uranium, whereas more than 1200 diffusion stages are needed for the same enrichment. The energy consumed by the nozzle separation process is reported to be about 4000 kWh/SWU, which is slightly higher than the energy used by gaseous diffusion. Improvements in the process are possible. However, there is no incentive to develop the nozzle method since commercially demonstrated centrifuge plants consume much less energy per SWU than the nozzle method. In addition, the AVLIS method is being pursued (see next section) and shows promise for commercial employment.

3.11 Enrichment of Uranium Using Lasers

As stated in Section 3.8, the United States abandoned the centrifuge in 1985 as the next method of uranium enrichment and decided instead to concentrate all its efforts on the development of the atomic vapor laser isotope separation (AVLIS) method as the sole advanced method for isotope enrichment.[11–13] The decision was based on the fact that the gaseous diffusion plants can provide adequate enrichment services for the foreseeable future; therefore, there is adequate time to develop the AVLIS method for commercial application. Also, in view of the increased competition for enrichment services from abroad, especially Europe, it was felt that the AVLIS method offered the best possibilities for success in the long run.

The principle of AVLIS was demonstrated in 1975 when milligrams of enriched uranium were obtained. What remains to be done is to upgrade the scale of the process to be able to enrich tons of uranium instead of just milligrams. New technologies are required for this major task, mostly in the area of powerful lasers.

AVLIS is based on the use of the absorption spectrum of uranium metal vapor, which consists of more than 300,000 lines at visible wavelengths.

However, many of these absorption lines are relatively sharp, with sufficient displacement between a ^{238}U and a ^{235}U absorption line for a transition to be instigated to one atom and not the other. To permit selective excitation of the ^{235}U atoms, a careful choice of the laser wavelength, one that would be most suitable for a practical process, must be made.

The AVLIS method is depicted in Figs. 3.9 and 3.10 and works as follows:

1. A pool of liquid uranium at 2300°C is formed at the bottom of a vacuum chamber inside a heated graphite crucible. Uranium vapor, consisting of ^{238}U and ^{235}U neutral atoms, rises and passes through the slit.

2. The beam of uranium atoms is exposed to an intense laser light of 5915 Å, which selectively excites ^{235}U atoms to a higher energy level, called *photoexcitation.*

3. Ultraviolet light "kicks" some of the excited electrons completely free, thus ionizing some of the ^{235}U atoms.

4. The positively charged ^{235}U ions are then attracted to a negatively charged Faraday cup through a quadrupole magnet.

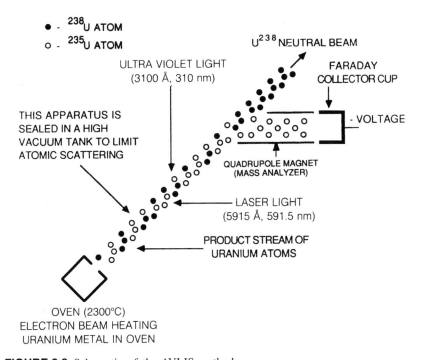

FIGURE 3.9 Schematic of the AVLIS method.

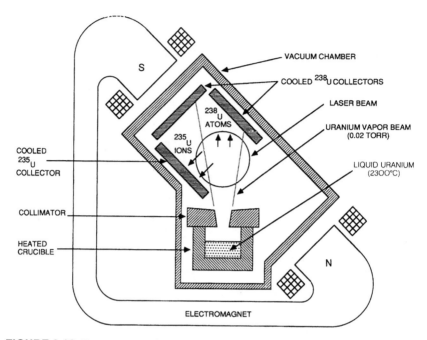

FIGURE 3.10 Transverse section of AVCO-Exxon laser uranium isotope separator.

The principal difficulties of AVLIS are the low throughput and the need to operate at very high temperatures (2300°C), at which the uranium vapor attacks almost all materials. The major potential advantages of the method are the obtaining of almost complete separation in one stage and low energy consumption (reported at 300 kWh/SWU).

A variation of AVLIS is the molecular isotope separation (MLIS) method[14] under development at Los Alamos National Laboratory. The MLIS method utilizes differences in the molecular vibrational and rotational states of the $^{235}U^{19}F_6$ and $^{238}U^{19}F_6$ molecules. MLIS proceeds in two steps: (1) excitation of the $^{235}UF_6$ molecules by the absorption of energy from infrared lasers and (2) dissociation of $^{235}UF_6$ molecules with energy absorbed from a source of ultraviolet light. The wavelengths used are such that the $^{238}UF_6$ molecules are not affected. The $^{235}UF_6$ molecule dissociates into $^{235}UF_5$ and free fluorine atoms. The $^{235}UF_5$ thus formed precipitates to a solid powder that can be filtered from the gas stream.

MLIS is more difficult because the use of UF_6 tends to cause overlapping of absorption lines at room temperature. To improve this situation, it is necessary to reduce the vapor pressure of the UF_6. However, the vapor pressure of UF_6 at 77 K is only 6.665×10^{-23} Pa (5×10^{-25} Torr). Robinson and Jenson[14] reported that an experiment was performed where UF_6 was mixed with hydrogen and the mixture cooled to 30 K by expansion to high speeds through a hypersonic nozzle. In this experiment, subcooled UF_6 molecules remained uncondensed long enough to assume the low-temperature energy distribution and display an absorption spectrum in which the $^{235}UF_6$ lines and $^{238}UF_6$ lines did not overlap. Because of classification of this research, we can only assume that the separation with laser light and ultraviolet light were similar to the atomic separation process.

A new enrichment process called SILEX, a variation of the AVLIS and MLIS methods, is under development. GE-Hitachi, through its subsidiary Global Laser Enrichment (GLE), submitted a license application in June 2009 to the NRC to construct a commercial laser enrichment plant in Wilmington, North Carolina, that will use SILEX. Initial capacity is announced to be 1×10^6 SWU, eventually to reach 3.5 to 6×10^6 SWU/yr.

The principles of laser enrichment have been proved in the laboratory. One major attraction to the method is the fact that a large separation factor (60% or more) is possible in one step. The energy consumption seems to be reasonable. The main additional development needed is the increase of the throughput from grams to tons.

3.12 Enrichment Prices and Contracts

Before the Privatization Act of 1996 and the creation of USEC, the price per SWU was determined by the U.S. government in accordance with the requirements set by the Atomic Energy Act of 1954. After the establishment of USEC as a private company, prices are set by USEC based on supply-and-demand market conditions, like any other product or service. The price of 1 SWU fluctuated over the years, reaching a maximum of $159/SWU in 1983. In 2012, the price is ~$110 to 130/SWU (current prices are available at the Ux Consulting Company website, www.uxc.com/review/uxc_Prices.aspx).

Two basic contract types are offered by USEC: requirements and utility services.

A requirements contract obligates the supplier to provide the services as and when needed. Under this type of contract, the supplier receives the benefit of increases in demand and assumes the risk of reductions in demand.

Utility services contracts were started in 1984 by DOE and had a term of 30 years. Customers could terminate future purchase obligations without penalty upon providing a 10-year notice; customers could terminate obligations on shorter notice by being penalized with substantial termination fees. USEC waived the 10-year notice provision for each year from fiscal 2003 through 2008. Under certain conditions a customer may be given the flexibility to vary its commitment between 70% and 100% of services if it agrees to purchase at least 70% of its annual commitment from USEC.

The price of enriched uranium may now be calculated. Let

PU = price of natural uranium ($/kgU)

PC = cost of conversion of U_3O_8 to UF_6 ($/kgU)

PS = price of one SWU (in $)

PE = price of enriched uranium ($/kgU).

Assuming no losses in conversion, the value of PE is

$$PE = (PU + PC)\frac{F}{P} + PS * SF \qquad (3.18)$$

where SF is given by Eq. (3.11). If uranium loss in conversion is taken into account, the equation for the cost of enrichment takes the form

$$PE = [PU/(1 - \ell_c)]\frac{F}{P} + PS * SF \qquad (3.19)$$

where ℓ_c is the fraction of uranium lost during conversion (the value of ℓ_c is <1%).

The expression for PE given by Eq. (3.18) may be considered as a function x_w, the tails assay. As such, one raises the question, Does this function have a minimum? To find out the answer, one takes the derivative with respect to x_w and sets it equal to zero. The result of this calculation is

$$\frac{PF}{PS} = \frac{(x_f - x_w)(1 - 2x_w)}{x_w(1 - x_w)} + (1 - 2x_f)\ln\left[\frac{x_w(1 - x_f)}{x_f(1 - x_w)}\right] \qquad (3.20)$$

where $PF = PU + PC$ is the price of UF_6 in $/kgU. Notice that the value of the tails that minimizes the cost depends on the ratio of the price of UF_6 divided by the price per SWU.

■ **Example 3.3:** Calculate the cost of enriched uranium (in dollars per kilogram) if the product is 3% enriched, the tails assay is 0.25%, and the conversion loss is 0.5%. Assume the price of natural uranium is $57/lbU_3O_8, the cost of conversion is $12/kg, and the price per SWU is $100.

Answer: First, it is necessary to calculate the feed and SWU factors [Eqs. (3.6) and (3.11)]:

$$F/P = (3 - 0.25)/(0.711 - 0.25) = 5.965$$

$$W/P = 4.965$$

$$V(x_f) = (2 * 0.00711 - 1)\ln[0.00711/(1 - 0.00711)] = 4.869$$

$$V(x_p) = (2 * 0.030 - 1)\ln[0.030/(1 - 0.030)] = 3.267$$

$$V(x_w) = (2 * 0.0025 - 1)\ln[0.0025/(1 - 0.0025)] = 5.959$$

$$SF = 3.267 + 4.965 * 5.959 - 5.965 * 4.869 = 3.810 \text{ SWU/kg}$$

Using Eq. (3.19) (price of U: $57/lb U_3O_8 * 2.6 = $148.20/kgU),

$$PE = [148.20/(1 - 0.005) + 12] * 5.965 + 100 * 3.810$$

$$= \$906.03 + \$381.00 = \$1341.04/kgU$$

The price is $1336.593/kgU if conversion loss is neglected.   ■

■ **Example 3.4:** Calculate the cost of enriched uranium (in dollars per kilogram) if the product is 4.5% enriched, the tails assay is 0.25%, and the conversion loss is 0.5%. Assume the price of natural uranium is $150/kg, the cost of conversion is $12/kg, and the price per SWU is $110.

Answer: First calculate the *FF* and *SF* using Eqs. (3.6) and (3.11):

$$F/P = (4.5 - 0.25)/(0.711 - 0.25) = 9.219$$

$$W/P = 8.219$$

$$V(x_p) = (2 * 0.045 - 1)\ln[0.045/(1 - 0.045)] = 2.780$$

$$V(x_f) = 4.869$$

$$V(x_w) = 5.959$$

$$SF = 2.780 + 8.219 * 5.959 - 9.219 * 4.869 = 6.870$$

$$PE = [150/(1 - 0.005) + 12] * 9.219 + 110 * 6.870 = \$2256.13/kgU$$

If conversion loss is neglected the price is $2249.18/kgU.   ■

3.13 World Enrichment Capacity

The world nuclear power industry operates under the "once-through" fuel cycle. In this mode, enrichment of uranium is a necessary step. For this reason, availability of adequate enrichment capacity is extremely important (obviously—without enrichment, the nuclear industry will come to a halt). Countries that operate nuclear power plants either have their own enrichment facilities or they contract their enrichment services to others that have the necessary enrichment capacity. Since the enrichment enterprise is large and expensive, for countries that operate a few plants, it costs less to obtain enrichment services from others than to build their own facilities.

The world enrichment capacity is not static; it is changing all the time. Table 3.1 shows capacity as of 2010 and projections for the future.

TABLE 3.1
World Enrichment Capacity*

	2010	2015	2020
France (AREVA)	8,500[a]	7,000	7,500
Germany, Netherlands, United Kingdom (URENCO)	12,800	12,200	12,300
Japan (JNFL)	150	750	1,500
United States (USEC)	11,300[a]	3,800	3,800
United States (URENCO)	200	5,800	5,900
United States (AREVA)	0	>1,000	3,300
United States (Global Laser Enrichment)	0	2,000	3,500
Russia (Tenex)	23,000	33,000	30,000 to 35,000
China (CNNC)	1,300	3,000	6,000 to 8,000
Pakistan, Brazil, Iran	100	300	300
Total (approximate)	57,350	69,000	74,000 to 81,000
Requirements (WNA reference scenario)	48,890	55,400	66,535

From World Nuclear Association, *WNA Market Report 2009*, and WNA Fuel Cycle: Enrichment Plenary Session, World Nuclear Fuel Cycle Conference, April 2011.
* Values are in thousand SWU/yr.
[a] See also www.world-nuclear.org/info/inf28.html.

Bibliography

Benedict, M., Pigford, T.H., and Levi, H.W., *Nuclear Chemical Engineering*, 2nd ed., McGraw-Hill (1981).

Centrifugation: A Practical Approach, D. Rickwood, Ed., Oxford University Press (1984).

Leung, W. Woon-Fong, *Industrial Centrifugation Technology*, McGraw-Hill (1998).

Rickwood, D., Ford, T., and Steensgaard, J., *Centrifugation: Essential Data*, John Wiley and Sons (1994).

Uranium Enrichment, S. Villani, Ed., Springer Verlag (1979).

General Websites

Energy Information Administration, U.S. Department of Energy: www.eia.gov

U.S. Department of Energy: www.energy.gov

World Nuclear Association: www.world-nuclear.org

References

1. "AEC Gaseous Diffusion Plant Operations," ORO-684, U.S. Atomic Energy Commission (Jan. 1972).

2. Benedict, M., Pigford, T.H., and Levi, H.W., *Nuclear Chemical Engineering*, 2nd ed., McGraw-Hill (1981).

3. *Uranium Enrichment*, S. Villani, Ed., Springer Verlag (1979).

4. Beams, J.W., "High Speed Centrifuging," *Rev. Mod. Phys.*, **10**, 245 (1938).

5. Beams, J.W., "Early History of Gas Centrifuge Work in the United States," University of Virginia, Charlottesville (1976).

6. Brouwers, J.J.H., "On Compressible Flow in a Gas Centrifuge and Its Effect on the Maximum Separative Power," *Nucl. Technol.*, **39**, 311 (1978).

7. *World Nuclear Industry Handbook*, Nuclear Engineering International, www.neimagazine.com.

8. Becker, E.W., and Schitte, R., *Z. Naturforsch. A*, **15**, 336 (1960).

9. Geppert, H., et al., "The Industrial Implementation of the Separation Nozzle Process," *Proc. Int. Conf. Uranium Isotope Separation*, London, England, March 5–7, 1975, British Nuclear Energy Society (1975).

10. Becker, E.W., Nogueria, B.P., and Volcker, H., "Uranium Enrichment by the Separation Nozzle Method within the Framework of German/Brazilian Cooperation," *Nucl. Technol.*, **52**, 105 (1981).

11. Levy, R.H., "Prospects for Uranium Laser Isotope Separation," AVCO-Exxon Nuclear report, presented at American Physical Society Meeting, New York, February 1976.

12. Robinson, P.B., and Marinuzzi, J.G., "Laser Isotope Separation," Los Alamos National Laboratory report, presented at American Physical Society Meeting, New York, February 1976.

13. Davis, J.I., "AVLIS: History of Development," *IEEE Trans. Nucl. Sci.*, **NS-30**, 24 (Feb. 1983).

14. Robinson, C.P., and Jenson, R.J., "Some Developments in Laser Enrichment at Los Alamos," LA-UR-76-91, Los Alamos National Laboratory (Feb. 1975).

Problems

3.1. An enrichment plant has a throughput of 32,000 kgU/day and produces 26,000 kgU as tails. What is the enrichment of the product if the feed is natural uranium and the tails are 0.25%?

3.2. A gaseous diffusion plant uses natural uranium feed and enriches it to 2.9% of ^{235}U. If the feed stream is 35,000 kgU/day and the product is 6000 kgU/day, what is the value of the tails and the amount of uranium per day going into tails?

3.3. Show that the SWU factor [Eq. (3.11)] can also be written as

$$SF = V(x_p) - V(x_w) - \frac{F}{P}[V(x_f) - V(x_w)]$$

3.4. Show that the ratio of the mass of natural uranium feed to the mass of ^{235}U in the enriched product is given by

$$\left(\frac{x_p - x_w}{x_f - x_w}\right)\frac{1}{x_p}$$

Calculate this ratio of natural uranium feed, 3% enrichment, 0.2% tails.

3.5. The gaseous diffusion method has been proposed for use in producing BF_3 enriched to 90% in ^{10}B. How many kilograms of BF_3 feed (natural boron) are needed to produce 1 kg of enriched product with 8% tails?

3.6. Assume that HEU from weapons dismantlement containing 90% ^{235}U is blended with depleted uranium with 0.2% ^{235}U. Under these conditions, how many kilograms of 4% enriched fuel can be made per kilogram of HEU?

3.7. In a place called Oklo, in Gabon, Africa, a nuclear fission reactor started operating on its own about 1.8 billion years ago using natural uranium ore of that time as its fuel. What was the percentage of ^{235}U at that time?

3.8. Calculate the natural uranium feed and SWU factors 1 billion years into the future. Assume tails of 0.20% and 4.5% enriched product. $t_{1/2}$ $(^{235}U) = 7.1 \times 10^8$ years, $t_{1/2}$ $(^{238}U) = 4.51 \times 10^9$ years.

3.9. Prove that Eq. (3.14) gives the result 0.0802 kW/(kg·SWU/yr) and 702 kWh/(kg·SWU).

3.10. Prove Eq. (3.20).

3.11. Starting with Eq. (3.20), develop an analytic expression for the function

$$x_w = f(PF/PS).$$

3.12. Using the prices listed below, calculate, for 1980 and for 2010, the value of tails that minimizes the cost of enriched uranium.

	1980 Prices	2010 Prices
U_3O_8 ($/kgU)	78.00	150.00
Conversion ($/kgU)	5.50	12.00
Price per SWU ($)	110.00	150.00

3.13. Assuming that the price per SWU is $80 and the cost of conversion is $4/kgU, what is the price of the U_3O_8 ($/lbU_3O_8$) beyond which it will cost less to enrich the already mined, purified, and converted (to UF_6) tails that contain 0.2% ^{235}U rather than mine new uranium? Assume the product will be 3% enriched in ^{235}U in either case and the new tails will be 0.1% (when the old tails are enriched). Tails stored as UF_6 cost nothing.

3.14. Repeat problem 3.13 assuming that the government will charge a price equal to 10% of the price of fresh UF_6 for the 0.2% tails.

3.15. Repeat problem 3.13 assuming enriched product of 4.5% and cost of tails given in problem 3.14.

3.16. It is stated in Section 3.6 that in the United States, 700,000 t of UF_6, tails of the enrichment process, are stored. How many kilograms of fuel enriched to 4.5% in ^{235}U can be produced if these tails are reinserted into the enrichment process? Assume that the tails contain 2.5% ^{235}U and the new tails will go down to 0.15% ^{235}U. At current prices, what would be the cost of 1 kg of such enriched fuel (leave out fabrication; consider just enriched fuel).

FOUR

REACTOR FUEL DESIGN AND FABRICATION

4.1 Introduction

For nuclear reactors, and especially power reactors, the performance of the nuclear fuel is of paramount importance, for obvious reasons: The construction costs of nuclear power plants are higher than those for other types of plants. Therefore, if nuclear power is to have an advantage over other methods of producing electricity, that advantage will have to come from reliable, uninterrupted operation over long periods. Such plant performance requires fuel that will produce the energy for which it was designed and fabricated, without any failures that may cause plant shutdowns or even operation at reduced power.

The three most important constraints imposed on the fuel are as follows: First, the cladding must not melt or reach a temperature that can initiate a chemical reaction between the cladding material and the hot water or steam (in LWRs); second, the fuel must not reach melting temperature; and third, no fission products should be released to the coolant (the tacit assumption made here is that once in the coolant, they will find their way into the environment). The first two constraints are absolute: The cladding and fuel temperatures must not reach the melting temperature. If this occurs, the condition is considered a major accident and the reactor will be shut down. The third constraint is not absolute, in the sense that some fission products may be released to the coolant (due to failed fuel cladding) and others (e.g., gaseous fission products) are allowed to be released to the environment without causing the plant to shut down.

Many factors affect fuel performance, but the two most important are the materials used and the design. The materials constitute an important consideration in overall reactor design and often pose the limiting condition of operation. Proper materials must be selected, based on their physical and chemical properties and their resistance to radiation damage, and their composition (e.g., alloys) and design configuration must be conceived. For the fuel, these considerations are complicated by chemical, physical, and isotopic changes during irradiation. Once the materials problem has been optimized, there remains the problem of designing and manufacturing to high precision and quality the enormous number of fuel rods involved in a power reactor core loading. For example, a 1000-MWe core requires about 37,500 rods.

Numerous nuclear and nonnuclear conditions must be satisfied for acceptable fuel performance. The most important are

1. Nuclear reactivity and control

2. Adequate thermal-hydraulic and heat transfer characteristics (i.e., adequate heat transfer surface and coolant flow rates to keep temperature everywhere at acceptable levels)

3. Containment of radioactive materials under both normal and abnormal conditions

4. Minimization of neutron-absorbing impurities in all materials

5. Cost competitiveness with other fuels, which implies

    (a) long fuel residency in reactor core (i.e., high burnup),
    (b) effective in-core fuel management (again for high burnup),
    (c) standardization of fuel design to permit efficient production methods,
    (d) reliability in both materials and workmanship, and
    (e) realistic specifications with stringent quality control within the acceptable tolerance range.

In today's nuclear reactors, the fuel consists of the nuclear material itself (UO_2 in most cases) and a cladding material that surrounds it. Both the nuclear fuel and the cladding materials must be specially designed to function properly in the reactor core, an environment of high temperatures and high levels of radiation, which can be particularly harmful to the fuel. Consider fresh fuel that is pure UO_2. As soon as this fuel is placed in the core and starts producing power, that is, the uranium fissions, its composition changes. It is no longer pure UO_2; it contains many other new chemical elements, the fragments of the fission process, in addition to transuranic elements that result from neutron capture by ^{238}U. The objective of the fuel design is to keep all of the products of the fission reaction inside the cladding and, preferably, inside the UO_2 crystal structure. This is only partially achieved, since some of the fission products are noble gases that escape from the UO_2. In most cases, the fission gas products are contained by the cladding. Most of the fission products are trapped in the UO_2 lattice, and as a result, they cause a change in the fuel density (see Section 4.4.1).

In the sections that follow, the fuel itself and the cladding materials for LWRs are discussed first, followed by fuel fabrication. Fuel problems, solutions to the problems, and improvements are then discussed. Finally, fuels for gas-cooled reactors, for liquid metal–cooled reactors, and for future reactor designs are presented briefly.

4.2 Reactor Fuel and Cladding Materials

4.2.1 Uranium Metal

Uranium was first used as a reactor fuel in the metal form. Uranium is a highly reactive metal that reacts with most of the nonmetallic elements and forms intermetallic compounds. Uranium metal oxidizes rather rapidly at room temperature. Initially, the metal has a shiny platinum-like surface. After being exposed to room temperature and air for 3 or 4 days, the surface becomes black. Uranium metal exists in three allotropic phases:

1. The α phase, which crystallizes in the orthorhombic system and is stable up to 600°C

2. The β phase, which has a tetragonal crystal structure and exists between 660°C and 700°C

3. The γ phase, which is a body-centered cubic and exists from 760°C up to the melting point of 1130°C.

The α crystal phase is anisotropic; when heated, it expands in two directions and contracts in the third direction. The β phase is probably also anisotropic; the γ phase, however, is isotropic. When uranium metal is deformed by rolling, swaging, or extrusion, the crystals orient themselves in preferred directions. Because of the anisotropic characteristics of α- and β-phase uranium, this preferred orientation results in dimensional changes when the uranium is thermal-cycled or exposed to radiation. Other than that, uranium metal can usually be worked and machined much like other metals.

The dimensional changes that occur upon irradiation of uranium metal used as reactor fuel represent a serious drawback to its use. Irradiation affects the microstructure of uranium metal, which causes the "growth" problem, as explained in the next section and in Section 4.4.1. In addition, irradiation of metal fuels in the core of the reactor has an adverse effect on their thermal conductivity.

Recently, new developments have been reported in uranium metal–alloy fuels that are to be used in liquid metal–cooled fast reactors. More details are given in Section 4.7.3.

4.2.2 Ceramic Fuels

A ceramic fuel is a solid inorganic material in which the interatomic bonding is predominantly ionic or covalent, and therefore it is a hard, brittle material. The ceramic fuel currently in use is uranium dioxide (UO_2). This material is

TABLE 4.1

Properties of Uranium Dioxide (UO$_2$)

Melting point	2865°C (5189°F)
Density (X-ray measurement)	10.97 g/cm^3
Thermal conductivity	~10 W/m·K at 20°C
	~5 W/m·K at 1000°C
Thermal expansion coefficient	~1 × 10^{-5}/°C (0 to 1000°C)
Tensile strength	6.9 × 10^7 Pa (10,000 psi)
Modulus of elasticity	1.72 × 10^{11} Pa (25 × 10^6 psi)
Cell type	Face-centered cubic[a]

[a] Uranium dioxide is not a simple material; thus, the cell type may vary.

attractive because oxygen has a very low thermal neutron capture cross section and thus does not cause a serious loss of neutrons. Additionally, UO$_2$ is chemically and structurally very stable, as demonstrated by the fact that there is no reaction with high-temperature water. Also, many of the fission products are retained within the UO$_2$ crystals even at high burnup. Finally, the fabrication cost is low. A summary of UO$_2$ properties is given in Table 4.1.

Uranium dioxide as a reactor fuel possesses some undesirable features. The thermal conductivity is relatively poor (Fig. 4.1), and the strength is inferior to that of the uranium metal. Although the thermal conductivity is low, relatively high temperatures are permissible in UO$_2$ because of its high melting point. The high temperatures and extreme thermal gradients used in

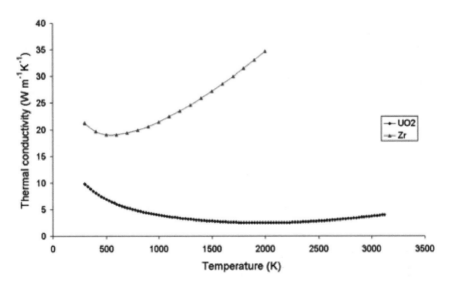

FIGURE 4.1 Thermal conductivity of zirconium metal and uranium dioxide as a function of temperature.

a power reactor do cause eventual grain growth in UO_2, accompanied by stresses and eventual cracking of the material. The cracking of the UO_2 will, of course, release some fission product gases after high burnup. However, the cracking of the UO_2 does not have an adverse effect on reactor operation, as long as the cladding retains the fission products. Uranium dioxide is not a simple material, and its fabrication strongly affects its irradiation behavior.

For every nuclear power plant, the objective is to operate in such a fashion that the burnup of the fuel, expressed in MWd/t, and the average linear power density, expressed in kW/ft, are as high as possible. For LWRs, typical maximum burnup values are between 40,000 and 50,000 MWd/t, and linear heat rates are between 10 and 17 kW/ft. However, this objective—of maximizing the two quantities just mentioned—is also a constraint imposed on the operator of the power plant because both burnup and linear heat rate may lead to fuel failure if they exceed their design values. Fuel failure is defined as the release of fission products into the primary coolant.

The maximum linear heat rate increases with burnup, up to 28,000 MWd/t at which point it reaches 17 kW/ft. It decreases beyond that point, reaching the value of 13 kW/ft at burnups beyond 39,000 MWd/t. This reduction is due to the fact that the linear heat rate is directly related to the temperature of the fuel, which in turn determines the degree of thermal expansion. Since the fuel thermal expansion is greater at the beginning of irradiation, the linear heat rate is also higher at lower burnups.

Fuel "growth" was mentioned earlier as one of the effects of irradiation. Three effects cause dimensional growth of the UO_2 fuel. One is irradiation growth directly connected with the anisotropy of the uranium crystal. The second, referred to as *fuel swelling*, is the result of the creation of fission products in the fuel. The third is the effect of neutron irradiation that causes swelling. Fission products interspersed in the UO_2 lattice decrease the density of the fuel; since the mass of the fuel changes very little (as a result of fission), its volume increases. Neutron bombardment, particularly by fast neutrons, knocks atoms out of their normal positions in the UO_2 lattice, creating interstitial and vacancy states that also contribute to fuel swelling. The rate of swelling, expressed in percent change of the volume ($\Delta V/V\%$), changes with burnup. It is 0.16% up to 4000 MWd/t, and it becomes 0.7% after all the internal voids of the UO_2 are filled. The rate of fuel swelling increases by a factor of 4 when burnup reaches a value of more than 50,000 MWd/t. This burnup value may be extended by decreasing the density of fresh fuel.

Another ceramic that has some interesting properties for reactor fuel (although it has not been used) is uranium monocarbide (UC). This type of ceramic fuel would be attractive for very high temperature reactors.

Work is also being done on other ceramic fuels such as the nitrides (UN). These fuel compositions appear attractive for space power systems. Ceramic fuels such as UC and UN have higher densities than UO_2 and thus may suffer less radiation damage.

4.2.3 Fuel Cladding

The fuel cladding serves several purposes: It prevents corrosion of the fuel by the coolant media, retains the fission products resulting from the splitting of uranium nuclei during power generation, accommodates the fuel volume changes, and provides a surface for the heat transfer from the fuel to the coolant. The cladding material must satisfy all these requirements while being subjected to neutron bombardment that changes its properties. From the requirements listed above, one realizes that the candidate cladding materials must have certain special mechanical, physical, chemical, and nuclear characteristics.

The cladding material must have a small thermal neutron absorption cross section so as not to affect seriously the neutron economy in the core. Table 4.2 gives the thermal neutron absorption cross sections for several metals considered as candidates for cladding materials. In addition, the cladding material must be compatible with the fuel and the coolant and it must be corrosion resistant. It must also provide good heat transfer from the fuel to the coolant. Thus, an intimate bond between fuel and cladding is necessary. In cases where bonding is not possible, an intermediate gaseous layer is used.

Beryllium, magnesium, and aluminum have cross sections similar to those of zirconium, but they all have one or more undesirable characteristics. Beryllium has inadequate corrosion resistance, lacks ductility, is expensive, and produces helium gas during irradiation. Aluminum and its alloys do not have adequate strength or corrosion resistance. Magnesium does not have adequate corrosion resistance in the water reactor environment.

Some of the early claddings were stainless steels. In fact, in sodium-cooled reactors, Type 304 stainless steel is still used as fuel cladding. However, because of the fairly high thermal neutron cross section of stainless steel, zirconium alloys are used in LWRs for fuel cladding. Actually, only two metals have melting temperatures above $1000°C$—beryllium ($1280°C$) and zirconium ($1845°C$). Zirconium is a relatively abundant element in the earth's crust. Unfortunately, it is always accompanied by hafnium, a very undesirable element because it has a very high neutron absorption cross section.

TABLE 4.2
Thermal Neutron Absorption Cross
Sections for Several Metals

Material	σ_a (b)	Material	σ_a (b)
Mg	0.063	Fe	2.6
Be	0.01	Mo	2.7
Zr	0.18	Cr	3.1
Al	0.23	Cu	3.8
Sn	0.63	Ni	4.6
Nb	1.10	Ti	5.8

TABLE 4.3

Composition of Zircaloy

Element	Zircaloy-2 (wt%)	Zircaloy-4 (wt%)
Sn	1.20 to 1.70	1.20 to 1.70
Fe	0.07 to 0.20	0.18 to 0.24
Cr	0.05 to 0.15	0.07 to 0.13
Ni	0.03 to 0.08	0.007 (maximum)
Fe + Cr + Ni	0.18 to 0.38	0.28 to 0.37

The hafnium is removed by using a process similar to that used to obtain U_3O_8 from uranium ore.

The form of zirconium used in LWR fuel is called Zircaloy, which is zirconium alloyed with a few weight percent of other elements. Table 4.3 shows the composition of Zircaloy-2, primarily used with BWRs, and Zircaloy-4, for PWRs.

Zircaloy-2 has an ultimate tensile strength (at 500°C) of about 2.965×10^8 Pa (43,000 psi) and a yield strength of 4.413×10^8 Pa (64,000 psi). These values depend on the methods of fabrication and annealing.

For PWRs, Westinghouse[1] introduced an improved PWR fuel called *VANTAGE-5* with an improved Zircaloy cladding referred to as *ZIRLO*. Westinghouse reports that ZIRLO is a specially developed alloy of Zr with Nb, Sn, and Fe that is an improvement on Zircaloy-4. The ZIRLO cladding can reach temperatures as high as 454°C (850°F) with no visible corrosion. Furthermore, ZIRLO is less sensitive to hydrogen embrittlement and suffers less creep. ZIRLO-clad fuel may exceed 60,000 MWd/t burnup without failure.

An improved BWR fuel cladding has also been developed by Advanced Nuclear Fuels Corporation that is referred to as *β-quenched* Zircaloy. This cladding material reportedly experiences less growth when irradiated. In addition, less corrosion has been observed. More information about advanced fuels appears in Section 4.7. Research is under way for completely new materials to be considered for cladding, such as SiC.

Silicon carbide (SiC) is the only chemical compound of carbon and silicon. It is used extensively in industry as an abrasive, in refractories and ceramics, in resistance heating, and in electronic components. SiC is considered as cladding material for nuclear fuel because it has some very useful properties.[2,3] It has a relatively high melting point of 2730°C (the melting point of Zircaloy is 1850°C); it is not attacked by any acids or alkalis or molten salts up to 800°C. In air, SiC forms a protective silicon oxide coating at 1200°C and maintains its strength; therefore, it can be used up to 1600°C. Compared to Zircaloy, SiC has a lower neutron absorption cross section, shows greater resistance to radiation damage, and can withstand higher temperatures. The main problem with using SiC as a tube for cladding nuclear fuel is the difficulty in manufacturing the tube in such a way as to show sufficient mechanical strength and be able to withstand the tensile stresses generated during fuel rod operation, particularly establishing strong end caps for the cladding.

4.2.4 Burnable Absorbers or Burnable Poisons

Burnable absorbers or burnable poisons are neutron-absorbing materials that are necessary to be incorporated in the fuel to accomplish a more efficient reactivity control that leads to better fuel utilization. A certain quantity of such absorbers is placed in the core; as the reactor operates, the amount of the absorber is reduced, that is, burned, as it absorbs neutrons. Burnable poisons are used for the following reasons:

1. A reactor core loaded with fresh fuel is supercritical; that is, if one considers the reactivity of the fuel alone, it has a multiplication factor $k > 1$ (or reactivity $\rho > 0$). This excess reactivity is needed to compensate for (a) fuel depletion; (b) fission products that, having high neutron absorption cross section, are neutron poisons; and (c) temperature effects that introduce negative reactivity.

2. The negative reactivity effects from the fission products and the temperature reach equilibrium in a matter of a few days and stay constant, as long as the power is constant. After that, only fuel depletion reduces the excess reactivity of the fuel (see Section 6.2.2).

3. The core must always have sufficient excess reactivity in order to increase the reactor power (see Section 5.1). Once the desired reactor power level is reached, however, the net reactivity of the core must become zero for constant power operation. The necessary reduction in reactivity, the "reactivity control," may be achieved by using control rods and/or chemical shim (see Section 5.6). Experience has shown that a more efficient reactivity control and better fuel utilization are achieved if burnable poisons are used in addition to other means of control.

4. The burnable poisons remove neutrons from the core by absorption, thus effectively reducing the excess reactivity of the fuel. At the beginning of the cycle, the excess reactivity of the fuel is highest, and so is the amount of burnable poisons; close to the end of the cycle, the fuel has been depleted considerably and the poisons have also been burned. Thus, with the presence of the burnable poisons, the demand for reactivity control during the cycle using control rods or chemical shim is reduced. In addition, burnable poisons placed judiciously in the core may help improve the power distribution. (See also Chapter 6.)

Materials that have been used as burnable poisons are chemical compounds of boron (B_4C), gadolinium (Gd_2O_3), and to a lesser extent, erbium (Er_2O_3); dysprosium has been considered for use in CANDU reactors. The reactor vendors have, over the years, designed several burnable absorbers showing continuous improvement in their performance. Brief descriptions follow of some representative designs.

- *Pyrex:* This is a borosilicate glass enclosed in stainless steel tubing, developed by Westinghouse. The primary neutron absorber is ^{10}B. An additional reduction in reactivity is achieved via neutron absorption by the stainless steel. Individual burnable absorber rods are inserted into selected control rod guide tube locations and removed after one cycle. The advantages of Pyrex are availability, ease of manufacture, uniform distribution of the boron in the glass, and relatively low swelling. The major disadvantage of Pyrex is its relatively high residual reactivity at the end of the cycle.

- *Wet annular burnable absorber (WABA):* This was also developed by Westinghouse as an improvement over Pyrex. It is called *wet* and *annular* because reactor coolant flows through a central annular channel. The neutron-absorbing material is a mixture of aluminum oxide and boron carbide (Al_2O_3-B_4C). The absorber is encased in a Zircaloy annular tube with water flowing through its center and around the outside, and there is no stainless steel. The improvement comes from the fact that the boron-containing pellet is thinner and the moderating effect of the water flowing through the center enhances the boron depletion (by increasing the ^{10}B absorption cross section), thus resulting in significantly reduced residual reactivity at the end of the cycle. WABA is installed in the same manner as Pyrex and removed after one cycle of operation.

- *Integral fuel burnable absorber*[4-6] *(IFBA):* The IFBA was developed by Westinghouse in connection with the VANTAGE-5 fuel (see Section 4.4.3); the absorber material is zirconium diboride (ZrB_2) and is applied as a thin coating on individual pellets. The IFBA coating does not affect pellet manufacturing or enrichment since it is applied to otherwise finished pellets; it can be selectively applied on the surface of pellets of a particular enrichment or, along the same fuel rod, over portions of the fuel rod's length for specific power peaking control. The use of IFBA requires a very accurate prediction of the fission gas release because the ^{10}B produces helium inside the fuel rod. Westinghouse[5] claims that its computer code successfully predicts the amount of gases released. The IFBA is better than the "discrete" burnable absorber rods for the following reason: A discrete burnable absorber displaces water, thus reducing neutron thermalization, which subsequently decreases the neutron fission probability. By contrast, the IFBA having the absorber applied directly on the pellet does not affect the volume of the water in the core, thus resulting in more efficient neutron use.

- *Gadolinium-uranium burnable poison:* This absorber has been developed, in different designs, by Combustion Engineering (CE) for its PWRs, by Westinghouse for its BWR customers, and by General Electric (GE) for its BWRs. The absorbing material is Gd_2O_3-UO_2 contained in selected fuel rods. In the CE design, the burnable poison rod consists of natural uranium-gadolinium pellets in the middle with natural uranium pellets at both ends of the fuel pin.

Gadolinium looks attractive as an alternative poison material because it can be mixed directly with UO_2. In this way, the advantages of a lumped burnable poison are obtained without having to displace uranium. Two major advantages offered by Gd_2O_3-UO_2 over the older B_4C-Al_2O_3 are a reduced linear heat rate and lower average enrichment of the fuel.

Natural gadolinium has two isotopes, ^{155}Gd and ^{157}Gd, with abundances of 14.7% and 15.7% and thermal neutron absorption cross sections equal to 58,000 and 2.4×10^5 b, respectively. Isotopic enrichment in the isotope ^{157}Gd has been reported[7] as a way of improving its performance. The gadolinium daughters produced by neutron absorption also exhibit moderate absorption cross sections.

Other isotopes considered for use as burnable poisons are ^{164}Dy ($\sigma_\gamma \sim$ 1000 b) and ^{167}Er ($\sigma_\gamma \sim$ 800 b).

Finally, it should be mentioned that there are also nonburnable poisons, which maintain almost all their reactivity through a fuel cycle. An example is Hf; absorption of a neutron by one isotope leads to another isotope, also an absorber. Specifically, the isotopes ^{176}Hf to ^{180}Hf are stable and are all neutron absorbers.

4.3 Fuel Element Fabrication

4.3.1 Fuel Pellet Production

To manufacture the fuel pellets, the UF_6 from the gaseous diffusion plant must first be converted to UO_2. Briefly, the procedure for converting UF_6 to UO_2 is as follows:

1. The enriched UF_6 is supplied to the manufacturer in a high-pressure steel cylinder. The UF_6 is initially a solid in the cylinder at room temperature.

2. The steel cylinder of UF_6 is placed in an oven and heated, and the UF_6 sublimes.

3. The UF_6 gas from the cylinder is bubbled through water, where it reacts to form UO_2F_2 in the water solution.

4. The above solution is then mixed with ammonia water and the uranium precipitates as ammonium diuranate $(NH_4)_2U_2O_2$ (ADU).

5. The precipitate is then dried and calcined (dried at high temperature) to form U_3O_8; then it is further reduced with hydrogen to form UO_2.

6. The UO_2 is then ground to form a fine, uniform powder. (There is 0.5% material loss in conversion from UF_6 to UO_2.)

7. Next, an adhesive agent is added to the powder, which is then pressed to form a right circular cylindrical pellet, referred to as a *green pellet*. An example of an adhesive agent would be the organic binder polyvinyl alcohol.

8. These green pellets are then sintered at high temperatures near the melting point, and densification occurs in a hydrogen atmosphere. This usually takes 24 h at 1650°C.

During the sintering process, the pellet density increases to ~94% of the theoretical density of the UO_2. Figure 4.2 shows fuel pellets ready to be

FIGURE 4.2 Fuel pellets ready for placement in a fuel rod.

TABLE 4.4
Fuel Rod Dimensions

BWR			
Array size	9×9	8×8	
Pellet o.d. (mm)	9.055	10.274	
Cladding o.d. (mm)	10.770	12.294	
Cladding thickness (mm)	0.7272	0.889	
PWR			
Array size	15×15	16×16	17×17
Pellet o.d. (mm)	9.1	8.3	~7.4
Cladding thickness (mm)	0.6	0.6	0.6

assembled into fuel pins. Remember that the fuel pellets must be kept in an inert atmosphere because of the rapid oxidation of UO_2. The pellet size varies, depending on the fuel element for which it is designed (see Table 4.4).

After the pellets have been sintered, they are ground to the dimensions given in Table 4.4. In the grinding process, each pellet end is cupped or dished so that there is space between pellets to contain fission products and allow for thermal expansion. "Cupping" and beveling the pellets, as shown in Fig. 4.3, prevents them from touching the cladding after power production begins and the pellet is distorted because of uneven thermal expansion (Fig. 4.4). After the pellets are ground to the required final diameter and properly cupped at the ends, each one is visually inspected and placed in

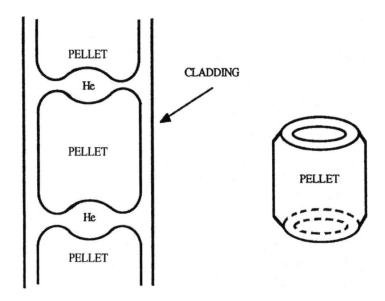

FIGURE 4.3 Fuel pellets, cupped at the ends.

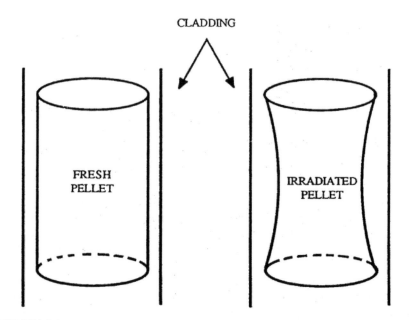

CLADDING

FRESH
PELLET

IRRADIATED
PELLET

FIGURE 4.4 Distortion of the fuel pellet because of uneven heat generation rates.

pellet stacks of desired length and weight. The pellet stacks are then out-gassed at high temperature in a vacuum oven to remove moisture and organic contaminants. It is well known that water causes pellet corrosion problems by breaking down at high temperatures.

4.3.2 Fuel Rod Loading

The dry fuel pellets are next loaded into clean, dry Zircaloy tubes in which one end has been plugged by welding (see Fig. 4.5). These pellet-loaded tubes are inspected and then placed in a welding machine. The pellets are loaded into the tube (along with plenum springs; see Fig. 4.5), which is first evacuated, then backfilled with helium gas, and finally plug-welded at the top. The PWR fuel pins are pressurized to 1.38×10^7 Pa (2000 psi), and then the end plug is inserted and welded into place. BWR fuel is also pressurized, but to 6.9×10^6 Pa (1000 psi). Notice in Fig. 4.5 that fuel rods are provided with additional volumes (plenums) at both the top and bottom ends for the collection of fission product gases. A spring holds the fuel pellets in contact. This spring also reduces axial stresses in the rod. These fully fabricated fuel rods (or pins; the term *fuel rod* will be used here) are placed in a vacuum chamber and tested for leaks. Assuming no indication of a leak, the rods are then etched in a nitric-hydrofluoric acid bath. Next the fuel rods are autoclaved with high-pressure steam. The fuel rods have now developed an

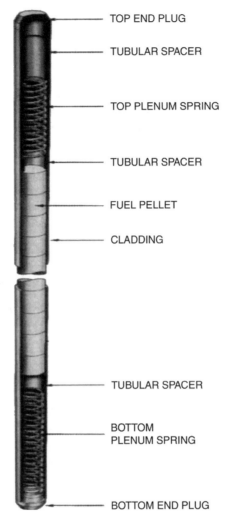

TOP END PLUG

TUBULAR SPACER

TOP PLENUM SPRING

TUBULAR SPACER

FUEL PELLET

CLADDING

TUBULAR SPACER

BOTTOM
PLENUM SPRING

BOTTOM END PLUG

FIGURE 4.5 Fuel rod design. (Courtesy of Babcock & Wilcox Fuel Company.)

outer surface film, which is corrosion resistant, and are ready to be put together in bundles to form fuel assemblies.

4.3.3 Fuel Assembly for a PWR

It is not fuel rods that are loaded in a reactor core but fuel assemblies. An assembly (also called a *fuel bundle*; the term *assembly* will be used here) is made up of many fuel rods bundled and secured together in one unit, the fuel assembly.

The process of making a fuel assembly, starting with fuel rods, is shown in Fig. 4.6. Obviously, all the assemblies are not exactly the same; they depend on the customer's needs. Some assemblies may need burnable poison installed at some positions in the fuel assembly, instead of fuel rods. Others may require one or more water holes to satisfy the reactor core power distribution limitations. In the case of a PWR, some fuel positions must be left vacant for control rods. Another factor that the fuel manufacturer must be responsive to is that some PWRs use 15 × 15 fuel pin arrays, others use 17 × 17 arrays, and 18 × 18 arrays are also being tested. Figure 4.7 shows

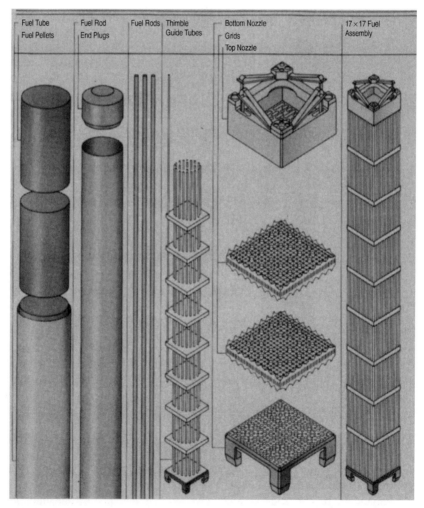

FIGURE 4.6 Steps involved in making a fuel assembly. (Courtesy of Westinghouse.)

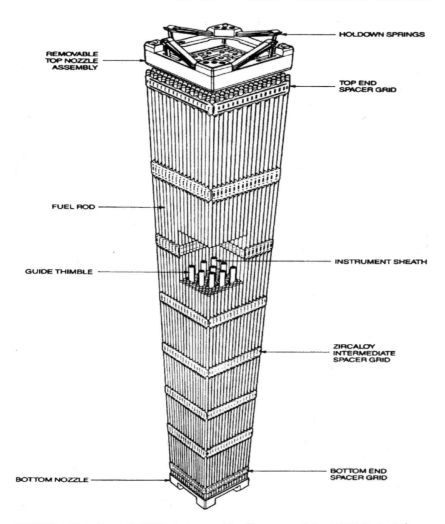

FIGURE 4.7 A 17 × 17 PWR fuel assembly. (Courtesy of the B&W Fuel Co.)

the Babcock & Wilcox Co. 17 × 17 array fuel assembly. Note that in Fig. 4.7, the fuel assembly has an upper support grid plate and a lower grid plate serving as the lower nozzle. Along the length of the fuel assembly are several intermediate spacer grids to restrain the fuel pins and prevent bulging. In this particular design, the upper nozzle can be detached to allow reconstitution of the assembly by removing and replacing defective fuel rods or removing burnable poison rods.

A typical 1100-MWe PWR core consists of 180 to 190 assemblies, more than 50,000 fuel rods, and ~18 million UO_2 pellets. Each assembly is ~4 m

($\sim$13 ft) high and weighs $\sim$660 kg; it generates power for 3 to 5 years (during three 18- to 24-month cycles), reaching a burnup of $\sim$50,000 MWd/t.

4.3.4 Fuel Assembly for a BWR

Figures 4.8a and 4.8b show a typical BWR assembly in a four-cluster formation with a cruciform control rod. Initially, BWR reactors used 7 × 7 fuel assemblies. However, some difficulties were experienced with these assemblies in the form of a phenomenon called *pellet/cladding interaction* (PCI; see Section 4.4.1). This problem required the operation of reactors containing this fuel to follow strict ramping power changes to minimize PCI effects. The cause of the PCI problem, as reported by GE, was due to the linear heat generation rate. Thus, 8 × 8 assemblies and 9 × 9 assemblies, which decreased the linear heat rate, were developed. Currently, GE is offering a new 10 × 10 array design designated as GNF2 (Global Nuclear Fuel 2). This new design offers the latest in corrosion and debris resistance.

These larger-array fuel assemblies are designed to fit the same reactor core support plates and have a much lower linear heat generation rate. Thus, the improved design of the 9 × 9 arrays permits the restrictions of ramp-rate limits imposed by the 7 × 7 arrays to be removed. This improved fuel assembly design is reported to give a 20% increase in fuel burnup.

Notice in the BWR assembly that no provision is made for control rods in the fuel assembly like those used in the PWR fuel assemblies. As Figs. 4.8a and 4.8b show, the BWR reactor uses a cruciform-shaped control rod that moves up and down between four fuel assemblies. The BWR fuel assemblies are designed, much like the PWR assemblies, to accommodate burnable poison tubes in some positions. The differences between BWRs and PWRs are shown in Fig. 4.9.

A typical 1100-MWe BWR core consists of $\sim$750 assemblies, more than 70,000 fuel rods, and $\sim$25 million UO_2 pellets. Each assembly is $\sim$4.4 m ($\sim$14.5 ft) high and weighs $\sim$320 kg; it generates power for 3 to 5 years (during three 18- to 24-month cycles), reaching a burnup of $\sim$50,000 MWd/t.

4.3.5 Fuel Assembly Identification Scheme

Every assembly fabricated in the United States is assigned a unique identification code based on American National Standard N18.3-1972. The assembly identification (ID) consists of six characters: a prefix of two alphabetic characters, identifying the fabrication facility, followed by four alphanumeric characters. The characters used for the ID are selected from the Arabic numerals 0 through 9 and letters of the English alphabet, except I and O, for a total of 34 different characters. The ID should be provided by casting, machining, engraving, or other method of marking on the end fitting or other integral part of the assembly.

1.TOP FUEL GUIDE
2.CHANNEL FASTENER
3.UPPER TIE PLATE
4.EXPANSION SPRING
5.LOCKING TAB
6.CHANNEL
7.CONTROL ROD
8.FUEL ROD
9.SPACER
10.CORE PLATE ASSEMBLY
11.LOWER TIE PLATE
12.FUEL SUPPORT PIECE
13.FUEL PELLETS
14.END PLUG
15.CHANNEL SPACER
16.PLENUM SPRING

FIGURE 4.8a Typical BWR fuel assembly. (Courtesy of General Electric.)

The sequence to be used in this 34-base numerical system is shown in Table 4.5, which gives the 1156 different characters, which provides (1156) (1156) = 1.336×10^6 combinations per fabricator. As an example, the first 1156 combinations start with 0000, followed by 0001, 0002, ..., 0009, 000A,

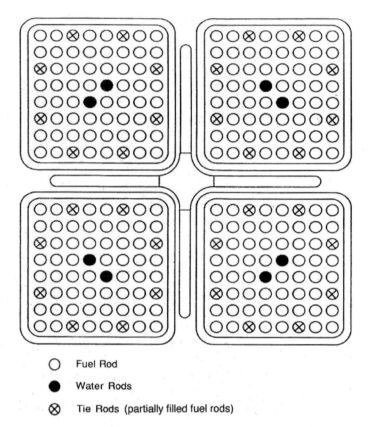

○   Fuel Rod

●   Water Rods

⊗   Tie Rods (partially filled fuel rods)

FIGURE 4.8b A cruciform control rod for the BWR fuel is placed in the space between the four assemblies shown in 4.8a. (Courtesy of General Electric.)

000B, . . . , 000Z. Then comes 0010, etc. The last of the first 1156 combinations is 00ZZ. The next 1156 combinations start with 0100, . . . all the way to 01ZZ. The very last combination is ZZZZ.

4.4 LWR Fuel Problems and Solutions

4.4.1 Nuclear Fuel Problems

As mentioned in the previous sections, nuclear fuel is required to satisfy very rigid criteria under operation in a hostile environment of high pressures, temperatures, and radiation. Both the physical dimensions and shape as well as the chemical composition of the uranium pellets and the cladding change during operation in a geometry that allows very small tolerance in the space between different materials. With this condition in mind, it should not come

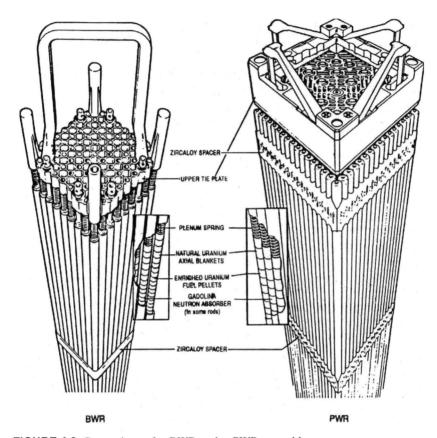

ZIRCALOY SPACER
UPPER TIE PLATE
PLENUM SPRING
NATURAL URANIUM AXIAL BLANKETS
ENRICHED URANIUM FUEL PELLETS
GADOLINA NEUTRON ABSORBER (in some rods)
ZIRCALOY SPACER

BWR   PWR

FIGURE 4.9 Comparison of a BWR and a PWR assembly.

as a surprise that certain unanticipated fuel problems have been encountered, particularly in the early 1970s. The nuclear industry has studied these problems and has redesigned the fuel, and as the operational history of the plants shows, most of the difficulties have disappeared. Brief descriptions of the most important fuel problems, their causes, and their solutions follow. The early problems were as follows:

- *Fuel swelling:* As explained in Section 4.3.1, the fuel pellet swells primarily because of the generation of fission products and the bombardment by neutrons. In LWRs, fuel swelling is not a big problem because the fast neutron component, which causes most of the swelling, is not dominant. By designing fuel pellets and cladding with proper margins, fuel swelling does not seem to be a factor.

- *Fuel densification:* Under certain circumstances, the density of the UO_2 pellet increases during the first few months of operation. Densification

TABLE 4.5

Numerical Sequence of Characters Used for Assembly Identification

	0	1	2	3	4	5	6	7	8	9	A	B	C	D	E	F	G	H	I	J	K	L	M	N	P	Q	R	S	T	U	V	W	X	Y	Z
0	00	01	02	03	04	05	06	07	08	09	0A	0B	0C	0D	0E	0F	0G	0H	0I	0J	0K	0L	0M	0N	0P	0Q	0R	0S	0T	0U	0V	0W	0X	0Y	0Z
1	10	11	12	13	14	15	16	17	18	19	1A	1B	1C	1D	1E	1F	1G	1H	1I	1J	1K	1L	1M	1N	1P	1Q	1R	1S	1T	1U	1V	1W	1X	1Y	1Z
2	20	21	22	23	24	25	26	27	28	29	2A	2B	2C	2D	2E	2F	2G	2H	2I	2J	2K	2L	2M	2N	2P	2Q	2R	2S	2T	2U	2V	2W	2X	2Y	2Z
3	30	31	32	33	34	35	36	37	38	39	3A	3B	3C	3D	3E	3F	3G	3H	3I	3J	3K	3L	3M	3N	3P	3Q	3R	3S	3T	3U	3V	3W	3X	3Y	3Z
4	40	41	42	43	44	45	46	47	48	49	4A	4B	4C	4D	4E	4F	4G	4H	4I	4J	4K	4L	4M	4N	4P	4Q	4R	4S	4T	4U	4V	4W	4X	4Y	4Z
5	50	51	52	53	54	55	56	57	58	59	5A	5B	5C	5D	5E	5F	5G	5H	5I	5J	5K	5L	5M	5N	5P	5Q	5R	5S	5T	5U	5V	5W	5X	5Y	5Z
6	60	61	62	63	64	65	66	67	68	69	6A	6B	6C	6D	6E	6F	6G	6H	6I	6J	6K	6L	6M	6N	6P	6Q	6R	6S	6T	6U	6V	6W	6X	6Y	6Z
7	70	71	72	73	74	75	76	77	78	79	7A	7B	7C	7D	7E	7F	7G	7H	7I	7J	7K	7L	7M	7N	7P	7Q	7R	7S	7T	7U	7V	7W	7X	7Y	7Z
8	80	81	82	83	84	85	86	87	88	89	8A	8B	8C	8D	8E	8F	8G	8H	8I	8J	8K	8L	8M	8N	8P	8Q	8R	8S	8T	8U	8V	8W	8X	8Y	8Z
9	90	91	92	93	94	95	96	97	98	99	9A	9B	9C	9D	9E	9F	9G	9H	9I	9J	9K	9L	9M	9N	9P	9Q	9R	9S	9T	9U	9V	9W	9X	9Y	9Z
A	A0	A1	A2	A3	A4	A5	A6	A7	A8	A9	AA	AB	AC	AD	AE	AF	AG	AH	AI	AJ	AK	AL	AM	AN	AP	AQ	AR	AS	AT	AU	AV	AW	AX	AY	AZ
B	B0	B1	B2	B3	B4	B5	B6	B7	B8	B9	BA	BB	BC	BD	BE	BF	BG	BH	BI	BJ	BK	BL	BM	BN	BP	BQ	BR	BS	BT	BU	BV	BW	BX	BY	BZ
C	C0	C1	C2	C3	C4	C5	C6	C7	C8	C9	CA	CB	CC	CD	CE	CF	CG	CH	CI	CJ	CK	CL	CM	CN	CP	CQ	CR	CS	CT	CU	CV	CW	CX	CY	CZ
D	D0	D1	D2	D3	D4	D5	D6	D7	D8	D9	DA	DB	DC	DD	DE	DF	DG	DH	DI	DJ	DK	DL	DM	DN	DP	DQ	DR	DS	DT	DU	DV	DW	DX	DY	DZ
E	E0	E1	E2	E3	E4	E5	E6	E7	E8	E9	EA	EB	EC	ED	EE	EF	EG	EH	EI	EJ	EK	EL	EM	EN	EP	EQ	ER	ES	ET	EU	EV	EW	EX	EY	EZ
F	F0	F1	F2	F3	F4	F5	F6	F7	F8	F9	FA	FB	FC	FD	FE	FF	FG	FH	FI	FJ	FK	FL	FM	FN	FP	FQ	FR	FS	FT	FU	FV	FW	FX	FY	FZ
G	G0	G1	G2	G3	G4	G5	G6	G7	G8	G9	GA	GB	GC	GD	GE	GF	GG	GH	GI	GJ	GK	GL	GM	GN	GP	GQ	GR	GS	GT	GU	GV	GW	GX	GY	GZ
H	H0	H1	H2	H3	H4	H5	H6	H7	H8	H9	HA	HB	HC	HD	HE	HF	HG	HH	HI	HJ	HK	HL	HM	HN	HP	HQ	HR	HS	HT	HU	HV	HW	HX	HY	HZ
I	I0	I1	I2	I3	I4	I5	I6	I7	I8	I9	IA	IB	IC	ID	IE	IF	IG	IH	II	IJ	IK	IL	IM	IN	IP	IQ	IR	IS	IT	IU	IV	IW	IX	IY	IZ
J	J0	J1	J2	J3	J4	J5	J6	J7	J8	J9	JA	JB	JC	JD	JE	JF	JG	JH	JI	JJ	JK	JL	JM	JN	JP	JQ	JR	JS	JT	JU	JV	JW	JX	JY	JZ
K	K0	K1	K2	K3	K4	K5	K6	K7	K8	K9	KA	KB	KC	KD	KE	KF	KG	KH	KI	KJ	KK	KL	KM	KN	KP	KQ	KR	KS	KT	KU	KV	KW	KX	KY	KZ
L	L0	L1	L2	L3	L4	L5	L6	L7	L8	L9	LA	LB	LC	LD	LE	LF	LG	LH	LI	LJ	LK	LL	LM	LN	LP	LQ	LR	LS	LT	LU	LV	LW	LX	LY	LZ
M	M0	M1	M2	M3	M4	M5	M6	M7	M8	M9	MA	MB	MC	MD	ME	MF	MG	MH	MI	MJ	MK	ML	MM	MN	MP	MQ	MR	MS	MT	MU	MV	MW	MX	MY	MZ
N	N0	N1	N2	N3	N4	N5	N6	N7	N8	N9	NA	NB	NC	ND	NE	NF	NG	NH	NI	NJ	NK	NL	NM	NN	NP	NQ	NR	NS	NT	NU	NV	NW	NX	NY	NZ
P	P0	P1	P2	P3	P4	P5	P6	P7	P8	P9	PA	PB	PC	PD	PE	PF	PG	PH	PI	PJ	PK	PL	PM	PN	PP	PQ	PR	PS	PT	PU	PV	PW	PX	PY	PZ
Q	Q0	Q1	Q2	Q3	Q4	Q5	Q6	Q7	Q8	Q9	QA	QB	QC	QD	QE	QF	QG	QH	QI	QJ	QK	QL	QM	QN	QP	QQ	QR	QS	QT	QU	QV	QW	QX	QY	QZ
R	R0	R1	R2	R3	R4	R5	R6	R7	R8	R9	RA	RB	RC	RD	RE	RF	RG	RH	RI	RJ	RK	RL	RM	RN	RP	RQ	RR	RS	RT	RU	RV	RW	RX	RY	RZ
S	S0	S1	S2	S3	S4	S5	S6	S7	S8	S9	SA	SB	SC	SD	SE	SF	SG	SH	SI	SJ	SK	SL	SM	SN	SP	SQ	SR	SS	ST	SU	SV	SW	SX	SY	SZ
T	T0	T1	T2	T3	T4	T5	T6	T7	T8	T9	TA	TB	TC	TD	TE	TF	TG	TH	TI	TJ	TK	TL	TM	TN	TP	TQ	TR	TS	TT	TU	TV	TW	TX	TY	TZ
U	U0	U1	U2	U3	U4	U5	U6	U7	U8	U9	UA	UB	UC	UD	UE	UF	UG	UH	UI	UJ	UK	UL	UM	UN	UP	UQ	UR	US	UT	UU	UV	UW	UX	UY	UZ
V	V0	V1	V2	V3	V4	V5	V6	V7	V8	V9	VA	VB	VC	VD	VE	VF	VG	VH	VI	VJ	VK	VL	VM	VN	VP	VQ	VR	VS	VT	VU	VV	VW	VX	VY	VZ
W	W0	W1	W2	W3	W4	W5	W6	W7	W8	W9	WA	WB	WC	WD	WE	WF	WG	WH	WI	WJ	WK	WL	WM	WN	WP	WQ	WR	WS	WT	WU	WV	WW	WX	WY	WZ
X	X0	X1	X2	X3	X4	X5	X6	X7	X8	X9	XA	XB	XC	XD	XE	XF	XG	XH	XI	XJ	XK	XL	XM	XN	XP	XQ	XR	XS	XT	XU	XV	XW	XX	XY	XZ
Y	Y0	Y1	Y2	Y3	Y4	Y5	Y6	Y7	Y8	Y9	YA	YB	YC	YD	YE	YF	YG	YH	YI	YJ	YK	YL	YM	YN	YP	YQ	YR	YS	YT	YU	YV	YW	YX	YY	YZ
Z	Z0	Z1	Z2	Z3	Z4	Z5	Z6	Z7	Z8	Z9	ZA	ZB	ZC	ZD	ZE	ZF	ZG	ZH	ZI	ZJ	ZK	ZL	ZM	ZN	ZP	ZQ	ZR	ZS	ZT	ZU	ZV	ZW	ZX	ZY	ZZ

results in reduction of pellet diameter and length, with subsequent formation of gaps in the fuel stack. The presence of gaps is undesirable because of the possibility of the cladding collapsing into the gap. The mechanism causing densification is not completely understood. Experiments have shown that pellets in which a large fraction of the void volume is made up of very small pores are subject to more densification than those with a small fraction of the void volume having large pores. Current pellet specifications normally include a requirement for a pore size distribution that minimizes densification. Westinghouse[8] reported that densification is essentially complete at ~30,000 MWd/t. In general, fuel densification is more of a problem for BWRs than it is for PWRs because of the size of the core.

- *Thermal expansion/deformation:* Because of nonuniform heating rates, the pellets not only expand but also deform as shown in Fig. 4.4. To prevent the pellet from touching the cladding inner surface, "cupping" or "dishing" of the pellet is used (Fig. 4.3). This particular design seems to have solved this problem.

- *Pellet/cladding interaction (PCI):* Experience with LWR and CANDU fuel[9] has shown that cladding failures may occur after a sufficiently high burnup as a result of a power ramp (i.e., a fast power increase). These fuel defects are the result of local stress loading combined with chemical reactions between the pellets and cladding. The pellet expands, stresses the cladding, and cracks; fission products are released through the cracks, some of them corrosive. Stresses under these conditions may cause the fuel cladding to crack with little or no plastic deformation. *Stress corrosion cracking* (SCC) is the term describing this phenomenon of the chemical attack of a metal under stress in the atmosphere of a corrosive material. It is believed that the fission product iodine is one of the substances causing the attack on the cladding. Available PCI data indicate[8] that the PCI dependence on burnup seems to saturate after 15,000 MWd/t. New fuel designs have been proposed to avoid, or reduce to acceptable levels, the effects of PCI (see Section 4.4.2).

- *Formation of hydrides:* Under normal operating conditions, hydrogen is generated in the reactor from radiolysis of the H_2O or from hydrogen picked up by the pellet surface during pressing or grinding. (Under accident conditions hydrogen is produced by the reaction $Zr + 2H_2O \rightarrow ZrO_2 + 2H_2$; this reaction is exothermic but becomes important only at temperatures >900°C.) Hydrogen absorbed by the Zircaloy lattice may lead to the formation of ZrH_2, which can cause embrittlement of the cladding if the hydride is present in large quantities or if it is adversely oriented, even in small quantities. Large reductions in strength and ductility were found when hydride platelets (a platelet is a small round or oval disk) were oriented at a right angle to the tensile stress

TABLE 4.6
Common Fuel Failure Mechanisms
in LWRs (2000–2006)

Mechanism (Cause)	Percentage of Failures	
	PWR	BWR
Grid-to-rod fretting	83	~0
Crud/corrosion	2	51
Duty related	3	19
Debris fretting	5	20
Fabrication	2	1
Unknown	5	9

From K. Edsinger et al., "Zero by 2010 and Recent U.S. Fuel Reliability Experience," Water Reactor Fuel Performance Meeting, China (Sep. 2011).

of the Zircaloy tube. Negligible effects were noticed when the platelets were aligned parallel to the stress axis.

After about 50 years of operating experience, the major causes of fuel failure are quite different from the early ones. Table 4.6 gives the latest data[10] for the period 2000–2006. Notice the big differences for percentage of failures from the different causes for PWRs and BWRs; these differences are due to the quite different modes of operation of the two plants. For PWRs, the major cause of fuel failure is grid-to-rod fretting; it results from the interaction between a vibrating fuel rod and the spacer grid. For BWRs, the major cause is debris fretting and still considerable contribution from PCI. Debris fretting is the result of solid (mostly metal) objects that circulate with the coolant and collide with fuel rod cladding. During cleanup of the coolant loop, types of debris collected include washers, bolts, and even bigger objects and numerous pieces of much smaller size. Obviously, reducing debris fretting requires filtering of the coolant, and this is what is practiced, especially in BWRs.

4.4.2 Barrier Fuel

Initial BWR fuels suffered failures due to PCI, and as a result, rather severe operating restrictions were imposed on BWR power plants, as mentioned previously. General Electric and other fuel manufacturers have approached this problem in several ways. One way, as mentioned, was to reduce the linear heat rate by going to a 9 × 9 fuel pin array in fuel assemblies. Another improvement was the introduction of "barrier" fuel construction. In this process, pure zirconium is metallurgically bonded to the Zircaloy cladding inner surface, forming an integral part of the cladding tube. Since pure zirconium is softer than the Zircaloy tube, the zirconium barrier material effectively inhibits PCI crack propagation. Without the fear of PCI-caused failure, BWR plants can be brought to full power quickly and respond swiftly to power changes. Other significant benefits from the use of barrier fuel are lower plant radiation exposures and higher burnup.

4.4.3 VANTAGE-5 Fuel

Another fuel element improvement previously mentioned in this chapter is the Westinghouse-designed VANTAGE-5 fuel.[11] The VANTAGE-5 fuel also has a PCI barrier and a better fuel cladding material developed by Westinghouse, ZIRLO (see Section 4.2.3). In addition, the burnable poison that has been put in the VANTAGE-5 fuel is zirconium diboride (ZrB_2) enriched in ^{10}B, which is sputtered directly on the fuel pellets.

4.5 Examination of Irradiated Fuel for Defects: Fuel Sipping

From the point of view of satisfactory fuel performance, it is important to remove defective fuel rods from the core. Defective rods release fission products into the coolant, which in turn increase the radiation exposure to personnel in the plant and, potentially, to the general public. Since the uranium fuel is valuable, it is also important not to reject nondefective fuel rods. Therefore, the methods of examining the fuel should be extremely reliable.

The quality control for fuel fabrication is excellent. Yet, in a reactor that contains more than 50,000 rods, even if the failure rate is 0.1% (the reported industry average), one would expect ~40 to 50 rods to fail.

The examination of the fuel for defects is performed during refueling outages, using a procedure called *sipping*.[12] There are many methods of sipping; the principles of the most important ones are discussed next. The various companies that provide sipping services give them special names.

Wet sipping is based on monitoring the leaching of fission products from fuel rods in a controlled isolated volume of water. For wet sipping, the fuel assembly under examination is placed in a sealed container filled with water. To reduce the radioactive background, the pool water is replaced with demineralized water. After keeping the assembly in this environment for 30 to 60 min, the water is sampled and analyzed in the laboratory for the presence of specific radionuclides.

Wet sipping is considered to be 95% efficient. It has two disadvantages. First, there is a rapid decrease of leachable fission products following shutdown. Second, significant quantities of fission products may be present in crud layers on the fuel elements in concentrations that may show considerable variations. This causes considerable scatter of the background concentrations of sound assemblies. As a result, questionable assemblies have to be reexamined. Using several containers, the rate of examination is about two to five assemblies per hour.

Dry sipping is based on the expulsion of fission gases from the defective rod. The assembly is placed in a container from which the water is removed and replaced with air. The decay heat of the fuel raises the temperature of the assembly (and the air) and causes the release of fission gases if it is a leaker. When the required temperature is reached, the air is sampled and analyzed for fission product activity. Dry sipping is more sensitive than wet sipping because fission gas atoms migrate more readily. Another advantage of dry sipping is the long duration of the signal after fuel discharge. The main disadvantage of this method is the possibility of overheating the cladding, since the water has been removed. Because of this potential effect, dry sipping is used less frequently than wet sipping.

Vacuum sipping combines the high sensitivity of dry sipping with the inherent safety of wet sipping. The fuel assembly is placed in an isolated chamber, which is sealed and flushed with demineralized water. A gas space is established above the assembly. The gas is removed by a vacuum pump and is directed to an online scintillation beta detector. The vacuum that is formed enhances the release of fission gases. It takes about 8 to 10 min to examine an assembly.

A sipping method named *ECHO-330* has been developed by B&W; it is based on an ultrasonic probe, in the form of a flexible blade, on which are mounted a transmitter and a receiver of ultrasonic signals. An ultrasonic pulse emitted by the transmitter creates a wave that travels 330 deg (hence the name) around the fuel rod cladding before it meets the receiver. The detection of defects is based on the fact that a signal passing through dry cladding is stronger than that going through a wet one. With proper calibration, the strength of the transmitted ultrasonic pulse is used to identify cladding defects. According to its promoter, ECHO-330 may detect as little as 0.1 cm^3 of water in a fuel rod; it can operate underwater, up to 40 ft deep, and at temperatures from 75°F to 150°F. It takes about 5 min to examine an assembly.

4.6 Axial and Radial Blankets

The objective of the axial and radial blankets is to improve the neutron economy in the reactor. The neutron economy will improve if the number of neutrons escaping from the core (neutron leakage) is reduced. The "traditional" fuel rods contain pellets with the same enrichment over the total length of the rod. An axial blanket is created by placing pellets of natural uranium, instead of enriched uranium, at both ends of the rod. The length of the axial blanket is 6 to 8 in. at either end. The presence of the axial blanket reduces neutron leakage through the top and bottom of the core (therefore improving the neutron economy) because the natural uranium of the axial blanket produces less power, and therefore fewer neutrons. Neutron leakage may be reduced by as much as 50%.

To create radial blankets, one places assemblies with a certain level of burnup at the core periphery. Burned-up assemblies contain less ^{235}U, produce fewer neutrons, and, in the same fashion as axial blankets, reduce the leakage through the radial surface of the core. The radial blanket is an extension of the so-called "low-leakage core loading" that is employed to reduce the fast neutrons bombarding the pressure vessel (details are given in Chapter 6).

4.7 Other Types of Power Reactor Fuels

4.7.1 The Gas-Cooled GT-MHR and Pebble Bed Reactor Fuel

The General Atomics (GA) company designed a gas-cooled reactor that utilizes a fuel quite different from that of LWRs. In the gas-turbine modular helium-cooled reactor (GT-MHR), the fuel consists of microspheres encapsulated in a material that retains the fission products; that is, the coating of these fuel particles replaces the cladding. The fuel elements of the GT-MHR are composed of fuel particles that are bonded together in fuel rods. The rods are emplaced in sealed vertical holes in hexagonal graphite blocks, as shown in Fig. 4.10. The GT-MHR fuel[13,14] will be close to 20% enriched fissile uranium oxycarbide (UCO) and fertile thorium oxide (ThO$_2$) in the form of spheres of 650 to 850 μm in diameter, coated first with a pyrolytic

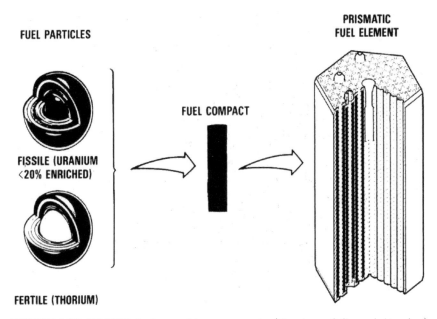

FUEL PARTICLES

PRISMATIC FUEL ELEMENT

FUEL COMPACT

FISSILE (URANIUM <20% ENRICHED)

FERTILE (THORIUM)

FIGURE 4.10 GT-MHR fuel assembly components. (Courtesy of General Atomics.)

carbon, then with silicon carbide, and then with another coating of pyrolytic carbon. The particles coated in such a manner are referred to as *TRISO-coated* particles. This coating system is shown in detail in Fig. 4.11. The core will consist of 102 columns of the hexagonal fuel elements stacked 10 elements high to form an annular core. Graphite blocks (without fuel) will surround the core and serve as reflectors in both the radial and axial directions. According to GA, no fission products escape from the refractory coating for temperatures below 1800°C (3272°F), as Fig. 4.12 shows. The GT-MHR is designed to operate using the Brayton cycle, which means that the hot He will drive the gas turbine and no steam will be generated.

The only reactor constructed that was operated using such fuel was the High Temperature Gas Reactor (HTGR), known as the Fort St. Vrain Nuclear Power Generating Station in Colorado. Fort St. Vrain used as fuel highly enriched (90%) UO_2 particles, as well as ThO_2, all of which were ceramic coated. Experience at Fort St. Vrain has shown that the ceramic-coated particles do indeed retain the fission products at extremely high temperatures [2000°C (3632°F)]. Temperatures higher than this are the only means of causing

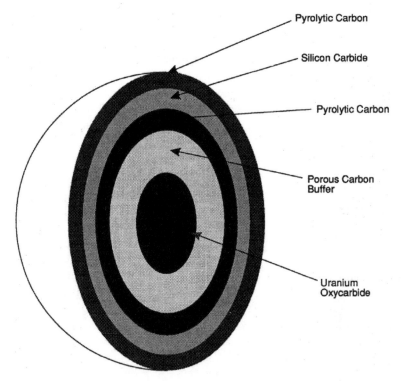

FIGURE 4.11 Detail of a fuel kernel to be used by the GT-MHR. (Courtesy of General Atomics.)

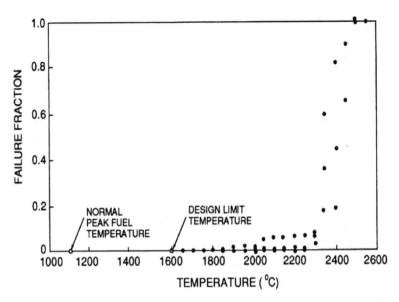

FIGURE 4.12 Fission product retention of GT-MHR refractory-coated fuel. (Courtesy of General Atomics.)

the release of fission products. Since the GT-MHR is designed to operate at fuel temperatures of 1600°C (2912°F), there is justified confidence that the fission products will not be released.

In the pebble bed reactor, the fuel particles are formed into large spheres with a diameter of ~60 mm. About 400,000 of these fuel balls will make up the reactor core, placed within a graphite-lined vessel that will be about 10 m high and 3.5 m in diameter. Helium gas will be the coolant and, as with the GT-MHR, the Brayton cycle will be used. Refueling is expected to be done online with the used fuel balls passing pneumatically to a storage tank at the base of the plant and fresh ones replacing them.

4.7.2 The MOX Fuel

The term *mixed oxide fuel* (MOX), as already mentioned in Chapter 1, refers to nuclear fuel consisting of a mixture of UO_2 and PuO_2. The UO_2 may be natural, enriched, or depleted uranium, depending on the application of the MOX fuel. The MOX fuel was designed for use in liquid-metal fast breeder reactors (LMFBRs) and in LWRs, if reprocessing and recycling are used. In the United States, MOX fuel has been used for research purposes in the Experimental Breeder Reactor II (EBR-II) in Idaho and the Fast Flux Test Facility (FFTF) in Washington state; both the EBR-II and FFTF have been shut down. In other countries, France has used MOX in the PHENIX and SUPERPHENIX breeder reactors, both also shut down. More important, however, is the fact that Electricité de France is using MOX to partially fuel the cores of many of its PWRs. Plutonium for the MOX fuel comes from reprocessing LWR used nuclear fuel. The reprocessing plant produces the Pu in the form of $Pu(NO_3)_4$. This compound is first transformed into PuO_2 powder, which is then mechanically blended with ceramic-grade UO_2 to produce the mixed oxide that is fabricated into pellets. Alternatively, MOX can be produced by coprecipitation of ammonium diuranate $[(NA_4)_2U_2O_2]$, known as *ADU*, and plutonium hydroxide in mixed crystal form by the addition of ammonia. A MOX fuel fabrication plant is under construction in Aiken, South Carolina, scheduled to begin operations in 2016 (ground broken in 2007); its estimated cost is ~\$4.6 billion. Most of the Pu used for this MOX fuel will come from dismantled nuclear weapons.

4.7.3 Future Fuel Designs

Since the fuel is so important for the performance of a nuclear power plant, continuous effort is made for its improvement; new fuel designs are proposed and (some) tested all the time.

Interest in and work on the development of metallic fuels continues. Experiments at EBR-II and at the FFTF have shown that the proposed metallic uranium fuels perform well under the reactor operating conditions.[15] It has been reported that this fuel is extremely easy to fabricate using newly developed pyrometallurgical procedures that combine reprocessing and fuel fabrication (see Section 7.4). Because of its higher thermal conductivity, metallic fuel cools faster than oxide fuel, thus reducing the chance for a dangerous temperature rise in the core during a loss of flow of the liquid sodium coolant.

Metallic fuel has been tested in EBR-II. Metallic fuel assemblies irradiated in EBR-II have reached burnups in excess of 50,000 MWd/t with satisfactory performance; the goal for this fuel is 140,000 MWd/t. Fuel swelling, one of the early problems of fast reactor fuels, has been solved by giving the fuel enough space to expand.[16]

A UZr_2 metallic fuel[17] with pellets not cylindrical but in a four-lobe shape (Fig. 4.13) that is believed will increase power density considerably is

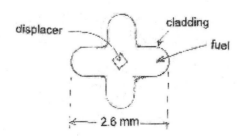

FIGURE 4.13 The four-lobe fuel design.

under development. The lobe design increases the fuel surface area, thus increasing the heat conduction rate. The developer claims that the fabrication cost of the lobe fuel will be less than that of a pellet; irradiation experiments are scheduled to start in 2012.

Annular fuel has also been studied with the same objective as the four-lobe fuel, namely, to increase surface-to-volume ratio and thus improve heat transfer. In the annular fuel, the pellet has a coolant channel at the center, which necessitates, obviously, cladding on the inside channel in addition to the outside surface of the pellet. The most comprehensive reference for annular fuel is Ref. 18.

DUPIC (direct use of pressurized water reactor used fuel in CANDU) is not really a new fuel design but an innovative idea for use of used fuel. Considerable effort has been devoted by Korea on this topic[19,20] since 1992.

Th-U fuel has also been studied for present and, especially, future reactor designs. Most of the work on Th-U fuels is presented in Ref. 21.

4.8 Fuel Fabrication Cost

In the United States the cost of fabricated fuel includes transportation costs; that is, the client pays the fuel manufacturer for fuel delivered on-site. In 2011, this cost was reported to be between \$220 and \$240 per kilogram.

The calculation of the cost of fabricated fuel is based on Eq. (3.19), with the addition of the cost of fabrication. A small loss of uranium occurs during fabrication, usually 1%. If one defines PF to be the cost of fabrication plus transportation (in \$/kg) and l_f to be the fraction of uranium lost in fabrication, the equation for the cost of fabricated fuel (FF) becomes

$$FF = \left\{ \frac{PU}{(1 - \ell_c)(1 - \ell_f)} + \frac{PC}{(1 - \ell_f)} \right\} \frac{F}{P} + \frac{PS}{(1 - \ell_f)} * SF + PF \qquad (4.1)$$

■ **Example 4.1:** What is the cost of fabricated fuel if the price for fabricated fuel delivered on-site is \$220/kg and there is an 0.8% loss of uranium during fabrication? Use the numbers of Example 3.4, p. 81, for natural uranium cost, conversion, and enrichment.

Answer: Based on Eq. (4.1),

$$FF = \left\{ \frac{150}{(1 - 0.005)(1 - 0.008)} + \frac{12}{(1 - 0.008)} \right\} * 9.219$$

$$+ \left\{ \frac{150}{(1 - 0.008)} \right\} * 6.870 + 240.00 = \$2531 + \$240 = \$2771/kgU$$

Neglecting conversion and fabrication losses, the cost is FF \$2764/kg. ■

4.9 Materials Concerns Relative to Reactor Plant Life Extension

The operating license given by the NRC for new reactors is valid for 40 years,[22] but after more than 50 years of operating history, experience has shown that a nuclear power plant may operate safely for a longer period. As a result, most of the nuclear plants (especially in the United States) have applied and received an extension of the operating license for up to 20 years.[23] Life extension is approved after the NRC has been convinced that all critical components (the word *critical* refers to materials and components that may impact the safe operation of the plant) still satisfy pertinent specifications that guarantee continuous and reliable performance of the plant for its extended licensed operational life.

Materials in a reactor degrade with time due to two major factors: One is irradiation, especially by fast neutrons. It is well established that fast neutron irradiation may cause, for example, embrittlement in steel. The second is corrosion caused by the coolant as a result of a combination of effects such as coolant flow, stresses generated by temperature and pressure, and coolant chemistry. The effects of aging manifest themselves as structural damage, deformation, cracking, and degradation of material properties.

When lifetime extension is considered, the components/structures in a nuclear power plant may be divided into two groups. The first is made up of replaceable components; in this case the main consideration is the cost involved in the replacement of such equipment and structures. The second consists of irreplaceable components; for these, the company that operates the plant must persuade the NRC that such components are sound enough to operate safely for the period of the extension of the license. The most important component in this group is the steel pressure vessel. As mentioned above, steel suffers radiation damage as a result of bombardment by fast neutrons leaking from the core. To ensure that the pressure vessel will not fail, a very detailed program has been established by every operator of a reactor (especially a PWR due to the high pressure), based on measurements and computations, that determines the physical state of the pressure vessel steel.

The most recent and most comprehensive reference about this topic is the book *Understanding and Mitigating Ageing in Nuclear Power Plants*, a compilation of articles edited by P.G. Tipping[24] (see also the Bibliography).

Bibliography

Advances in Materials Science for Environmental and Nuclear Technology II: Ceramic Transactions, Sundaram, S.K., Tatsuki, O., Fox, K., and Hoffman, E., Eds., Wiley (Ceramic Transactions Series) (2011).

Kaufmann, A.R., *Nuclear Reactor Fuel Elements, Metallurgy, and Fabrication*, Interscience Publishers (1962).

Kopelman, B., *Materials for Nuclear Reactors*, McGraw-Hill (1959).

Olander, D.R., "Fundamental Aspects of Nuclear Reactor Fuel Elements," TID-26711, U.S. Department of Commerce, National Technical Information Service (1976).

Proc. ANS Topl. Mtg. Light Water Reactor Fuel Performance, Portland, Oregon, April 29–May 2, 1979, American Nuclear Society (1979).

Proc. IAEA Symp. Fuel Element Fabrication, Vienna, Vols. 1 and 2, Academic Press (1961).

Proc. Int. Conf. Fundamental Aspects of Radiation Damage in Metals, Gatlinburg, Tennessee, October 6–10, 1975, Vols. 1 and 2, CONF-751006-P1 and P, M.T. Robinson and F.W. Young, Eds., U.S. Government Printing Office (1976).

Simnad, M.T., and Howe, J.P., in *Materials Science in Energy Technology*, G.G. Libowitz and M.S. Whitingham, Eds., Academic Press (1979).

Understanding and Mitigating Ageing in Nuclear Power Plants: Materials and Operational Aspects of Plant Life Management (PLM), Tipping, P.G., Ed., Woodhead Publishing (2010).

Was, G.S., *Fundamentals of Radiation Materials Science: Metals and Alloys*, Springer (2007).

References

1. Frank, F.J., and Scherpereel. L.R., "Fuel Cycle Cost Reduction through Westinghouse Fuel Design and Core Management," *Trans. Am. Nucl. Soc.*, **50,** 101 (1985).

2. Patnaik, P. *Handbook of Inorganic Chemicals*, McGraw-Hill (2002).

3. Carpenter, D., Ahn, K., Kao, S., Hejzlar, P., and Kazimi, M.S., "Assessment of Silicon Carbide for High Performance Light Water Reactors," MIT-NFC-TR-098, Massachusetts Institute of Technology (Nov. 2007).

4. Pritchett, J.E., and Mueller, D.E., "Operational Experience with a ZrB_2 Integral Fuel Burnable Absorber," *Trans. Am. Nucl. Soc.*, **56,** 117 (1988).

5. Miller, R.S., Kaiser, R.S., and Roberts, E., "Westinghouse PWR Extended Burnup Experience and Related Product Improvements," *Proc. Int. Symp. Improvements in Water Reactor Fuel Technology and Utilization*, Stockholm, Sweden, September 15–19, 1986, International Atomic Energy Agency (1986).

6. Srinilta, S., Schmidt, R.F., and Pritchett, J.E., "A Comparison of Gd and ZrB_2 as Integral Fuel Burnable Absorbers in PWRs," *Trans. Am. Nucl. Soc.*, **55,** 124 (1987).

7. Hove, C.M., and Spetz, S.W., "Improvement of Gd Fuel Cycle Economics by Isotopic Enrichment of ^{157}Gd," *Trans. Am. Nucl. Soc.*, **50,** 102 (1985).

8. "Extended Burnup Evaluation of Westinghouse Fuel," S.L. Davidson and W.P. Kramer, Eds., WCAP-10126-NP-A, Westinghouse Electric Corp. (1985).

9. Roberts, J.T.A., Smith, E., Fuhrman, N., and Cubicciotti, D., "On the Pellet-Cladding Interaction Phenomenon," *Nucl. Technol.*, **35,** 131 (1977).

10. Edsinger, K., Cheung, B., Daum, R., Deshon, J., Hussey, D., Kucuk, A., Mader, E.V., Pytetl, M., Reitmeyer, M., Yagnik, S.K., and Yueh, K., "Zero by 2010 and Recent U.S. Fuel Reliability Experience," Water Reactor Fuel Performance Mtg., China (Sep. 2011).

11. Doshi, P.K., Chapin, D.L., and Scherpereel, L.R., "Westinghouse VANTAGE Fuel Assembly to Meet Future PWR Operating Requirements," *Trans. Am. Nucl. Soc.*, **56**, 118 (1988).

12. Green, T.A., and Laurent, M.S., "Examining Fuel for Defects," *Nucl. Plant Safety*, p. 16 (Sep.–Oct. 1984).

13. Blue, L.S., "Safety of the Next Generation Power Reactors," *Proc. ANS Topl. Mtg.*, Seattle, Washington, May 1–5, 1988, American Nuclear Society (1988).

14. Northup, T.E., Stansfield, O.M., and Stewart, H.B., "An Assessment of the Modular HTGR Containment System," *Proc. Intersociety Energy Conversion Engineering Conf.*, Philadelphia, Pennsylvania, August 10–14, 1987.

15. Till, C.E., and Chang, Y.I., "The Integral Fast Reactor Concept," *Proc. American Power Conf.*, Chicago, Illinois, April 14–16, 1986, Illinois Institute of Technology, Vol. 48, p. 688 (1986).

16. Till, C.E., "The IFR," *Trans. Am. Nucl. Soc.*, **59**, 2 (1989).

17. Malone, J., Totemeier, A., Shapiro, N., and Vaidyanathan, S., "Lightbridge Corporation's Advanced Metallic Fuel for LWRs," *Nucl. Technol.*, **180**, 3 (2012); see also www.ltbridge.com.

18. Annular Fuel Special Issue, *Nucl. Technol.*, **160** (Oct. 2007).

19. Ko, W.I., and Kim, H.D., "DUPIC Proliferation Resistance," *J. Nucl. Sci. Technol.*, **38**, 9, 757 (2001).

20. Choi, H., et al., "Progress of the DUPIC Fuel Compatibility Analysis," *Nucl. Technol.*, Part I: **153**, *1*, 25 (2006); Part II: **153**, 2, 164 (2006); Part III: **155**, 2, 176 (2006); Part IV: **157**, *1*, 1 (2007).

21. Th-U Fuels Special Issue, *Nucl. Technol.*, **147** (July 2004).

22. Licenses, certifications, and approvals for nuclear power plants; *Code of Federal Regulations* (10CFR52), Title 10, "Energy," Part 52.104, "Duration of Combined License" (Jan. 2010).

23. Requirements for renewal of operating licenses for nuclear power plants; *Code of Federal Regulations* (10CFR54), Title 10, "Energy," Part 54.31, "Issuance of a Renewed License" (Jan. 2010).

24. *Understanding and Mitigating Ageing in Nuclear Power Plants: Materials and Operational Aspects of Plant Life Management (PLM)*, P.G. Tipping, Ed., Woodhead Publishing (2010).

Problems

4.1. At a uranium pellet fabrication plant, the average pellet density is 9.5×10^3 kg/m^3, with a standard deviation equal to 0.5×10^3 kg/m^3. What is the probability that a pellet at random has a density less than 8.0×10^3 kg/m^3?

4.2. A PWR core contains about 50,000 fuel rods. If the probability to find one defective rod is 0.1%, what is the probability to find 10 defective rods in a random sample of 1000?

4.3. Calculate the cost of nuclear fuel fabricated and delivered on-site using the following data:

Cost of natural uranium, $60/lb; U_3O_8 enrichment, 4.2%; conversion, $11.50/kgU; tails, 0.25%; price of SWU, $110; conversion loss, 0.6%; fabrication/transportation cost, $230/kgU; fabrication loss, 0.7%.

4.4. If the enrichment changes by 0.4%, that is, goes from 4.2% to 4.6%, by what percentage does the cost of fuel in problem 4.3 change?

FIVE

REACTOR PHYSICS CALCULATIONS

5.1 Introduction

This chapter presents a relatively brief discussion of reactor physics calculations. (A complete description of the topic would require an entire book.) It is assumed that the reader is somewhat familiar with this subject.

A reactor physics calculation determines, essentially, the neutron population in the core expressed by the neutron flux φ (n/cm$^2\cdot$s); once the neutron flux is known, all information pertinent to the safe operation of the reactor can be obtained. The topic is presented with power reactors in mind, the focus of this book; however, most of the information applies to research reactors as well.

For a reactor to be able to operate over a period of time, it must have enough fissile material in the core so that the multiplication factor k (also known as the effective multiplication factor, k_{eff}; in this chapter it will be designated simply as k) must be at least equal to 1, or the reactivity defined by

$$\rho = (k - 1)/k \tag{5.1}$$

must be greater than or equal to zero. Practically, the reactor should be designed to have enough fuel so that k can be greater than 1 for the following four reasons, as mentioned in Section 4.2.4:

1. To accommodate fuel depletion (if $k = 1.00$, just after the first fission k will become less than 1).

2. To overcome the negative reactivity introduced by several fission products (primarily ^{135}Xe and ^{149}Sm produced in the core as fission products).

3. To overcome the negative reactivity effect introduced as a result of the elevated temperature in which the reactor operates. (For details about these effects, the reader should consult the general Bibliography given at the end of the chapter.)

4. To be able to increase power. A power change from one level to a higher one can be accomplished only if the reactor operator has positive reactivity at his disposal during the change.

The first task of a reactor physics calculation is, therefore, the determination of the value of the *multiplication factor k*.

If the reactor core has enough fissile material to become supercritical, a mechanism must be provided to hold down the excess reactivity when it is not needed (which is the case most of the time since power reactors operate at constant power for as long as possible). Therefore, except during power increases or shutdown, an amount of neutron absorbers sufficient to make the reactor exactly critical should be provided. The neutron poisons are introduced into the core in the form of control rods and other burnable poisons, and in the case of PWRs, directly in the coolant. How much neutron poison is needed and how that poison changes with time constitute another part of reactor physics calculations.

A nuclear reactor should operate in such a way that design safety limits are not violated. These limits are expressed as maximum temperature (T), maximum power (P), maximum deviation from nucleate boiling ratio (DNBR) anywhere in the core, and so on. In addition to these limits, the power distribution should have a certain shape. It is very desirable, not only from the safety point of view but also for better fuel utilization, to have a power distribution in the core that is as flat as possible both radially and vertically. Therefore, the reactor physicist or engineer will have to calculate not only the fissile mass that will result in the desired value of k at all times in core life, but also the specific distribution of the assemblies in the core, that is, the core loading that will produce the desired power shape. The calculation of T, P, and heat flux and their distribution in the core requires the combined computation of reactor physics and thermal-hydraulic parameters.

The values of all of the parameters mentioned above can be obtained if the neutron flux is known everywhere in the core, as a function of space and neutron energy, for steady-state operation. This is true because almost all of the calculations involve computations of reaction rates of the form

$$R_{i,j}(\mathbf{r}) = N_j(\mathbf{r}) \int dE \, \varphi(\mathbf{r}, E) \sigma_{i,j}(E) \qquad (5.2)$$

where the subscript i indicates the type of nuclear reaction involved (scattering, absorption, fission, etc.), j indicates the isotope with N nuclei participating in the reactions, $\sigma_{i,j}(E)$ is the value of the corresponding cross section for reaction type and isotope j, $\varphi(\mathbf{r}, E)$ is the neutron flux, and $R_{i,j}(\mathbf{r})$ is the reaction rate (reaction/cm$^3 \cdot$s) for reaction type i with isotope j at the location $\mathbf{r}$. Since the information about the cross sections is assumed to be known (see Section 5.3), the problem of "reactor physics calculations" is reduced to the determination of the neutron flux.

In the sections that follow, the fundamental neutron transport equation is derived first, and then the most important approximations for its solution are discussed. Information regarding nuclear cross sections is given in Section 5.3. Reload and fuel depletion calculations follow. Finally, reactor control is discussed.

5.2 The Neutron Transport Equation

5.2.1 General Comments and Derivation of the Transport Equation

Neutrons in a reactor move in different directions and at different speeds (different kinetic energies). As they move inside a material, sometimes they collide with nuclei, sometimes they are absorbed, sometimes they leak out of the reactor. The neutron absorptive reactions may lead to neutron capture, in which case the neutron disappears from the system, or may result in the generation of more neutrons, for example, fission, and $(n,2n)$, $(n,3n)$, etc., reactions.

To describe completely the state of a neutron, one needs the following seven variables (Fig. 5.1):

1. Position in space—three variables (x, y, z or r, ϑ, z or r, ϑ, ψ)
2. Direction of motion—two variables (θ, ϕ) defining the unit vector $\hat{\Omega}$
3. Kinetic energy E—one variable
4. Time t—one variable.

The quantity that describes the neutron population in a reactor, whether it is the neutron density or the neutron flux, is a function of these seven variables.

The neutron transport equation (TE), also called the Boltzmann transport equation because it is very similar to the particle transport equation derived by Boltzmann in the late 1800s, expresses the following fundamental neutron balance:

$$\text{Rate of change of neutron density} = (\text{sources}) - (\text{losses})$$

In terms of the neutron angular flux $\phi(\mathbf{r}, E, \hat{\Omega}, t)$ having the meaning

$$\phi(\mathbf{r}, E, \hat{\Omega}, t) \, dE d\hat{\Omega}$$

$$= \begin{pmatrix} \text{number of neutrons per square centimeter per second} \\ \text{at point } \mathbf{r}, \text{ at time } t, \text{ with energy between } E \text{ and } E + dE, \\ \text{moving in the direction } \hat{\Omega} \text{ inside the solid angle } d\hat{\Omega} \end{pmatrix},$$

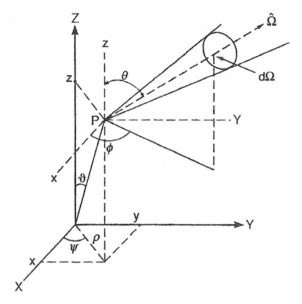

FIGURE 5.1 The position P of the neutron is defined by the three variables x, y, z (in Cartesian coordinates), or r, ϑ, z (in cylindrical coordinates), or r, ϑ, ψ (in spherical coordinates). The direction of motion is defined by the angles θ and ϕ.

the neutron transport equation has the form (for derivation, see the Bibliography)[a]:

$$(1/v) \frac{\partial \phi(\mathbf{r}, E, \hat{\Omega}, t)}{\partial t} + \nabla[\hat{\Omega}\phi(\mathbf{r}, E, \hat{\Omega}, t) + \Sigma_t(E)\phi(\mathbf{r}, E, \hat{\Omega}, t)]$$

$$= \int_{E'} dE' \int_{\Omega'} d\hat{\Omega}' \, \Sigma_s(E' \rightarrow E, \hat{\Omega}' \rightarrow \hat{\Omega})\phi(\mathbf{r}, E', \hat{\Omega}', t) + S(\mathbf{r}, E, \hat{\Omega}, t) \quad (5.3)$$

where $\Sigma_t(E)$ is the total macroscopic cross section at neutron energy E, and $\Sigma_s(E' \rightarrow E, \hat{\Omega}' \rightarrow \hat{\Omega})$ is the differential scattering cross section (per unit energy E, per unit solid angle Ω). Note that neutron density, n (n/cm^3), and flux, ϕ, are related by $\phi = n * v$, where v (cm/s) is the neutron speed.

The cross sections may be functions of space, that is, $\Sigma_i(\mathbf{r}, E)$, since they depend on the material. However, this dependence is normally not indicated explicitly because, as is shown in subsequent sections, the TE is usually solved "piecewise" over homogeneous regions.

---

[a] A form equivalent to the integrodifferential equation presented here is an integral transport equation (see, e.g., the Bell and Glasstone and Ott and Bezella entries in the Bibliography). Most computer codes solve Eq. (5.3).

The source term takes the form

$$S(\mathbf{r}, E, \hat{\Omega}, t) = S_{ext} + \chi(E) \int dE' \int d\hat{\Omega}' \, \nu(E') \Sigma_f(E') \phi(\mathbf{r}, E', \hat{\Omega}', t) \qquad (5.4)$$

where

$S_{ext} = f(\mathbf{r}, E, \hat{\Omega}, t)$ = given nonfission external source

$\nu(E)$ = number of neutrons per fission caused by a neutron with energy E

$\chi(E) \, dE$ = neutron fission spectrum = fraction of fission neutrons with energy between E and $E + dE$.

Equation (5.3) is exact except for neglecting neutron/neutron interactions, which in a reactor environment are negligible. It is an integrodifferential equation that cannot be solved analytically, with all seven variables included, even in the simplest geometries. Add to the problem the complicated geometry of a real nuclear reactor and the task becomes impossible even if one seeks a numerical solution. In view of these difficulties, what is done, in practice, is to solve various approximations of the TE considering only some of the variables. The validity of these approximations is limited, of course, to the cases where the "suppressed" variables can be neglected.

In general, if the time t is omitted, the solution represents a steady-state case; since the subject of this book deals with steady-state operation of a plant and not with time-dependent conditions, the time variable will be dropped from here onward.

If the angular variable $\hat{\Omega}$ is included, the approximation is designated by the word "transport"; if the variable $\hat{\Omega}$ is not kept, the approximation is usually a "diffusion" approximation.

Because the energy variable spans seven decades (0 to 2×10^7 electronvolts) and the neutron cross sections depend strongly (and without a regular pattern) on the neutron energy, the variable E cannot be abandoned. The use of average quantities over the whole energy range does not lead to meaningful results either. What reactor physicists have discovered to be very useful is to divide the energy range into a certain number of energy groups and solve the TE by treating all the neutrons in each energy group as having the same (average) energy of that group; cross sections for that average energy are used. This approach is the well-known multigroup method discussed in Section 5.2.3.

As computers become more powerful, in terms of speed and storage capacity, the TE solutions that can be obtained become more accurate.

The various approximations of the TE, assuming a steady-state case, are discussed next.

5.2.2 The Diffusion Approximation

The diffusion approximation of the transport equation gives the neutron flux as a function of space and energy, $\phi(\mathbf{r}, E)$, that is, the angular variable has been suppressed. To obtain the equation for the function $\phi(\mathbf{r}, E)$, the TE is integrated term by term over all directions. The result is[1,2]:

$$\nabla \mathbf{J}(\mathbf{r}, E) + \Sigma_t(E)\phi(\mathbf{r}, E) = \int_{E'} dE' \, \Sigma_S(E' \rightarrow E)\phi(\mathbf{r}, E') + S(\mathbf{r}, E) \qquad (5.5)$$

where the flux $\phi(\mathbf{r}, E)$ is obtained from the integration

$$\phi(\mathbf{r}, E) = \int_{4\pi} d\hat{\Omega} \, \phi(\mathbf{r}, E, \hat{\Omega}) \qquad (5.6)$$

and the function $\mathbf{J}(\mathbf{r}, E)$, called the neutron current, is defined by

$$\mathbf{J}(\mathbf{r}, E) = \int_{4\pi} \hat{\Omega} \, \phi(\mathbf{r}, E, \hat{\Omega}) \, d\hat{\Omega} \qquad (5.7)$$

Since Eq. (5.5) requires two functions, the flux $\phi(\mathbf{r}, E)$ and the current $\mathbf{J}(\mathbf{r}, E)$, to solve it, one needs an expression linking the neutron flux and current. In the diffusion approximation, that expression takes the form

$$\mathbf{J}(\mathbf{r}, E) = -D\nabla\phi(\mathbf{r}, E) \qquad (5.8)$$

where D is the diffusion coefficient. In general, the diffusion coefficient is written as

$$D = 1/(3\Sigma_{tr}) \qquad (5.9)$$

where Σ_{tr} is the neutron transport cross section given by

$$\Sigma_{tr}(E) = \Sigma_t(E) - \bar{\mu}\Sigma_s(E) \qquad (5.10)$$

and $\bar{\mu}$ is the average of the cosine of the neutron scattering angle.

Over the years, many different "prescriptions" have been developed for the calculation of the diffusion coefficient D, prescriptions that constitute variations of the basic definition given by Eqs. (5.9) and (5.10).

Substituting Eq. (5.8) into Eq. (5.5), one obtains the energy-dependent, steady-state diffusion equation:

$$-\nabla D\nabla \phi(\mathbf{r}, E) + \Sigma_t(E)\phi(\mathbf{r}, E)$$

$$= \int_{E'} dE' \, \Sigma_s(E' \to E)\phi(\mathbf{r}, E') + S(\mathbf{r}, E) \qquad (5.11)$$

It has been shown that the diffusion approximation is not valid in regions of space where the neutron flux varies drastically over short distances (short compared to the neutron mean free path). Places where this can happen are at interfaces between a dense medium and a vacuum (or a much less dense medium, e.g., air), close to neutron sources, in media with high-absorption cross sections (e.g., control rods), and inside media with a strongly aniso-tropic scattering cross section. Therefore, in such cases the neutron flux should not be obtained as the solution of the diffusion equation.

5.2.3 The Multigroup Diffusion Approximation Formalism

To set up a multigroup calculation, one needs to know

1. The basic nuclear data, that is, cross sections, $\chi(E)$, $\nu(E)$, etc., for all the isotopes involved (see Section 5.3)

2. The geometry and composition of the system under study

3. The boundaries of the energy groups to be used in the calculation.

The multigroup method is based on the assumption that one can calculate average quantities, such as flux, cross sections, diffusion coefficients, etc., for each group. Then, the TE is solved group by group for the flux as a function of the space variables.

The division of the energy range into energy groups is up to the person performing the calculation. The choice of the number of groups and of energy boundaries depends on the objective of the calculation. If the objective is to calculate the fast neutron flux ($E >$ keV), few if any neutron groups are employed below the keV energy range. If, on the other hand, the objective is to calculate the thermal neutron ($E < 100$ eV) flux, one may lump together into a few groups or a single group all neutrons with energies above a few hundreds of electron-volts. In general, fast neutron flux calculations involve more groups (20 or more) than the corresponding thermal neutron calcula-tions (sometimes 5 or less).

To derive the multigroup equations, assume that the energy range is divided into G groups, as shown in Fig. 5.2, with the g'th group having boundaries between E_g and E_{g-1}. Since the function $\phi(\mathbf{r}, E)$ of Eq. (5.6) is the neutron flux per unit energy, the neutron flux from all the neutrons in the g'th group will be

$$\phi_g(\mathbf{r}) = \int_{E_g}^{E_{g-1}} \phi(\mathbf{r}, E) \, dE \, | \, g = 1, G \qquad (5.12)$$

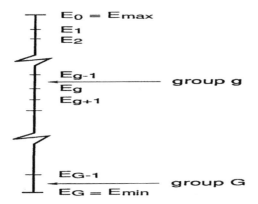

FIGURE 5.2 The energy range from $E_{max} = E_0$ to $E_{min} = E_G$ is divided into G energy groups.

It is these fluxes, called group fluxes, that are obtained as the result of a multigroup calculation.

Consider now Eq. (5.11) and integrate term by term from E_g to E_{g-1} [notice that E_{g-1} is the upper (higher energy) boundary of the group]. The result is as follows, with the space dependence of cross sections shown explicitly and the four terms indicated as I, II, III, IV:

$$\int_{E_g}^{E_{g-1}} dE\,[\underset{\text{(I)}}{-\nabla D(\mathbf{r},E)\nabla\phi(\mathbf{r},E)} + \underset{\text{(II)}}{\Sigma_t(\mathbf{r},E)\phi(\mathbf{r},E)}]$$

$$= \int_{E_g}^{E_{g-1}} dE\,\left[\underset{\text{(III)}}{\int_{E'} dE'\,\Sigma_s(\mathbf{r},E'\to E)\phi(\mathbf{r},E')} + \underset{\text{(IV)}}{S(\mathbf{r},E)}\right] \qquad (5.13)$$

Let us look at each term of Eq. (5.13) separately, starting with term II, the easiest to handle. Term II is written as

$$\int_{E_g}^{E_{g-1}} \Sigma_t(\mathbf{r},E)\phi(\mathbf{r},E)\,dE = \Sigma_{t,g}(\mathbf{r})\int_{E_g}^{E_{g-1}} \phi(\mathbf{r},E)\,dE = \Sigma_{t,g}(\mathbf{r})\phi_g(\mathbf{r}) \qquad (5.14)$$

where

$$\Sigma_{t,g}(\mathbf{r}) = \frac{\displaystyle\int_{E_g}^{E_{g-1}} \Sigma_t(\mathbf{r},E)\phi(\mathbf{r},E)\,dE}{\displaystyle\int_{E_g}^{E_{g-1}} \phi(\mathbf{r},E)\,dE} \qquad (5.15)$$

Equation (5.15) gives the definition and method of computation of the average total cross section for group g. Note, however, that the calculation of any average group cross section (e.g., scattering, absorption, fission) is done as shown by Eq. (5.15)—just substitute the subscript t with s, a, f, etc.

Term I is written as

$$\int_{E_g}^{E_{g-1}} \nabla D(\mathbf{r}, E) \nabla \phi(\mathbf{r}, E)\, dE = \nabla D_g(\mathbf{r}) \nabla \phi_g(\mathbf{r})$$

and the average diffusion coefficient for group g, $D_g(\mathbf{r})$, is defined as

$$D_g(\mathbf{r}) = \frac{\displaystyle\int_{E_g}^{E_{g-1}} D(\mathbf{r}, E) \nabla \phi(\mathbf{r}, E)\, dE}{\displaystyle\int_{E_g}^{E_{g-1}} \nabla \phi(\mathbf{r}, E)\, dE} = \frac{\displaystyle\int_{E_g}^{E_{g-1}} D(\mathbf{r}, E) \nabla \phi(\mathbf{r}, E)\, dE}{\nabla \phi_g(\mathbf{r})} \tag{5.16}$$

Consider now term III:

$$\int_{E_g}^{E_{g-1}} dE \int_0^{E_{max}} dE'\, \Sigma_s(\mathbf{r}, E' \to E) \phi(\mathbf{r}, E')$$

$$= \int_{E_g}^{E_{g-1}} dE \sum_{g'=1}^{G} \int_{E_{g'}}^{E_{g'-1}} dE'\, \Sigma_s(\mathbf{r}, E' \to E) \phi(\mathbf{r}, E')$$

$$= \sum_{g'=1}^{G} \int_{E_g}^{E_{g-1}} dE \int_{E_{g'}}^{E_{g'-1}} dE'\, \Sigma_s(\mathbf{r}, E' \to E) \phi(\mathbf{r}, E')$$

$$= \sum_{g'=1}^{G} \Sigma_s^{g' \to g}(\mathbf{r}) \phi(\mathbf{r})$$

where the cross section $\Sigma_s^{g' \to g}(\mathbf{r})$ is the average group-to-group transfer scattering cross section in the sense that the quantity

$$\int_{E_g}^{E_{g-1}} dE \int_{E_{g'}}^{E_{g'-1}} dE'\, \Sigma_s(\mathbf{r}, E' \to E) \phi(\mathbf{r}, E') = \Sigma_s^{g' \to g}(\mathbf{r}) \phi(\mathbf{r}) \tag{5.17}$$

gives the number of neutrons per $cm^3 \cdot s$ having a collision in group g' and ending up, after the collision, in group g.

Note that the replacement of the integral from E_0 to E_{max} by a summation of integrals across the group boundaries is not an approximation.

Finally, consider term IV, the source term. In analogy with Eq. (5.12), using Eq. (5.4),

$$S_g(\mathbf{r}) = \int_{E_g}^{E_{g-1}} dE\, S_{ext} + \int_{E_g}^{E_{g-1}} dE\, \chi(E) \int_0^{E_{max}} dE'\, \nu(E')\Sigma_f(E')\phi(\mathbf{r}, E')$$

$$= S_{g,ext} + \int_{E_g}^{E_{g-1}} dE\, \chi(E) \sum_{g'=1}^{G} \int_{E_{g'}}^{E_{g'-1}} dE'\, \nu(E')\Sigma_f(E')\phi(\mathbf{r}, E')$$

$$= S_{g,ext} + \chi_g \sum_{g'=1}^{G} (\nu\Sigma_f)_{g'}\, \phi_{g'}(\mathbf{r}) \tag{5.18}$$

Normally in reactors, $S_{ext} = 0$ except at startup. The average $(\nu\Sigma_f)_g$ is defined by

$$(\nu\Sigma_f)_g = \frac{\displaystyle\int_{E_g}^{E_{g-1}} dE\, \nu(E)\Sigma_f(E)\phi(\mathbf{r}, E)}{\phi_g(\mathbf{r})} \tag{5.19}$$

The quantity

$$\chi_g = \int_{E_g}^{E_{g-1}} \chi(E)\, dE\, | g = 1, G \tag{5.20}$$

represents the fraction of neutrons emitted in fission with energy in group g; therefore,

$$\sum_{g=1}^{G} \chi_g = 1$$

Collecting all the terms (with $S_{ext} = 0$), one obtains

$$-\nabla D_g(\mathbf{r})\nabla\phi_g(\mathbf{r}) + \Sigma_{t,g}(\mathbf{r})\phi_g(\mathbf{r})$$

$$= \sum_{g'=1}^{G} \Sigma_s^{g'-g}(\mathbf{r})\phi_{g'}(\mathbf{r}) + \chi_g \sum_{g'=1}^{G} (\nu\Sigma_f)_{g'}\phi_{g'}(\mathbf{r}) | g = 1, G \tag{5.21}$$

Frequently, the terms involving the total cross section and the first summation term on the right-hand side are combined by splitting the summation term into two parts:

$$\sum_{g'=1}^{G} \Sigma_s^{g'\to g}(\mathbf{r})\phi_{g'}(\mathbf{r}) = \Sigma_s^{g\to g}(\mathbf{r})\phi_g(\mathbf{r}) + \sum_{g'\neq g}^{g'\to g}(\mathbf{r})\phi_{g'}(\mathbf{r})$$

and a "removal" cross section is defined as

$$\Sigma_{R,g}(\mathbf{r}) = \Sigma_{t,g}(\mathbf{r}) - \Sigma_s^{g\to g}(\mathbf{r}) \tag{5.22}$$

Notice that the removal cross section is the difference between the total and the "in-group" scattering cross section. The in-group scattering does not remove the neutron from the group; therefore, that part of the scattering collisions does not represent a loss; hence, the subtraction. With the introduction of the removal cross section, the multigroup equations take the form

$$-\nabla D_g(\mathbf{r})\nabla\phi_g(\mathbf{r}) + \Sigma_{R,g}(\mathbf{r})\phi_g(\mathbf{r})$$

$$= \sum_{g'\neq g}^{G} \Sigma_s^{g'\to g}(\mathbf{r})\phi_{g'}(\mathbf{r}) + \chi_g \sum_{g'=1}^{G} (\nu\Sigma_f)_{g'}\phi_{g'}(\mathbf{r})|g=1,G \tag{5.23}$$

A few remarks are in order about Eq. (5.23):

1. Starting with Eq. (5.11), which involves the flux in terms of four variables (three for space and one for energy), Eq. (5.23) has been obtained for a function of three variables only. It is easier to solve any single equation in Eq. (5.23) than Eq. (5.11); but, the price to pay is that instead of solving one equation, G equations have to be solved.

2. The multigroup equations are coupled because of the first summation term on the right-hand side.

3. That same summation term takes into account the neutrons that enter an energy group after they have collided inside another group. In principle, the transfer of neutrons from group to group, as a result of scattering, may go both ways, that is, up or down in energy. In practice, however, only downscattering is considered, except in very special cases where an accurate determination of the thermal flux is required, which is generally the case for graphite-moderated reactors. For the discussion here, only downscattering is assumed.

4. The multigroup equations provide the space variation of the group fluxes $\phi_g(\mathbf{r})$, which, in turn, represent the energy dependence of the flux in a histogram form (group by group). But there is a contradiction here: The neutron fluxes (the unknowns) have been used for the computation of the average group cross sections [see Eqs. (5.15), (5.16), and (5.17)]. This is possible because the fluxes used for the calculation

of the group constants are essentially functions of energy only $[\phi(E)]$, with a very "mild" space dependence. These fluxes are obtained by solving the TE for $\phi(E)$, that is, by concentrating on the energy variable only. The solution is not an easy task, but it has to be done only once and the result can be used for a large class of problems. More details about how this calculation is performed are given in Section 5.3.

5.2.4 Criticality Calculation Using the Multigroup Equations

In obtaining Eq. (5.23), a steady state was assumed, that is, the reactor is exactly critical. In reality, however, it is highly unlikely that in choosing a material composition and a certain geometry, the system will be exactly critical with the first guess. Recognizing this fact, the multigroup equations are rewritten in the following form:

$$
-\nabla D_g(\mathbf{r})\nabla \phi_g(\mathbf{r}) + \Sigma_{R,g}(\mathbf{r})\phi_g(\mathbf{r}) = -\sum_{g' \neq g}^{G} \Sigma_s^{g' \to g}(\mathbf{r})\phi_{g'}(\mathbf{r})
$$

$$
= \frac{1}{k}\chi_g \sum_{g'=1}^{G} (\nu\Sigma_f)_{g'}\,\phi_{g'}(\mathbf{r})\,|\,g=1,G \qquad (5.24)
$$

where the constant k balances the equations for noncritical conditions and has the meaning of the effective multiplication factor for the reactor core under study. To show the coupling between the groups, the equations are written below explicitly, group by group. [For simplicity, the summation in the fission source is suppressed and that source is indicated as $S(\mathbf{r})$.] As indicated in Section 5.2.3, only downscattering is assumed.

$$
g = 1 \qquad -\nabla D_1(\mathbf{r})\nabla \phi_1(\mathbf{r}) + \Sigma_{R,1}(\mathbf{r})\phi_1(\mathbf{r}) = \frac{1}{k}\chi_1 S(\mathbf{r})
$$

$$
g = 2 \qquad -\nabla D_2(\mathbf{r})\nabla \phi_2(\mathbf{r}) + \Sigma_{R,2}(\mathbf{r})\phi_2(\mathbf{r}) - \Sigma_s^{1\to2}(\mathbf{r})\phi_1(\mathbf{r}) = \frac{1}{k}\chi_2 S(\mathbf{r})
$$

$$
g = 3 \qquad -\nabla D_3(\mathbf{r})\nabla \phi_3(\mathbf{r}) + \Sigma_{R,3}(\mathbf{r})\phi_3(\mathbf{r}) - \Sigma_s^{1\to3}(\mathbf{r})\phi_1(\mathbf{r}) - \Sigma_s^{2\to3}(\mathbf{r})\phi_2(\mathbf{r})
$$

$$
= \frac{1}{k}\chi_3 S(\mathbf{r})
$$

$$
\vdots
$$

$$
g = G \qquad -\nabla D_G(\mathbf{r})\nabla \phi_G(\mathbf{r}) + \Sigma_{R,G}(\mathbf{r})\phi_G(\mathbf{r}) - \Sigma_s^{1\to G}(\mathbf{r})\phi_1(\mathbf{r})
$$

$$
- \Sigma_s^{2\to G}(\mathbf{r})\phi_2(\mathbf{r}) - \ldots - \Sigma_s^{G-1\to G}(\mathbf{r})\phi_{G-1}(\mathbf{r}) = \frac{1}{k}\chi_G S(\mathbf{r}) \qquad (5.25)
$$

The criticality search proceeds as follows[2]:

1. An initial value is guessed for the fission source and k:

$$S(\mathbf{r}) = S^{(0)}(\mathbf{r}) , \quad k = k^{(0)} \tag{5.26}$$

2. The flux $\phi_1^{(0)}(\mathbf{r})$ is next calculated for the first group by solving

$$-\nabla D_1(\mathbf{r})\nabla\phi_1^{(0)}(\mathbf{r}) + \Sigma_{R,1}(\mathbf{r})\phi_1^{(0)} = \frac{1}{k^{(0)}} \chi_1 S^{(0)}(\mathbf{r}) \tag{5.27}$$

which is solved numerically because the geometry of the core is complicated.

3. The fluxes $\phi_g^{(0)}(\mathbf{r})|g = 2,G$ are next obtained successively for the rest of the groups. Note that the fission source, $S^{(0)}(\mathbf{r})$, is the same for all groups.

4. A new source is calculated, using the fluxes just obtained,

$$S^{(1)}(\mathbf{r}) = \sum_{g=1}^{G} [\nu\Sigma f(\mathbf{r})]_g \phi_g^{(0)}(\mathbf{r}) \tag{5.28}$$

and a new value of k, $k^{(1)}$, is also calculated:

$$k^{(1)} = \frac{\int d^3 r S^{(1)}(\mathbf{r})}{\frac{1}{k^{(0)}} \int d^3 r S^{(0)}(\mathbf{r})} \tag{5.29}$$

5. The new values of the source, $S(\mathbf{r})$, and k are compared with the previous ones. In general, after the n'th iteration, one compares

$$\left| \frac{S^{(n)}(\mathbf{r}) - S^{(n-1)}(\mathbf{r})}{S^{(n)}(\mathbf{r})} \right| < \varepsilon_s \tag{5.30}$$

and

$$\left| \frac{k^{(n)} - k^{(n-1)}}{k^{(n)}} \right| < \varepsilon_k \tag{5.31}$$

The values of the convergence criteria ε_s and ε_k are of the order of 10^{-3} to 10^{-5}. If Eqs. (5.30) and (5.31) are satisfied, this part of the calculation is completed.

6. If the value of k is the desired one, the problem is solved. If, however, a different value of k is desired, the calculation is repeated

(steps 1 to 5) with a new composition. Obviously, the composition is changed in such a way as to lead toward the desired value of k. A change in k will also result from a change in geometry or from a combination of geometry-composition. Because operating reactors have a fixed geometry, it is only the composition that is usually changed when criticality with new fuel has to be calculated.

The process followed in the calculation of k is called the power or source iteration method (Fig. 5.3). The iterations themselves (steps 1 to 5) are called

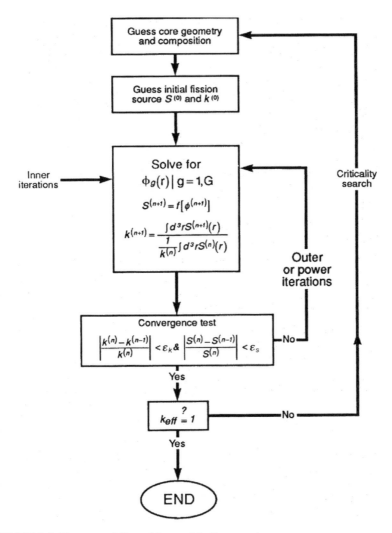

FIGURE 5.3 The steps followed in a criticality search.

outer iterations. The solution of each multigroup equation by numerical techniques also involves iterations over guesses of the flux $\phi(\mathbf{r})$ at different space points. These iterations are called inner iterations. The inner iterations are stopped when the flux of a particular group satisfies a convergence criterion similar to that shown by Eqs. (5.30) and (5.31).

Criticality searches are performed with the help of computer codes that use an algorithm based on the process described here. Examples of such codes are PDQ,[3] VENTURE,[4] PHOENIX/ANC,[5] CASMO/SIMULATE,[6–8] and others.

5.2.5 One- and Two-Group Diffusion Equation Calculations

It is useful to consider two special cases of the multigroup equations because the results provide an opportunity to make some general comments about criticality and the flux in a homogeneous reactor without a reflector. Although commercial reactors are heterogeneous and have reflectors, the cases considered in this section are still interesting because they introduce the concepts of the buckling and criticality equations.

Consider first the one-group case. From Eq. (5.24) one obtains, assuming a homogeneous core (D and Σ not functions of space),

$$-D\nabla^2\phi(\mathbf{r}) + \Sigma_a\phi(\mathbf{r}) = \frac{1}{k}\nu\Sigma_f\phi(\mathbf{r}) \tag{5.32}$$

If only one group of neutrons is used, the removal cross section is equal to the absorption cross section and all the fission neutrons appear in this group; therefore $\chi_1 = 1$. Notice that Eq. (5.32) expresses the logical statement that in a critical reactor ($k = 1$)

$$(\text{leakage}) + (\text{absorption}) = (\text{source})$$

The source may also be written as

$$\nu\Sigma_f\phi(\mathbf{r}) = \nu\frac{\Sigma_f}{\Sigma_{a,fuel}}\frac{\Sigma_{a,fuel}}{\Sigma_a} = \eta f\Sigma_a\phi(\mathbf{r}) = k_\infty\Sigma_a\phi(\mathbf{r}) \tag{5.33}$$

where

$$\eta = \nu\frac{\Sigma_f}{\Sigma_{a,fuel}} = \text{number of neutrons produced per neutron absorbed by the fuel}$$

$$f = \frac{\Sigma_{a,fuel}}{\Sigma_a} = (\text{thermal}) \text{ neutron utilization factor} = \text{fraction of neutrons absorbed by the fuel}$$

$$k_\infty = \eta f = \text{infinite multiplication factor.}$$

Defining the neutron diffusion length as

$$L^2 = D/\Sigma_a \qquad (5.34)$$

and the buckling as

$$B^2 = \frac{1}{L^2}\left(\frac{k_\infty}{k} - 1\right) \qquad (5.35)$$

Eq. (5.32) takes the familiar form

$$\nabla^2 \phi(\mathbf{r}) + B^2 \phi(\mathbf{r}) = 0 \qquad (5.36)$$

Equation (5.35) for the buckling is rearranged to become

$$k = \frac{k_\infty}{1 + L^2 B^2} \qquad (5.37)$$

which is also known as the reactor criticality equation in the one-group case.

The one-group diffusion equation gives inaccurate results. It is used primarily to illustrate the concept of the buckling and the shape of the flux in a bare homogeneous reactor. The buckling, as given in Eq. (5.35), depends on the composition of the system. From the point of view of Eq. (5.36), B^2 is the eigenvalue (or eigenvalues) of that equation, subject to the boundary condition $\phi(\mathbf{r}_s) = 0$, where $\mathbf{r}_s$ indicates a position vector on the surface of the reactor (including extrapolation distance). The solutions of Eq. (5.36) and the corresponding eigenvalues for a critical reactor subject to this boundary condition are shown in Table 5.1.

TABLE 5.1
Neutron Flux and Buckling for Critical Bare, Homogeneous Reactors

Reactor Geometry	Flux	Buckling
Slab (thickness a)	$\cos(\pi x/a)$	π^2/a^2
Parallelepiped (volume abc)	$\cos(\pi x/a)\cos(\pi y/b)\cos(\pi z/c)$	$\pi^2/a^2 + \pi^2/b^2 + \pi^2/c^2$
Cylinder (height H, radius R)	$J_0(\nu_0 r/R)\cos(\pi z/H)$[a]	$\dfrac{\nu_0^2}{R^2} + \dfrac{\pi^2}{H^2}$
Sphere (radius R)	$(1/r)\sin(\pi r/R)$	π^2/R^2

[a] $\nu_0 = 2.405 = $ first zero of the Bessel function $J_0(\nu_0 r/R)$.

The two-group equations are

$$-D_f\nabla^2\phi_f(\mathbf{r}) + \Sigma_{R,f}\phi_f(\mathbf{r}) = \frac{1}{k}\chi_f[(\nu\Sigma_f)\phi_f(\mathbf{r}) + (\nu\Sigma_f)_{th}\phi_{th}(\mathbf{r})]$$

$$-D_{th}\nabla^2\phi_{th}(\mathbf{r}) + \Sigma_{a,th}\phi_{th}(\mathbf{r}) - \Sigma_s^{1\rightarrow2}\phi_f(\mathbf{r})$$

$$= \frac{1}{k}\chi_{th}[(\nu\Sigma_f)\phi_f(\mathbf{r}) + (\nu\Sigma_f)_{th}\phi_{th}(\mathbf{r})] \tag{5.38}$$

where, instead of the subscripts 1 and 2, the more familiar subscripts f (for fast) and th (for thermal) are used. The equations are usually simplified by recognizing that almost all fission neutrons are fast (i.e., $\chi_f = 1, \chi_{th} = 0$). Also, for the thermal group, $\Sigma_R = \Sigma_a$ since there is no group below the thermal one to which neutrons may be lost.

For a bare, homogeneous reactor, it is an acceptable approximation to assume that the flux has the same space dependence in both groups and satisfies the equation

$$\nabla^2 f(\mathbf{r}) + B^2 f(\mathbf{r}) = 0 \tag{5.39}$$

that is, one can write

$$\phi_f(\mathbf{r}) = \phi_f f(\mathbf{r}) \ , \quad \phi_{th}(\mathbf{r}) = \phi_{th} f(\mathbf{r}) \tag{5.40}$$

where $f(\mathbf{r})$ represents the space dependence of the flux and ϕ_f and ϕ_{th} are constants, scaling factors independent of space.

Upon substitution of Eqs. (5.39) and (5.40) into Eq. (5.38), one obtains two algebraic equations for the two unknowns ϕ_f and ϕ_{th} (with $\chi_{th} = 0$):

$$\left[D_f B^2 + \Sigma_{R,f} - \frac{1}{k}(\nu\Sigma_f)_f\right]\phi_f - \frac{1}{k}(\nu\Sigma_f)_{th}\phi_{th} = 0$$

$$- \Sigma_s^{1\rightarrow2}\phi_f + (D_{th}B^2 + \Sigma_{a,th})\phi_{th} = 0 \tag{5.41}$$

For this equation to have a solution other than zero, the determinant of the coefficients of ϕ_f and ϕ_{th} must be zero. This condition leads, after some algebra, to

$$k = \frac{(\nu\Sigma_f)_f}{\Sigma_{R,f} + D_f B^2} + \frac{\Sigma_s^{1\rightarrow2}}{\Sigma_{R,f} + D_f B^2}\frac{(\nu\Sigma_f)_{th}}{\Sigma_{a,th} + D_{th}B^2} \tag{5.42}$$

Traditionally, k is given by the so-called "six-factor" formula:

$$k = \varepsilon \eta f p \, P_{FNL} P_{TNL} \tag{5.43}$$

where η and f have been defined earlier

p = resonance escape probability

ε = fast fission factor (fraction of neutrons generated by fissions caused by fast neutrons)

P_{FNL} = fast neutron nonleakage probability

P_{TNL} = thermal neutron nonleakage probability.

Equation (5.42) may be cast into the form of Eq. (5.43) after properly defining the various factors.[1,2]

The shape of the neutron flux, obtained after a two-group calculation, is the same as that from a one-group calculation (see Table 5.1). However, the magnitude of the two-group fluxes is different since the factors ϕ_f and ϕ_{th} of Eq. (5.40) are not equal. These two factors are calculated using the second equation of Eq. (5.41),

$$\frac{\phi_f}{\phi_{th}} = \frac{(D_{th} B^2 + \Sigma_{a, th})}{\Sigma_s^{1 \to 2}} \tag{5.44}$$

plus the equation giving the reactor power,

$$P = E_f \int \phi_f f(\mathbf{r}) \Sigma_{f, f} \, dV + E_f \int \phi_{th} f(\mathbf{r}) \Sigma_{f, th} \, dV \tag{5.45}$$

where E_f is the energy released per fission.

For a given reactor power level, the values of ϕ_f and ϕ_{th} can be obtained from Eqs. (5.44) and (5.45).

5.2.6 Numerical Solution of the Multigroup Equations

It is impossible to obtain an analytical solution of the multigroup equations, even for the simplest geometry. The standard method of solution is a numerical one, based on the discretization of the space variables. For details of the method, the reader should consult the Bibliography and Refs. 3, 4, and 9. In this section we discuss only the basic steps on which the numerical solution is founded. Some comments are made about the value and pitfalls of numerical techniques.

For any numerical solution, the fundamental idea is, first, the discretization of a variable and, second, the replacement of differential and integral operators, involving that variable, with algebraic equivalents. For simplicity in writing, we assume in the following that only one variable is involved. In the case of the multigroup equations, assume that the space variable in question is x. Therefore, we expect to obtain solutions for the functions $\phi_g(x) | g = 1, G$.

The discretization is achieved by deciding to evaluate the unknown functions $\phi_g(x)$ at a certain finite number of points $x = i = 1, M$, and for each point one writes

$$\phi_g(x_i) = \phi_{g,i} | i = 1, M, g = 1, G \qquad (5.46)$$

where M is the number of spatial points at which the unknown functions will be computed. In the mathematical sense, the numerical solution has the limitation of giving the value of the functions $\phi_g(x)$ only at M points $x_i | i = 1, M$ (Fig. 5.4), as opposed to an analytical solution, which would result in a continuous function that could be used to calculate the value of $\phi_g(x)$ at any point x. In the practical sense, however, this is not a real limitation for two main reasons: One, a numerical solution is better than none and, two, the actual "detail" of the solution is only limited by the amount of computer time one is willing to spend on (and pay for) the solution. Experience has shown that numerical solutions do adequately represent quantities of interest (in the present case the neutron flux) and are extremely helpful in designing and constructing reactors that perform according to the design. The criterion for the adequacy of a solution of an equation that represents any phenomenon

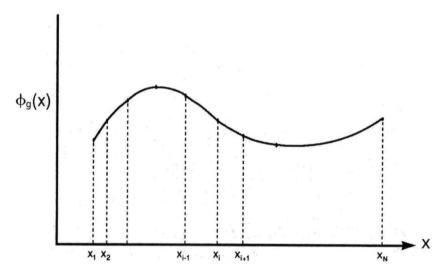

FIGURE 5.4 In a numerical solution, the variable is discretized and the unknown function is computed at a finite number of N points.

(physical, chemical, nuclear, etc.) is how well the calculated value of a quantity (whether analytical or numerical) compares to its measured value. In that sense, numerical solutions are successful and continue to improve as better models are used to represent the phenomenon under study and more powerful computing capabilities become available.

Numerical solutions are obtained by using rather large and sophisticated computer codes. The chances are small that an engineer out in the field will have to write such a code. The chances are very high, however, that an engineer will have to use one. In that case, the user of the code will have to provide the input information and be able to understand and analyze the results of the computation. Correct preparation of the input requires that the user-engineer understand the basics of the computer code structure, the approximations used by the code (are they valid for the problem under study?), and the effect of all the input parameters on the outcome of the computation. One of the fundamental input parameters of a numerical solution code is the number of discrete points M to be used or, equivalently, the size of the "mesh" $\Delta x_i = x_{i+1} - x_i | i = 1, M$.

The replacement of a differential operator by a "numerical" one is based on the validity of the equation

$$\frac{df}{dx} = \frac{f_i - f_{i-1}}{x_i - x_{i-1}} = \frac{f_i - f_{i-1}}{\Delta x_i} \tag{5.47}$$

where $f_i = f(x_i)$ is the function to be computed. The second derivative is given by a similar equation:

$$\frac{d^2 f}{dx^2} = \frac{\left(\dfrac{df}{dx}\right)_i - \left(\dfrac{df}{dx}\right)_{i-1}}{x_i - x_{i-1}} \tag{5.48}$$

which, in view of Eq. (5.47) and assuming a constant Δx, becomes

$$\frac{d^2 f}{dx^2} = \frac{f_i - 2f_{i-1} - f_{i-2}}{(\Delta x)^2} \tag{5.49}$$

Clearly, the accuracy of this approximation depends on how fast the function $f(x)$ changes over the interval $\Delta x = x_i - x_{i-1}$. Since the function $f(x)$ is not known, how is the decision going to be made about the size of Δx? To be specific, if one attempts to calculate the neutron flux, how can the decision be made if the flux is not known? There is no general rule about such a decision. What helps is experience, knowledge about similar systems, and a basic understanding of neutron physics. If nothing else is known, one uses the assumption that, in any medium, the attenuation of neutrons is, essentially, exponential of the type

$$\phi(x) \sim \exp(-\Sigma_t x) = \exp(-x/\lambda) \qquad (5.50)$$

where $\lambda = 1/\Sigma_t$ is the mean free path of the neutron in the medium. The size of the space mesh Δx should be definitely less than one mean free path since attenuation over such a distance is equal to $1 - \exp(-1) = 0.63$, which is considered excessive for any numerical calculation. Therefore, the decision about the size of Δx is made by checking the mean free path of the neutrons in the medium for which the flux is calculated and making sure that $\Delta x < \lambda$.

After the decision is made regarding the mesh size, the differential equations are transformed into algebraic equations by substituting the approximations in Eqs. (5.47) and (5.49) for the derivatives.

The result is G linear algebraic equations for the $G * M$ unknown values of the fluxes, $\phi_g(x) = \phi_{g,i} | i = 1, M$ and $g = 1, G$. Normally, the value of one group flux at one mesh point is decided arbitrarily; next, the flux values are obtained sequentially for that group at the M spatial points. Setting the value of one flux at one point arbitrarily is not an approximation since the fluxes in a criticality calculation are determined within a constant. The absolute values are determined based on the reactor power.

The numerical solutions discussed in this section represent the inner iterations of the criticality calculation presented in Section 5.2.4 (Fig. 5.3). Various schemes have been developed over the years that connect inner and outer iterations with the goal of improving accuracy and accelerating convergence.

5.2.7 The Transport Approximations P_N and S_N

The transport approximations involve the handling of the angular variables: the azimuthal angle and the polar angle (Fig. 5.1) (see the Duderstadt and Hamilton and the Lewis and Miller bibliographical entries and Refs. 10–12). Although the differential scattering cross section appears to depend on the initial and final neutron directions [see Eq. (5.3)], in reality it depends only on the angle between initial and final direction θ_0 (Fig. 5.5), because most media are "isotropic." An isotropic medium has the same properties in all directions, as a result of which the azimuthal angle does not play a role in scattering collisions. This is fortunate because it means that one more variable can be eliminated from the transport equation.

Without any loss in generality, Eq. (5.3) (steady state) can be integrated over the azimuthal angle ϕ from 0 to 2π, and the polar angle can be replaced by the cosine of the angle:

$$\mu = \cos \theta_0 \qquad (5.51)$$

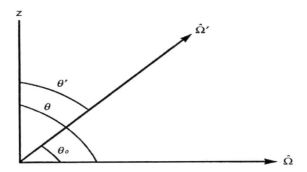

FIGURE 5.5 If $\hat{\Omega}$ is the direction of motion of the incident neutron and $\hat{\Omega}'$ the direction of motion of the scattered one, the differential scattering cross section depends on $\cos\theta_0 = \mu = \hat{\Omega}\cdot\hat{\Omega}'$ and not on the two $\hat{\Omega}$'s independently.

This permits the transport equation to become, in an operator form,

$$T(E,\mu)\phi(\mathbf{r},E,\mu) = S(\mathbf{r},E,\mu) \qquad (5.52)$$

The equation is written in an operator form because only the principles of the transport approximations will be discussed, not the actual derivations (for which the reader should consult the references). Notice that the operator $T(E,\mu)$ is not a function of space if the cross sections are not functions of space.

At this point, the multigroup approach (as explained in Section 5.2.3) can be applied and the following equation obtained:

$$T_g(\mu)\phi_g(\mathbf{r},\mu) = S_g(\mathbf{r},\mu)\,|\,g = 1, G \qquad (5.53)$$

Two general methods are used for treating the angular variable beyond this point: series expansion in terms of Legendre polynomials or numerical solution using discretization. The first approach leads to the P_N method and the second to the S_N method.

Using Legendre polynomials, one tries to represent the solution as a series of the form

$$\phi(\mathbf{r},\mu) = \sum_{l=0}^{\infty} \phi_{g,l}(\mathbf{r})P_l(\mu) \qquad (5.54)$$

where the Legendre polynomials are the functions with the orthogonality property

$$\int_{-1}^{1} P_l(\mu)P_m(\mu)\,d\mu = \frac{2}{2l+1}\,\delta_{lm} \qquad (5.55)$$

Substituting Eq. (5.54) for the flux in Eq. (5.53), multiplying all terms by $P_m(\mu)$, and integrating term by term over the range $-1 \leq \mu \leq +1$, one obtains [making use of the orthogonality condition expressed by Eq. (5.55)]

$$T_{g,l}\phi_{g,l}(\mathbf{r}) = S_{g,l}(\mathbf{r})|g = 1, G \text{ and } l = 0, \infty \qquad (5.56)$$

The derivation of Eq. (5.56) results in the elimination of the angular variable at the expense of going from one equation (for the variable μ) to an infinite number of equations. In practice, the series in Eq. (5.54) is truncated after N terms; that is, one sets

$$\phi_{g,l}(\mathbf{r}) = 0|l > N$$

which is known as the P_N approximation.

One particular difficulty of the P_N equation, Eq. (5.56), is the fact that for every value of l there is a coupling among several flux coefficients; for example, in the equation for value l, three coefficients are coupled:

$$\phi_{g,l-1}(\mathbf{r}), \quad \phi_{g,l}(\mathbf{r}), \quad \phi_{g,l+1}(\mathbf{r})$$

The use of the P_N approximation, particularly for neutrons, has declined in favor of one of the S_N methods. The S_N methods are based on the discretization of the angular variable in a manner similar to that used for the space variable (Section 5.2.6). In the original S_N method, the neutron flux was computed at N points, that is, at N distinct directions in the range of $-1 \leq \mu \leq +1$. Thus, one computes the values

$$\phi_g(\mathbf{r}, \mu_n) = \phi_{g,n}(\mathbf{r})|n = 1, N$$

Derivatives involving μ are handled in the manner shown by Eqs. (5.47) and (5.49). Hidden in the operator $T_g(\mathbf{r}, \mu)$ is an integral over μ. The integral is represented numerically as a summation of the form

$$\int_{-1}^{1} d\mu \, T_g(\mathbf{r}, \mu) = \sum_{j=1}^{J} W_j T_{g,j} \qquad (5.57)$$

where the W values are J "weights" chosen for the particular numerical integration scheme employed.

The integral over μ involves the differential scattering cross section

$$\Sigma_s(\mathbf{r}, \mu)$$

Before the numerical integration of [Eq. (5.57)] is performed, the cross section Σ_s is represented by a series similar to that used for the flux [Eq. (5.54)]:

$$\Sigma_s(\mathbf{r}, \mu) = \sum_l \Sigma_{s,l}(\mathbf{r}) P_l(\mu) \tag{5.58}$$

This series is also truncated after a few terms, in a manner analogous to the representation of the flux in the P_N approximation. Note that the neutron cross-section files (see Section 5.3) provide the values of these Legendre expansion coefficients ($\Sigma_{s,l}$).

After discretization, the transport equation is transformed into a set of algebraic equations for which the unknowns are the values of the fluxes $\phi_{g,n}(\mathbf{r})$ at the specified values of μ.

The differences among the various S_N methods stem from different treatment of the directions chosen and the weights used to represent the angular integral [Eq. (5.57)]. The original S_N method represented the flux as N straight-line segments in the range of $-1 \le \mu \le +1$. Methods developed later use more elaborate treatment of the angular variable. In modern transport codes, the S_N method calls for the use of $N(N + 4)/4$ discrete directions in one-dimensional (1-D) problems and $N(N + 4)/2$ discrete directions in two-dimensional (2-D) problems. Thus, if one chooses S_8, then the flux will be discretized in 24 directions for 1-D problems, and in 48 directions for 2-D problems. Well-known codes based on the S_N method are ANISN[12] and XSDRNPM[13] for 1-D problems, DOT[14] for 2-D problems, and ATTILA,[15] which is a three-dimensional (3-D) code.

5.2.8 Nodal Methods

When the neutron transport equation is solved numerically, the demand for computer time increases dramatically with the number of energy groups and the number of mesh points. Even using today's fastest computers, the time required to calculate the neutron flux in a commercial power reactor in three dimensions and with a modest number of energy groups may be prohibitive. Yet there are many cases where a 3-D representation of the flux is necessary to provide an adequate study of the changes taking place in the core because of fuel depletion, control rod insertion or ejection, burnable poison depletion, and so on, and such calculations have to be repeated many times. How can one perform the necessary calculations satisfactorily while at the same time keeping the computer time used and money spent to a reasonable amount? An answer to this question seems to be the use of nodal methods (see the Henry and the Duderstadt and Hamilton entries in the Bibliography and Refs. 16–18).

The nodal method is based on a division of the reactor into a certain number of cells, also called nodes or nodal cells. Each node is treated as a region with homogeneous properties for which a neutron balance equation is written in the general form (steady state):

$$(\text{leakage out} + \text{absorption}) = (\text{leakage in} + \text{source}) \tag{5.59}$$

Each of the terms in Eq. (5.59) is expressed mathematically and the equations for all of the nodes are solved to give the neutron flux in each node. This statement sounds fine in principle; however, in practice, to solve the equations one needs to compute neutron transfer (leakage, if you will) from each node to every other node in the core. Thus, if the reactor has been divided into N nodes, a calculation is required for $N * N$ leakage or "coupling" coefficients, which may be considered the elements of an $N * N$ matrix. Since the flux and the source have N values, they may be represented by column matrices and the complete equation for the reactor takes the matrix form

$$\Phi = \mathbf{T} * \mathbf{S} \tag{5.60}$$

where

Φ = the flux matrix (N elements)

$\mathbf{S}$ = the source matrix (N elements)

$\mathbf{T}$ = the transfer matrix with elements T_{ij} representing transfer of neutrons from node i to node j ($N * N$ *elements*).

One may say that physically the T_{ij} elements represent the probability that a neutron from node i will end up in node j.

It is not difficult to see the connection between the nodal method and the numerical techniques described earlier: As N becomes very large, the size of the cell becomes, eventually, the volume element defined by the space mesh division of the numerical calculation. To obtain an idea of the difference in size of numerical mesh versus node in the nodal method, consider the following. In typical numerical calculations, an LWR assembly may be represented by 5 to 10 mesh points per direction; nodal methods calculations have been reported with four nodes per assembly.

Obviously the question to be asked is how accurate the result of the nodal method is, in view of the fact that a rather coarse reactor representation is involved. The answer is that the success of the method depends on the satisfactory calculation of the matrix $\mathbf{T}$. Computer codes based on the nodal method have been successful in computing the 3-D reactor flux in commercial power reactors.[18]

5.2.9 The Monte Carlo Method

It has been shown in the previous sections that all transport calculations involve the determination of the neutron flux $\phi(\mathbf{r}, E, \hat{\Omega})$. The flux is obtained as the solution of the transport equation and as such it represents a deterministic quantity because it is a solution of a deterministic equation relating average (but single-valued) neutronic parameters. By contrast, the Monte Carlo (see Spanier and Gelbard in the Bibliography and Refs. 19–24) method starts with the understanding that the behavior of a single neutron is not at all deterministic. Knowing everything about a neutron (energy, position, direction of motion) and the properties of the medium in which it travels does not allow one to predict that particle's future with certainty. The most we can say is that the neutron might participate in certain collisions or leak out of the medium. Considered as an event, a neutron–nucleus collision is a stochastic phenomenon, that is, there is a probability for the collision to take place, a probability given by a nuclear cross section.

Once the collision takes place, its outcome is also another stochastic phenomenon. There is a probability (expressed by a cross section) that the neutron will be reemitted (scattering), will stay in the nucleus (capture), will cause the emission of one or more other particles (γ, n, $2n$, α, etc.), or cause fission. Thus, if one had the means to follow individual neutrons with identical initial parameters, that observer would find out that the individual histories of the neutrons would be different. However, if one calculates the "average" of outcomes of interest (e.g., flux, radiation dose), based on the results from the histories of many neutrons, the calculations will result in averages that agree quantitatively with the corresponding measured quantities.

The Monte Carlo method can be considered an experiment that is performed in a computer, involving the transport of particles through a medium. In a real experiment, there is a source of particles, a real medium, and real detectors that record the particles. Based on the numbers recorded by the detectors, one can say something about the medium and behavior of the particles studied. The experimenter knows very well that the numbers recorded by the counters have an inherent statistical uncertainty (an uncertainty that depends on the numbers recorded in the scaler) and can be estimated, based on those same numbers.

Using the Monte Carlo method, a model of the medium under study is set up in the computer and individual particles are thrown at the medium or are generated in it, as if coming from a source. The particles are followed, one by one, and the various events in which they participate (collision, absorption, fission, escape, etc.) are recorded. All the events associated with one particle constitute the history of that particle. Of course, the history of every particle should have an end, the particle should eventually "die" or be "killed." The death of the particle is decided by the person doing the "experiment," that is, by the person doing the computation. Typical particle deaths are absorption, leakage out of the system, or reaching a lower energy threshold.

The type of outcome of such a Monte Carlo "experiment" is what the observer decides it to be. Based on the objective, the observer records events of interest. After many particle histories have been recorded, average quantities can be calculated and conclusions can be drawn about the behavior of the particles in that medium. As the number of histories increases, the sample averages will approximate the expected value of the quantity of interest. As in the real experiment, the result of a Monte Carlo calculation has a statistical uncertainty that can be estimated in a manner similar to that used to determine the standard error of radiation counting results.

A fundamental requirement for a Monte Carlo calculation is the knowledge of probability distributions associated with all the possible events in which a particle may participate, as well as all the variables involved with such events. The decision about a particular event taking place or not and about a particular variable taking on a certain value is made on the basis of the corresponding probability distributions: Consider a variable x and define $f(x)dx$ as the probability that the value of the variable x is between x and $x + dx$. The function $f(x)$ is known as the probability distribution function (pdf) of the variable x [Fig. 5.6(a)] and is normalized to 1. A cumulative distribution function (cdf), $F(x)$, is defined as

$$F(x) = \int_{x_1}^{x} f(x)\, dx \ , \quad x_1 \le x \le x_2 \tag{5.61}$$

where $F(x)$ is the probability that the value of x is less than or equal to x [Fig. 5.6(b)]. Based on its definition, $F(x)$ is bounded between 0 and 1.

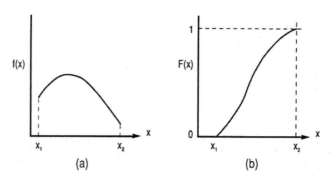

FIGURE 5.6 (a) A possible pdf for the variable x. (b) A typical cdf for the variable x ($x_1 \le x \le x_2$).

To select values of x correctly for a Monte Carlo calculation, the distribution of the selected x values should follow the pdf $f(x)$. This is accomplished by selecting a random number (RN) between zero and one, setting

$$RN = F(x) \tag{5.62}$$

and inverting it to obtain

$$x = F^{-1}(RN) \tag{5.63}$$

It can be shown (see Problem 5.9) that if the x's are selected as shown by Eqs. (5.62) and (5.63), based on RN values uniformly distributed between 0 and 1, their distribution is that of $f(x)$. There are many ways to select the RN values. In this age of computers, the RN values are generated by the machine. Computers are able to generate a set of "random" numbers between 0 and 1, uniformly distributed in this range—in other words, with equal probability of finding any RN anywhere between 0 and 1.

There are cases where the pdf is a discrete function. Then, if the number of possible outcomes is N, one has

$$\sum_{i=1}^{N} f(x_i) = 1 \tag{5.64}$$

and the cdf is given by

$$F(x_i) = \sum_{j<i} f(x_j) \tag{5.64a}$$

Examples of discrete functions are the probability of throwing a coin and getting heads or tails, the probability of a neutron colliding with a nucleus and causing either fission or being absorbed, and so forth.

To illustrate the use of random numbers for the selection of a variable, consider a neutron of energy E entering a medium. Assume that answers are needed to the following questions (Fig. 5.7):

1. Where does the first collision take place?

2. What type of collision is it?

3. What is the direction of motion of the neutron after the collision?

To decide at what distance s the neutron will have the first interaction, one needs to determine the probability that a neutron will have a collision between s and $s + ds$. That function is known and is (assuming a uniform medium)

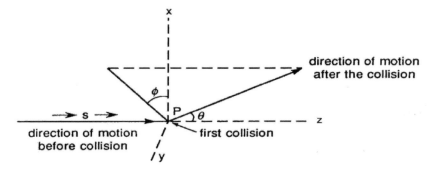

FIGURE 5.7 The particle enters the medium and has its first collision at point P. A decision has to be made about the distance s and the angles θ and ϕ.

$$f(s)\,ds = \exp(-\Sigma_t s)\Sigma_t\,ds \tag{5.65}$$

The cdf is

$$F(s) = \int_0^s f(s)\,ds = 1 - \exp(-\Sigma_t s) \tag{5.66}$$

Selecting a random number RN, setting it equal to $F(s)$, and solving for s, one obtains

$$s = -\left(\frac{1}{\Sigma_t}\right)\ln(1 - RN) \tag{5.67}$$

This equation determines the distance s to the first interaction.

Assume that the scattering cross section is Σ_s and the absorption cross section is $\Sigma_a(\Sigma_s + \Sigma_a = \Sigma_t)$. Obviously, the probability that the outcome of the collision is absorption is equal to Σ_a/Σ_t, and the probability for scattering is equal to Σ_s/Σ_t.

A new random number is selected and compared to these probabilities:

- If $RN \le \Sigma_a/\Sigma_t$, the event is absorption.

- If $RN > \Sigma_a/\Sigma_t$, the event is scattering.

The determination of the direction of motion requires the decision about the azimuthal angle ϕ and the polar angle θ. Since any azimuthal angle is equally probable, its pdf is

$$f(\phi)\,d\phi = (1/2\pi)d\phi|0 \le \phi \le 2\pi \tag{5.68}$$

and the cdf is

$$F(\phi) = \int_0^\phi \frac{1}{2\pi} \, d\phi = \frac{\phi}{2\pi} \tag{5.69}$$

Selecting a new random number and setting it equal to $F(\phi)$ gives the value of ϕ:

$$\phi = 2\pi RN \,|\, 0 \le \phi \le 2\pi \tag{5.70}$$

For the determination of the polar angle θ, one obtains the pdf using the definition of the differential scattering cross section:

$$f(\theta)d\theta = \frac{\sigma_s(\theta)\sin\theta \, d\theta}{\sigma_s} \tag{5.71}$$

where σ_s is the total scattering cross section. The cdf is

$$F(\theta) = \frac{\displaystyle\int_0^\theta \sigma_s(\theta)\sin\theta \, d\theta}{\sigma_s} \tag{5.72}$$

A new random number is selected and is set equal to $F(\theta)$. Then, the value of θ is obtained by inverting that relationship as shown in Eq. (5.63). One very common case is that of isotropic scattering. Then, the differential scattering cross section is independent of the polar angle and Eq. (5.72) gives

$$\theta = \arccos(1 - 2RN) \,|\, 0 \le \theta \le \pi \tag{5.73}$$

Spanier and Gelbard (see the Bibliography) indicate that the following features are common in all Monte Carlo calculations:

1. Description of the physical process
2. Formulation of the probability model
3. Definition of the basis that estimates a random variable
4. Construction of sampling distributions, using random numbers
5. Processing of samples and statistical analysis of data.

The most useful aspect of the Monte Carlo method is its ability to represent and study phenomena in complicated geometries, involving shapes that would be practically impossible to represent by a differential equation. A second useful feature is its ability to provide the result in any detail desired; all the user has to do is to record all of the pertinent events. (Of course, detail does not come cheaply. Monte Carlo–based computer codes have a voracious appetite for computer memory and computer time!)

Many computer codes have been developed over the years that are based on the Monte Carlo method. Five well-known codes are:

- KENO, a Monte Carlo code[24] that calculates the value of k

- MORSE (Multigroup Oak Ridge Stochastic Experiment), a code[22] that can be used for neutrons, gammas, or a mixed neutron-gamma calculation

- MCNP,[21] which has the capability to read cross-section values directly from the nuclear data files, thus avoiding the need for multigroup cross sections

- TRIPOLI, a Monte Carlo code[23] developed by the French

- FLUKA, a code developed at CERN[25] primarily for charged particles.

One of the objectives of every Monte Carlo code user is to obtain a result that gives the desired precision, but uses the minimum possible amount of computer time. To achieve this, all Monte Carlo codes utilize biasing techniques that alter the history of particles in such a way that the probabilities for individual events are changed, but the outcome over many events and particles is the correct one. Particularly sophisticated biasing techniques are employed by MCNP and TRIPOLI. An excellent report on biasing techniques is given in Ref. 26.

5.3 Nuclear Cross-Section Data

5.3.1 The ENDF/B Library

In the United States, the national repository for all information about nuclear cross sections is the National Cross Section Center (NCSC) at the Brookhaven National Laboratory (BNL) in Upton, New York. Cross-section data obtained either by calculation, or experiment, or by a combination of the two approaches anywhere in the world are collected at the NCSC for evaluation.[27,28] There is a team of experts called the Cross Section Working Evaluation Group whose sole and continuous function is to evaluate cross-section data for nuclear reactions of neutrons, gammas, and charged particles. At BNL, all information about nuclear cross sections is stored in a huge computer-data library known as the Evaluated Nuclear Data Files (ENDF).[b] There are two types of files, file type A and file type B. The data in file A are, generally, incomplete in terms of their evaluation, and for this reason the

---

[b] The first comprehensive publication containing most of the data known at the time appeared in 1955 as report BNL-325, "Neutron Cross Sections," which was known as the "barn book."

information contained there and known as ENDF/A is used only by the specialists who evaluate the cross sections. File B contains the evaluated cross-section data known as ENDF/B, the data used by all persons involved in reactor physics calculations.

Although the evaluation of nuclear cross sections is a continuous process, for practical reasons, evaluated data are not released to the users on a continuous basis. Instead, every few years a new complete version is released for general use. As of 2012, the latest version available was version VII, known and indicated in reports, books, and so on, as ENDF/B-VII.

As mentioned above, the ENDF library contains information about cross sections for neutron, gamma, and charged-particle interactions. For reactor physics calculations, one needs data primarily about neutron and neutron-producing reactions and, secondarily, about gamma and alpha particle reactions.

5.3.2 Information Provided by ENDF/B

The following type of information is contained in ENDF/B for all isotopes of interest, some molecules, and some special mixtures (e.g., some fission products are lumped together as single pseudomaterials) for all known nuclear reactions:

1. The decay constant

2. Type of decay

3. Cross-section values, as a function of neutron energy, from very low energies up to 20 MeV, as well as scattering cross-section values, as a function of the scattering angle, for the same energy range

4. Resonance parameters for nuclear cross sections

5. Fission product yields

6. Secondary neutron energy and angular distribution [for fission neutrons, this is the value of $\chi(E)$, the fission neutron energy spectrum]

7. (γ, n) reaction cross sections.

In the ENDF/B, the cross sections are represented as a combination of tabulated cross sections and resonance parameters. To solve the transport equation in any approximation, cross sections must be defined at all energies. In energy regions where the cross sections are not tabulated, the required cross-section values are obtained with the help of interpolation schemes. The ENDF/B library provides the five interpolation schemes shown in Table 5.2.

Experience has shown that the choice of the interpolation law is important because the use of the wrong scheme may produce cross sections that lead to erroneous results when they are subsequently utilized for neutronic calculations. The errors are reduced if linearization schemes are used to represent the cross sections within a range where a particular interpolation

TABLE 5.2
ENDF Interpolation Schemes

Scheme	Function
Constant (E)	$\sigma(E) = A$
Linear-linear (E)	$\sigma(E) = A + BE$
Linear-log (E)	$\sigma(E) = A + B \ln(E)$
Log-linear (E)	$\sigma(E) = A \exp(BE)$
Log-log	$\sigma(E) = A * E^B$

law has been used. A detailed description of these problems is given in Ref. 9.

The resonance parameters are used to reconstruct the cross sections in the energy range where the resonance occurs. This reconstruction is not a trivial matter. It may lead to significant errors if performed incorrectly. The person who performs this task should take into account whether at any particular energy region,

1. There is only one isolated resonance.

2. There are many, but resolved, resonances.

3. There are many, but unresolved, resonances.

In each of the cases mentioned, the treatment of the resonances is different and, therefore, the resulting cross-section values are also different.[9]

Another problem associated with resonances is the so-called "self-shielding." The term *self-shielding* is used to describe the following phenomenon: At the resonance energy, where the value of the cross section is extremely high, the neutron flux is depressed. Since the flux is depressed, the number of reactions at that energy also decreases, thus "shielding" the resonance from the neutron flux. The treatment of self-shielding is complicated by the fact that the phenomenon is spatially dependent (it depends on geometry and even on direction[9]).

The user of ENDF/B should remember that the values of cross sections are given under the assumption that neutrons collide with stationary nuclei. In reality, the nuclei have a thermal motion that is important, particularly in the case of resonances. Then, the Doppler effect comes into play and the absorption rate depends on temperature. Since the transport equation describes the neutron population in the laboratory frame of reference and for elevated temperatures, care should be exercised to use the proper cross sections for its solution.

5.3.3 Calculation of the Neutron Energy Spectrum $\phi(E)$

The ENDF/B library constitutes a tremendous volume of data. For the average user utilizing the nuclear cross-section data for a reactor physics calculation, starting with ENDF/B represents a monumental task that is not always necessary. Also, it must be mentioned that the ENDF/B data are not readily usable; they need special processing to make them compatible with the computer codes that require them in order to perform the computation. Many codes have been developed to perform such tasks.[29–32] Reference 33 describes the NJOY nuclear data processing system, widely used by the reactor physics community.

The overwhelming majority of calculations is performed by applying the multigroup formalism (see Section 5.2.3), which does not require all of the detail contained in ENDF/B. For this reason, the common approach taken is to develop sets of group constants for a certain number of groups (200) that apply to a whole class of problems (e.g., for LWRs, for fast reactors, for shielding, for fusion reactors). To perform a specific calculation, one would choose the cross-section set that applies best to the problem and either uses the group constants directly, in a multigroup calculation, or most frequently, produces constants for a smaller number of groups using a process called *cross-section collapsing*.

The development of group constants from the ENDF/B follows these steps:

1. The transport equation is solved for the neutron energy spectrum $\phi(E)$; that is, all of the variables except energy are suppressed.

2. Using the spectrum $\phi(E)$, a set of group constants is computed over a superfine- or fine-group structure. At this step, the number of groups is more than a thousand.

3. The group constants obtained in step 2 are used for the generation of new constants over a broad-group structure (e.g., 200 groups).

The transport equation, in terms of the energy variable alone, takes the following form (for a homogeneous medium):

$$\Sigma_t(E)\phi(E) = \sum_{j=1}^{J} \int_E^{E_{\alpha_j}} \frac{\Sigma_s^j(E' \to E)}{(1 - \alpha_j)E'} \phi(E')\, dE' + S(E) \qquad (5.74)$$

The summation $j = 1, J$ is over all J isotopes present in the medium. The source $S(E)$ is, for a reactor without external sources [see also Eq. (5.18)]:

$$S(E) = \frac{1}{k} \chi(E) \int_{E'=0}^{E_{max}} \nu(E')\Sigma_f(E')\phi(E')\, dE' \qquad (5.75)$$

The solution of Eq. (5.74) represents the neutron flux as a function of energy in an infinite homogeneous medium at steady state. The properties of the medium enter through the cross sections, the atom concentrations, and the constants

$$\alpha_j = [(A_j - 1)/(A_j + 1)]^2 \tag{5.76}$$

where A_j is the atomic weight of isotope j. In reality, the computer codes[29-32] that solve this equation keep a "mild" space dependence through a buckling B^2, but that detail is not important for our discussion here.

For a heterogeneous medium, the equation for $\phi(E)$ takes a different form because the flux is different in the separate media involved and neutrons may travel from one medium to another. As a result, the transport equation is transformed into coupled equations. Consider, for example, the usual case of two separate media—fuel and moderator. The two equations for the fuel and moderator are

$$
V_F \Sigma_{tF}(E)\phi_F(E) = V_F[1 - P^0_{F \to M}(E)] \int_E^{E_{\alpha F}} \phi_F(E') \Sigma_{sF}(E') \frac{1}{(1 - \alpha_F)} \frac{1}{E'} dE'
$$
$$
+ V_M P^0_{M \to F}(E) \int_E^{E_{\alpha M}} \phi_M(E') \Sigma_{sM}(E') \frac{1}{(1 - \alpha_M)} \frac{1}{E'} dE'
$$
$$\tag{5.77}$$

$$
V_M \Sigma_{tM}(E)\phi_M(E) = V_F P^0_{F \to M}(E) \int_E^{E_{\alpha F}} \phi_F(E') \Sigma_{sF}(E') \frac{1}{(1 - \alpha_F)} \frac{1}{E'} dE'
$$
$$
+ V_M[1 - P^0_{M \to F}(E)] \int_E^{E_{\alpha M}} \phi_M(E') \Sigma_{sM}(E') \frac{1}{(1 - \alpha_M)}
$$
$$
\times \frac{1}{E'} dE' \tag{5.78}
$$

where

V_F = volume of fuel

V_M = volume of moderator

$P^0_{F \to M}(E)$ = probability that a neutron of energy E escapes from the fuel, without a collision in the fuel, and ends up in the moderator

and the rest of the symbols have their usual meaning.

All of the cross sections necessary for the solution of Eqs. (5.74), (5.77), and (5.78) are taken directly from ENDF/B. The solution is achieved by numerical techniques. It is not a very difficult problem, but it is not a trivial one either. Because the energy spans seven decades, one has to consider the variation of the cross sections over that same range, which means that the resonances have to be treated properly, as discussed in Section 5.3.2.

Periodic array of infinite slabs:

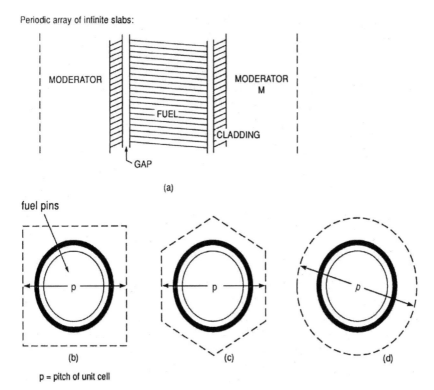

p = pitch of unit cell

FIGURE 5.8 Configurations of typical unit cells: (a) plane, (b) square, (c) hexagonal, and (d) cylindrical.

In modeling a reactor for Eq. (5.77) or (5.78), it is not necessary to consider the whole core. Normally, one chooses a unit cell, which may be regarded as the smallest repeating unit of a reactor core that has the properties of a critical assembly. The use of the unit cell simplifies the calculation considerably, since the alternative would be to model each fuel rod separately. (There are more than 50,000 rods in a large commercial LWR!)

The geometry of the unit cell depends on the assembly design. Traditional unit cells are shown in Fig. 5.8. It is assumed that the length of a unit cell in the direction perpendicular to its cross section is infinite and it is customary to treat square and hexagonal unit cells as cylindrical ones. In such a case, the radius R of the "cylindricized" unit cell is given, in terms of the pitch p, by

$$R = p/\sqrt{\pi}, \text{ for the square cell}$$

$$R = (\sqrt{3}/2\pi)^{1/2}p, \text{ for a hexagonal cell} \tag{5.79}$$

To calculate the neutron flux inside the unit cell, it is necessary to satisfy boundary conditions on the surface of the cell. Some examples of boundary conditions are zero current or specific reflection property on the surface (i.e., specified albedo).

Frequently, the unit cell is homogenized, based on the relative volumes of fuel and moderator. For example, the homogenized atom densities of fuel (N'_F) and moderator (N'_M) in a cell with volumes V_F and V_M, correspondingly, are given by

$$N'_F = N_F \frac{V_F}{V_F + V_M} \tag{5.80}$$

$$N'_M = N_M \frac{V_M}{V_F + V_M} \tag{5.81}$$

where N_F and N_M are the atom densities of fuel and moderator, respectively.

5.3.4 Cross-Section Libraries for Multigroup Calculations

After the neutron energy spectrum $\phi(E)$ is obtained, multigroup constants (i.e., average values of cross sections for each energy group) are computed based on the equation

$$\sigma_h = \left. \frac{\int_{E_h}^{E_{h-1}} \sigma(E)\phi(E)\, dE}{\int_{E_h}^{E_{h-1}} \phi(E)\, dE} \right| h = 1, H \tag{5.82}$$

for all isotopes and cross-section types. A set of multigroup constants is known as a *cross-section library*.

The group structure at this stage is a "fine" one. It is not unusual for H to be equal to a thousand or more groups. As mentioned earlier, most reactor calculations are performed with a smaller number of groups, in which case there is a need for a set of new group constants corresponding to the new group structure. This task, called cross-section collapsing, is accomplished in the following manner.

Consider H fine groups with energy group boundaries $E_h | h = 1, H$ and a new "broad"-group structure consisting of G groups with energy group boundaries $E_g | g = 1, G$. A basic requirement in going from H to G group constants is that the energy boundaries of the G groups must coincide with the boundaries of the H groups (Fig. 5.9). The system under study is modeled in one dimension and the transport equation is solved in H groups, thus providing

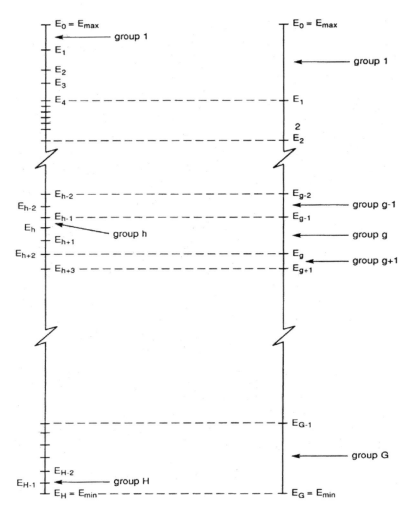

FIGURE 5.9 The fine-group (H-group) and broad-group (G-group) structures. Boundaries of the G-group structure must coincide with boundaries of the H-group structure.

the fluxes $\phi_h(\mathbf{r})|h = 1, H$. Any cross section in the broad-group structure is then obtained by

$$\sigma_g(\mathbf{r}) = \frac{\sum_h \sigma_h(\mathbf{r})\phi_h(\mathbf{r})(\Delta E)_h}{\sum_h \phi_h(\mathbf{r})(\Delta E)_h}\Bigg| \, g = 1, G \qquad (5.83)$$

and $(\Delta E)_h = E_{h-1} - E_h$ and the summation over h indicated in Eq. (5.83) covers all of the h groups whose energy boundaries lie within those of that g'th group. The group constants obtained by Eq. (5.83) constitute the collapsed cross-section set.

The G-group set may be the final one to be used for routine reactor calculations or it may still be an intermediate one. Frequently, this broad-group set consists of 200 groups. If it was derived based on a model of an LWR average composition, it may subsequently be used with a more detailed model of the particular reactor under study to produce yet another set of multigroup constants for a much smaller number of groups (anywhere from 2 to 50).

What is the optimum number of groups one should use? There is no unique answer to that question. The number of groups depends on the objective of the calculation, the reactor type (thermal or fast), the accuracy desired, and the amount of computer time for which one is willing to pay.

5.4 Fundamentals of Core Reload Calculations

5.4.1 Objectives of Reload Calculations

Two general objectives drive the reload calculations:

1. To guarantee that the new core will deliver the energy it is designed for; that is, to guarantee that the fuel can reach the desired burnup.

2. To ascertain that the safety characteristics of the fuel are equal to or better than those reported in the safety analysis report for the previous core.

The design of the reload consists of three parts:

1. Mechanical and thermal design of each assembly

2. Determination of enrichment and number of fresh assemblies

3. Determination of the new core loading pattern.

Since the design of the new fuel is completed before the previous cycle ends, that is, before the beginning of the cycle (BOC), there is no choice but to base the design on a certain projected condition of the core at the end of the cycle (EOC).

The safety parameters of the core fall into three categories:

1. Core reactivity parameters (for PWRs: moderator temperature coefficient, fuel Doppler reactivity coefficient, delayed neutron fraction, prompt neutron lifetime, boron worth). (The reactivity components of an LWR are shown in Table 5.3.)

TABLE 5.3

Reactivity Components in LWRs

	Associated Reactivity (%)	
	BWR	PWR
Changes in the core:		
1. Cold zero power to hot full power:		
Fuel temperature defect	1.5	1.5
Moderator temperature and voidage	2.0	2.5
2. Equilibrium fission product poisoning	3.3	3.5
3. Burnup[a] compensation	6.5	10.0
4. Control margin and xenon override	1.0	1.2
5. Shutdown margin	1.0	1.0
Total	15.3	19.7

[a] The excess reactivity reserved for depletion depends essentially on fuel management options selected, and may vary substantially.

2. Control rod worth parameters (differential and total rod worth, verification of rod insertion limits)

3. Other neutronic parameters (boron dilution effect, control rod ejection) and thermal-hydraulic parameters (loss-of-coolant accident, steam-line break, core power peaking factors, etc.).

In addition to the parameters mentioned above, the following must be known as a function of burnup:

1. Radial and axial power distribution

2. Fission product absorber worth (mostly xenon)

3. Boron concentration (for PWRs); control rod position (for BWRs).

The computation of the reload design proceeds along the following three steps:

1. Collect mechanical data and the material composition for each assembly.

2. Determine the temperature of the fuel during operation; thermal-hydraulic codes provide such information.[34–36]

3. Conduct neutronic calculations (Fig. 5.10); the starting point is the cross-section information provided by ENDF/B. The next step is the generation of cross-section libraries. Examples of computer codes that may be used to perform that task are MC-2,[30] the AMPX system,[13] and GGC-5.[29] The computer codes CASMO (now CASMO-5) and SIMULATE-3 have been adopted by many U.S. and foreign utilities[6–8]; they form an advanced 3-D two-group nodal computational package that can be used for fuel management studies of either a BWR or a

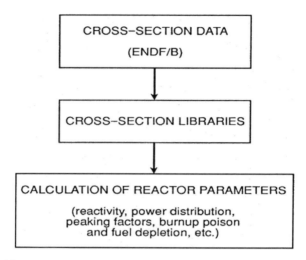

FIGURE 5.10 The major tasks involved in performing reactor physics calculations.

PWR. The CASMO-3/SIMULATE-3 package has been benchmarked against more detailed codes; it has been shown to compute reactor parameters with remarkable accuracy (2% or less), and seems to perform better than earlier codes like LEOPARD, PDQ, and HARMONY.[3,37,38] One important feature of SIMULATE-3 is that it requires no normalization of its results to operating data or to the results of other more sophisticated codes. Westinghouse also developed the system of codes termed PHOENIX-P/ANC,[5,39] which performs similar tasks.

5.4.2 Calculation of the Average Power per Assembly

A nuclear reactor core is designed to produce a certain thermal energy Q, with a fixed number of assemblies. For the same output Q, a BWR requires about three times more assemblies than a PWR. In both types of reactors, however, the fuel assemblies are placed in the core in such a way that the core shape approximates a cylinder. One of the principal design objectives in evaluating core performance and predicting fuel loading is the determination of the power density distribution within the core as a function of core life.

Although the core is loaded in such a way that the power profile across the core is as flat as possible, individual assemblies do not all produce the same power. Each assembly produces a certain thermal power, depending on its fuel and poison content and its core location. If the power density is $q(\mathbf{r})$ in watts per unit volume and the volume of assembly j is V_j, the power produced by assembly j, P_j, is given by the following equation, where E_f represents energy per fission:

$$P_j = \int_{V_j} q(\mathbf{r}) \, dV = E_f \sum_{g=1}^{G} \overline{\Sigma_{fgj}} \, \overline{\phi_{gj}} V_j \qquad (5.84)$$

where $\overline{\Sigma_{fgj}}$ and $\overline{\phi_{gj}}$ are the average values, over the assembly volume, of the fission cross section and the flux (by group), respectively. The summation over the G groups will be suppressed in what follows for simplicity in writing. By following the power produced by an assembly during its life in the core, the isotopic content of that assembly can be determined and, thus, its burnup.

If the total number of assemblies in the core is N, the average power per assembly is given by

$$\bar{P} = \frac{P}{N} = \frac{E_f \sum_{j=1}^{N} \overline{\Sigma_{fj}} \, \overline{\phi_j} V_j}{N} \qquad (5.85)$$

Let NP_j be the fraction of power produced by assembly j:

$$NP_j = \frac{P_j}{P} = \frac{\overline{\Sigma_{fj}} \, \overline{\phi_j} V_j}{\sum_{j=1}^{N} \overline{\Sigma_{fj}} \, \overline{\phi_j} V_j} \qquad (5.86)$$

If, as is the usual case, all assemblies have the same volume, Eq. (5.86) becomes

$$NP_j = \frac{\overline{\Sigma_{fj}} \, \overline{\phi_j}}{\sum_{j=1}^{N} \overline{\Sigma_{fj}} \, \overline{\phi_j}} \qquad (5.87)$$

The power P_j [Eq. (5.84)] produced by assembly j is given by

$$P_j = NP_j * \bar{P} \qquad (5.88)$$

With respect to the flux, in Eq. (5.87) relative values can be used, which, incidentally, are the values generated by the diffusion codes that compute these fluxes.

In practice, the online computer at the power plant records the fractions NP_j for all of the assemblies. The NP_j values are determined from signals proportional to the assembly power, obtained by detectors either permanently mounted on certain assemblies (in PWRs, these detectors are called self-powered neutron detectors) or detectors periodically inserted in certain assemblies (in BWRs, these detectors are called traversing in-core probes).

■ *Example 5.1:* As an example of the calculation of the power produced by an assembly, consider a reactor with $P = 3500$ MW(t) and $N = 180$ assemblies. Figure 5.11 shows, in one-quarter of the core, the burnup and the relative power distribution, that is, the fractions NP_j. Based on this information, what is the power produced by assemblies 15G, 8H, and 9D?

Answer: The average power per assembly is $P = 3500/180$ MW(t)/assembly = 19.44 MW(t)/assembly

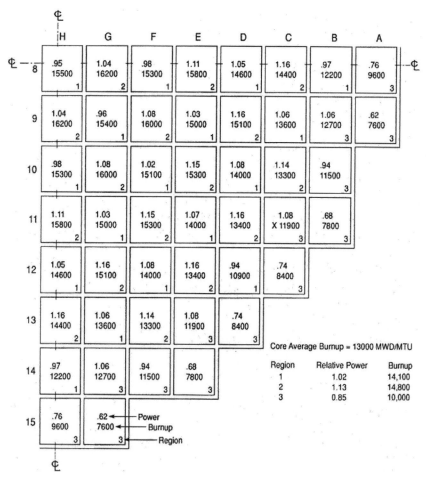

FIGURE 5.11 One-quarter of a power reactor loading showing burnup and power by assembly.

Using the NP_j values from Fig. 5.11,

$$P(15G) = 0.62 * 19.44 = 12.05 \text{ MW(t)}$$

$$P(8H) = 0.95 * 19.44 = 18.47 \text{ MW(t)}$$

$$P(9D) = 1.16 * 19.44 = 22.55 \text{ MW(t)} \quad \blacksquare$$

5.5 Fuel Depletion Calculations

As the reactor operates, the fuel composition changes and has an effect on the reactivity of the core. The following aspects of fuel depletion are particularly important to the nuclear engineer:

1. The relationship between reactivity loss and fuel burnup

2. The changes in core power distribution with fuel depletion

3. The reactivity control during operation and its effect on core power distribution

4. The change in fuel composition, as a result of depletion, and its overall effect on fuel performance

5. The expected energy produced during the cycle.

In LWRs, it is the isotopes ^{235}U and ^{238}U that are consumed. In the process, fission products are produced and also plutonium isotopes. Some of the fission products, particularly xenon and samarium, are strong neutron absorbers and, as a consequence, they reduce the core reactivity. On the other hand, ^{239}Pu has an overall positive effect because it contributes to the power generation and it is not uncommon to have 15% to 20% of the reactor power produced by fissions in plutonium. Another isotope, whose concentration is important for two reasons, is ^{238}U. First, ^{238}U contributes to reactivity through fast fissions (positive effect) and through resonance absorption (negative effect). Second, it leads to the production of plutonium. The production of actinides such as ^{241}Am, ^{236}Pu, and ^{236}U is also of interest because their presence causes an additional, albeit minor, reduction in reactivity.

The task of fuel depletion calculations is to determine the concentration, in each assembly, of all the isotopes of interest as a function of time, that is, as a function of burnup. The general equation for the calculation has the form

$$\frac{dN_i}{dt} = \sum_{m=1}^{M} l_{im} \lambda_m N_m + \phi \sum_{m=1}^{M} f_{im} \sigma_m N_m - (\lambda_i + \phi \sigma_i + r_i - c_i)N_i + F_i | i = 1, M$$

$$(5.89)$$

where

N_i = atom density of nuclide i

M = number of nuclides

l_{im} = fraction of decays of nuclide m, leading to formation of nuclide i

λ_i = radioactive decay constant of nuclide i

ϕ = neutron flux, position and energy averaged

f_{im} = fraction of neutron absorption by nuclide m, leading to the formation of nuclide i

σ_m = average neutron absorption cross section of nuclide m

r_i = continuous removal rate of nuclide i from the system

c_i = continuous feed rate of nuclide i

F_i = production rate of nuclide i directly from fission.

The various terms in Eq. (5.89) represent the following:

$$\sum_{m=1}^{M} l_{im} \lambda_m N_m = \text{production of species } i \text{ as a result of the decay of all the nuclides present}$$

$$\phi \sum_{m=1}^{M} f_{im} \sigma_m N_m = \text{production of species } i \text{ as a result of neutron capture by all nuclides present}$$

$$\lambda_i N_i = \text{loss of nuclide } i \text{ through its own decay}$$

$$\phi \sigma_i N_i = \text{loss of nuclide } i \text{ as a result of neutron capture}$$

$$F_i = Y_i \Sigma_f \phi = \text{production rate of nuclide } i \text{ directly from fission}$$

$$Y_i = \text{fission yield of nuclide } i.$$

For a particular isotope, one or more terms may be missing and multiple production terms may exist either for neutron absorption or for decay of other precursors. Following are examples of the form Eq. (5.89) takes for a few important isotopes.

^3H: Tritium is produced directly by fission ($Y = 1.26 \times 10^{-4}$) and by the following reactions:

$$^6\text{Li}(n,^3\text{H})^4\text{He}, \quad ^7\text{Li}(n,^3\text{H})^5\text{He}, \quad ^{10}\text{B}(n,^3\text{H})^8\text{Be} \ (2\ ^4\text{He}),$$

$$^{11}\text{B}(n,^3\text{H})^9\text{Be}, \quad ^2\text{H}(n,\gamma)^3\text{H}$$

$$\frac{dN_{^3H}}{dt} = -\lambda_{^3H} N_{^3H} + \phi(\sigma_{^7Li} N_{^7Li} + \sigma_{^6Li} N_{^6Li} + \sigma_{^{10}B} N_{^{10}B} + \sigma_{^{11}B} N_{^{11}B} + \sigma_{^2H} N_{^2H})$$

$$+ Y_{^3H} \Sigma_f \phi$$

$^{135}Xe:$ ^{135}Xe is produced directly by fission $(Y = 0.003)$ and from the decay of iodine, a fission product with a fission yield of $Y = 0.061$.

$$\frac{dN_{Xe}}{dt} = -\lambda_{Xe} N_{Xe} + \lambda_I N_I + Y_{Xe} \Sigma_f \phi - \sigma_{aXe} \phi N_{Xe}$$

$^{149}Sm:$ ^{149}Sm is produced by the decay of ^{149}Pm, the decay product of ^{149}Nd, a fission product with a fission yield of $Y = 0.0113$.

$$\frac{dN_{Sm}}{dt} = \lambda_{Pm} N_{Pm} - \sigma_{aSm} \phi N_{Sm}$$

$^{239}Pu:$ ^{239}Pu is produced by neutron absorption in ^{238}U. The cross section σ_U should be properly averaged over the neutron energy spectrum.

$$\frac{dN_{Pu}}{dt} = -\lambda_{Pu} N_{Pu} + \sigma_U \phi N_U - \sigma_{Pu} \phi N_{Pu}$$

For ^{239}Pu, the decay term is negligible compared to the other two, since its half-life is 24,400 yr.

Equation (5.89) becomes nonlinear if either the flux or any of the cross sections are functions of time. To maintain linearity, the equations are solved over individual time steps that are short relative to the cycle length. For each time step, the depletion calculation consists of three main tasks (Fig. 5.12):

1. Macroscopic cross sections are derived based on the known composition of the reactor at the beginning of the depletion step.

2. A 2-D or 3-D calculation is performed, using as input the isotope concentrations at the beginning of that depletion step, to produce the flux for that time step.

3. The reactor is divided into a number of regions and an average flux is calculated for each region. The flux is normalized based on the average power during the step. Using the flux obtained above and the known concentrations, Eq. (5.89) is solved for all the regions and all the isotopes of interest, thus providing the isotopic concentrations at the end of the step (which is also the beginning of the next one). Tasks 2 and 3 are usually performed by the same computer code.

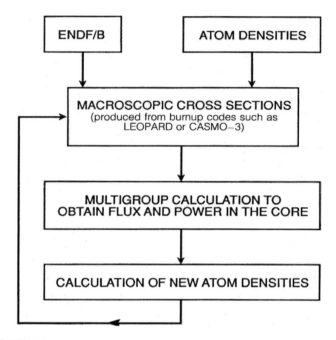

FIGURE 5.12 The computational process followed in fuel depletion calculations.

The length of the step may be given in time units or in terms of burnup. The latter, obviously, is more meaningful since it is the burnup that causes changes in the fuel. Typical burnup timestep lengths are of the order of 500 MWd/t or less, depending on reactor type and other changes that may have occurred (or be projected to occur) during the step. The following example shows how burnup is related to real time.

■ **Example 5.2:** A depletion calculation is performed for an 1100-MWe reactor with efficiency of 31%, a capacity factor of 85%, and a time step equal to 300 MWd/t. The core contains M = 90 tons of fuel. What is the real time corresponding to that depletion step?

Answer: The burnup (BU) is given by

$$\text{BU} = \frac{energy\ produced}{mass\ of\ fuel} = \frac{P * T * CF}{M}$$

where P is the maximum reactor power, T is the time, and CF is the capacity factor for time period T. Then,

$$T = (300\,\text{MWd/t} * 90\,\text{t})/[(1100\,\text{MW}/0.31) * 0.85] = 8.95\,\text{days}\quad ■$$

Since the core composition changes with burnup as well as the conditions in the moderator (boron concentration, control rod position) and the fuel (depletion of ^{235}U and ^{238}U, buildup of plutonium), the neutron spectrum also changes. Change in the neutron spectrum in turn means that the average microscopic cross sections may have to be recalculated in every step. The macroscopic cross sections must certainly be calculated for every step and for every region of the core. Composite codes like LEOPARD[37] and CASMO/ SIMULATE[6–8] take these changes into account.

5.6 Burnable Poison Calculations—Chemical Shim

As mentioned in Section 4.2.4, control of the excess reactivity of the core is accomplished by using control rods and burnable poisons (BPs). Experience has shown that the use of BPs offers advantages for better fuel utilization over use of control rods alone.[40–47]

The ideal BP would be one that matches the fuel depletion characteristics. To match the fuel depletion characteristics, the absorption cross section of the poison should be greater than that of the fuel for the first part of the cycle; during the last part of the cycle, the poison should burn out rapidly. By using lumped or heterogeneous poisons, the self-shielding factor (see Section 5.3.2) for the poison creates characteristics close to the ideal.

As indicated in Chapter 4, the lumped BPs are placed in the appropriate fuel assemblies to reduce the average neutron flux in that assembly. As the fuel cycle progresses, the depletion of the BP is represented by

$$\frac{dN^P_{(t)}}{dt} = -g(t)\sigma_{aP}N^P(t)\phi \qquad (5.90)$$

where

$$g(t) = \frac{average\ flux\ inside\ the\ BP}{average\ flux\ in\ the\ core}$$

σ_{aP} = neutron absorption cross section of the BP

$N^P(t)$ = number of atoms of the BP at time t.

The function $g(t)$ depends on the geometry and the initial concentration of the poison, and on the self-shielding effect. BP calculations will not be accurate if self-shielding is ignored.

An alternative to lumped poisons is the use of poisons dissolved in the coolant of the reactor, a process known as *chemical shim* control,[47] which is the main type of control used in commercial PWRs.

A suitable poison for chemical shim must be an isotope characterized by a large neutron absorption cross section and must be soluble in the reactor coolant. It should also be a noncorrosive material and relatively stable so that it does not become attached to reactor core components. Although cadmium sulfate ($CdSO_4$) has been used in some reactors, boric acid (H_3BO_3) is used almost exclusively in PWRs.

A controlled boron concentration in the coolant is used

1. To obtain optimum poisoning of fuel assemblies

2. To compensate for reactivity changes associated with major changes in reactor coolant temperature between cold shutdown and hot full-power operation

3. To compensate for fuel burnup

4. To compensate for fission product poison buildup

5. To provide a shutdown margin during refueling and maintenance operations.

The principal advantages of chemical shim are an improvement in reactor power distribution uniformity and a reduction in core mechanical complexity. The primary disadvantages of chemical shim are its slow introduction or removal rate from the coolant [because of this "slowness" chemical shim cannot be used to trip (scram) the reactor] and its adverse effect on the moderator temperature coefficient. Overall, substantial gains in PWR core design and performance have been achieved by employing chemical shim.

The calculation of the relationship between boron concentration and reactivity is derived on the basis that the chemical shim affects the reactivity of a thermal reactor core by altering the thermal utilization factor (f) (see Section 5.2.5). Since the boron concentration in the coolant is relatively low, in the parts per million range, the transport properties of the core stay essentially the same after the boron is introduced into the water. Assuming a uniform boron concentration in the moderator, the reactivity worth of the poison can be shown to be (see the Lamarsh and Baratta entry in the Bibliography)

$$\rho_B = \frac{\overline{\Sigma_{aB}}}{\overline{\Sigma_{aF}} + \overline{\Sigma_{aM}}} \tag{5.91}$$

where

$\overline{\Sigma_{aF}}$ = average thermal macroscopic cross section of the fuel

$\overline{\Sigma_{aB}}$ = average thermal macroscopic cross section of boron

$\overline{\Sigma_{aM}}$ = average thermal macroscopic cross section of the moderator (plus structural materials).

In terms of the thermal utilization factor without boron (f_0), Eq. (5.91) becomes

$$\rho_B = (1 - f_0) \frac{\overline{\Sigma_{aB}}}{\overline{\Sigma_{aM}}} \tag{5.92}$$

with

$$\frac{f_0}{1 - f_0} = \frac{\overline{\Sigma_{aF}}}{\overline{\Sigma_{aM}}} \tag{5.93}$$

If the boric acid concentration is C ppm, then in terms of the masses of water and boron, C is given by

$$C = 1.0 \times 10^6 (m_B / m_M) \tag{5.94}$$

Combining Eqs. (5.92) and (5.94) (also using the relationship between macroscopic and microscopic cross sections), the boron reactivity worth can be written as

$$\rho_B = (1 - f_0) C \frac{A_M \sigma_B}{A_B \sigma_M} \times 10^{-6} \tag{5.95}$$

where $A_M = 18$, $A_B = 10.81$, and σ_M and σ_B are the spectrum-averaged microscopic absorption cross sections for water and natural boron, respectively. If one uses the typical values of 0.66 and 759 b, respectively, Eq. (5.95) becomes:

$$\rho_B = 1.92 \times 10^{-3} C (1 - f_0) \tag{5.96}$$

■ **Example 5.3:** The value of the thermal utilization factor for a certain PWR is 0.965 at startup without any boron in the coolant. At that time, the total excess reactivity is 20.5%. If the control rods are worth 7.5% in reactivity, what is the minimum boric acid concentration, in parts per million, necessary to keep the reactor just critical?

Answer: Using Eq. (5.96) and solving for C, one obtains

$$C = \frac{0.13}{1.92 \times 10^{-3}(1 - 0.965)} = 1934 \text{ ppm boron}$$

since the chemical shim must be worth 20.5% − 7.5% = 13%. Notice that in this example the control rods do not have enough reactivity to keep the reactor from going critical at the beginning of cycle (BOC), which is the case for many PWRs. ■

Theoretically, chemical shim control would permit full-power operation at a steady-state condition, with all control rods pulled out of the core. In practice, however, there are some limitations regarding introduction and removal of the poison and the total amount that can be used. For this reason, some of the control rods are not completely pulled out of the core.

The major limitation on chemical shim stems from its effect on the moderator temperature reactivity coefficient. If the water temperature increases, the density of the moderator and that of the poison decrease. As a result, the reactivity effect of the chemical shim decreases, which amounts to the introduction of a positive component to the moderator temperature reactivity coefficient (MTC). Thus, if the concentration of the soluble boron is large enough, the net value of the MTC may become positive. The addition of burnable poisons helps keep the boron concentration sufficiently low, at BOC, so that the MTC can be kept within safe limits. This trend of having a positive MTC is real and important for a PWR during the power assent period after refueling. A positive MTC is allowed within a certain power level and MTC limits.

During early studies of chemical shim, there was concern about "hide-out" of the poison via plate-out on reactor components. This concern was based on the scenario that the selective accumulation of boron in the core and a sudden release of the boron could result in a ramp reactivity insertion. Fortunately, by controlling the pH of the water coolant, the hide-out problem can be prevented. The pH of the water in PWRs is now maintained in the 6.9 to 7.6 range.

The mechanical part of the chemical shim system is composed of a demineralizer, a filter, coolers, and a pump (Fig. 5.13). The piping to the reactor vessel has a small diameter to prevent rapid changes in the concentration of the boron in the primary loop. To change the concentration, the boric acid is either pumped into the reactor vessel or the primary water is pumped through the cooler to the demineralizer, which removes the boron. The pure water is then pumped back into the primary loop. This process is called "feed-and-bleed." The feed-and-bleed process removes coolant at a rate equal to the injection of the new fluid, so as to maintain a constant coolant volume. The system also provides the means for the disposal of impurities in the coolant and it also controls the amount of fluid in the loop, which expands and contracts according to changes in temperature.

The change in reactivity, as a result of boron removal, is calculated as follows: Consider a system containing a fluid of total volume V with soluble poison concentration $C(t)$ in kilograms per liter at time t. To increase the concentration of the poison, a more concentrated solution C_n, also in kilograms per liter, is added to the system at a rate of w liters per second, determined by the charging pumps. At the same time, fluid with concentration $C(t)$ must be removed in order for the total fluid volume to stay constant. The process is described by the differential equation[48]:

To insert boron

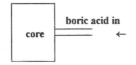

Boron removal system

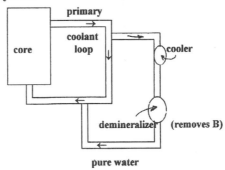

FIGURE 5.13 The mechanical parts of addition and removal of boron from the coolant of a PWR.

$$\frac{dC(t)}{dt} = [C_n - C(t)]\frac{w}{V} \qquad (5.97)$$

To reduce the poison concentration, pure water ($C_n = 0$) is added. Since the change in reactivity is proportional to the poison concentration, one can write

$$\rho_B(t) = \rho_0 + \alpha_B C(t) \qquad (5.98)$$

where α_B = reactivity per unit of boron concentration in the coolant and ρ_0 = core reactivity at time $t = 0$. Differentiating Eq. (5.98), one obtains

$$\frac{d\rho_B(t)}{dt} = \alpha_B[C_n - C(t)]\frac{w}{V} \qquad (5.99)$$

which indicates that the rate of reactivity change is proportional to the poison concentration.

In a reactor in which the fuel depletion component of the excess reactivity is compensated for by chemical shim, the concentration of the poison in the coolant is maximum at BOC and minimum at the end of the cycle. A typical boron concentration change with a burnup for a large commercial PWR is shown in Fig. 5.14. The sudden drop of the concentration at the beginning is due to fission poisons and temperature effects that saturate relatively early in the cycle (details are given in Chapter 6).

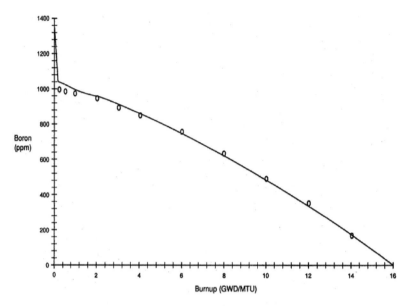

FIGURE 5.14 The change of boron concentration versus burnup in a typical PWR.

5.7 Control Rod Calculations

Generally, control rod calculations have three parts. The first is to determine the worth of a single control rod of a given material and geometric configuration. The second is to determine the worth of an array of control rods distributed in the reactor. The third is to evaluate the power distribution changes, and particularly power peaking, that may be caused locally by the insertion or removal of a control rod.

Control rods are generally characterized as "black" or "gray." Black control rods are very strong neutron absorbers of such size that, once neutrons enter the control rod, they have a negligible probability of exiting from it. Then, on an interface between such a rod and other material (fuel or moderator), no neutrons return from the interior of a black control rod. Gray control rods are made or contain milder neutron absorbers and have such physical size that some neutrons escape from them. The tendency in reactors is to use gray control rods because the black ones distort the neutron flux and, therefore, the power distribution excessively.

As an illustration of a control rod calculation, consider first the simplest case, that of a single control rod located at the center of the reactor. The reactivity worth of the rod is defined as

$$\rho_w = \frac{k - k'}{k'} \tag{5.100}$$

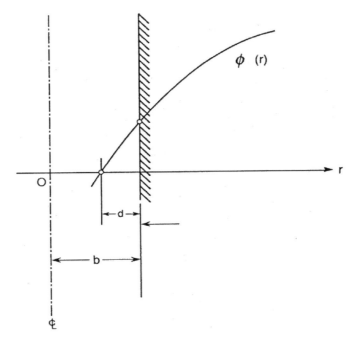

FIGURE 5.15 Extrapolation distance for a black control rod.

where k and k' are the values of the multiplication factor before and after the rod insertion, respectively. In principle, then, to obtain the rod worth, the value of k has to be calculated.

The criticality calculation without the rod is performed by using a multigroup approach, as described in Section 5.2.4. With the rod inserted, the method of calculation has to be modified because the diffusion equation is not valid close to the vicinity of a control rod, particularly a black one. In practice, the diffusion equation is solved in the fuel and moderator and a boundary condition is applied on the surface of the rod of the form

$$\frac{1}{\phi}\left(\frac{d\phi}{dr}\right)_b = \frac{1}{d} \tag{5.101}$$

where b is the radius of the rod and d is an extrapolation distance obtained by transport theory means. What Eq. (5.101) defines is, essentially, an equivalent radius for the control rod equal to $b - d$ (Fig. 5.15).

For a cylindrical reactor of radius R and height H, the flux with the control rod out of the core is given in one-group theory by

$$\phi(r, z) = AJ_0(2.405r/R)\cos(\pi z/H) \tag{5.102}$$

where $J_0(x)$ is the zero-order Bessel function of the first kind. With the control rod fully inserted, the equation for the flux takes the form (for $b \leq r \leq R$):

$$\phi(r, z) = A\left[J_0(\lambda r) - \frac{J_0(\lambda R)}{Y_0(\lambda R)} Y_0(\lambda r)\right]\cos(\pi z/H) \qquad (5.103)$$

where $Y_0(x)$ is the zero-order Bessel function of the second kind and the constant λ is the critical parameter and is related to the buckling by

$$B^2 = \lambda^2 + (\pi/H)^2 \qquad (5.104)$$

To determine the value of A (equivalent to determining the value of k), the flux given by Eq. (5.103) is applied to the boundary condition given by Eq. (5.101), and the resulting transcendental equation is solved for A. (For a complete derivation see reactor physics texts, e.g., Refs. 1 and 2.)

The method described above is not the most accurate one for the calculation of ρ_w. The intent was just to show the process. There are two-group calculations that give better results not only for a central control rod but also for control rods located off-center.

When clusters of control rods are considered, as is the case with large commercial reactors, a different approach[2,9] is taken based on an equivalent unit cell. Consider the geometry of control rods in PWRs (Fig. 5.16) and in

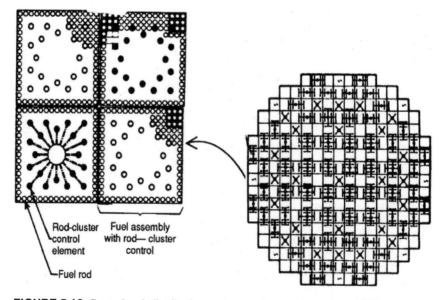

FIGURE 5.16 Control rod distribution and control rod clusters in a PWR.

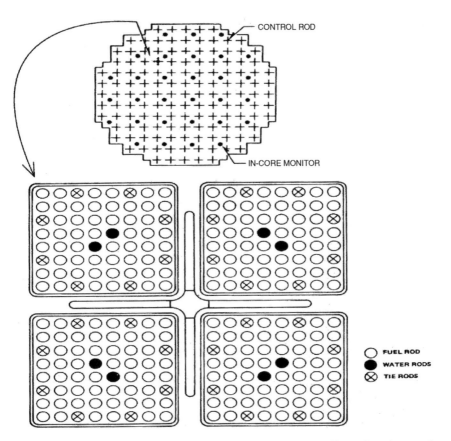

FIGURE 5.17 Control rod distribution and detail of the cruciform-shaped control rod in a BWR. (Courtesy of General Electric.)

BWRs (Fig. 5.17). In PWRs, the control rods are interspersed, in the form of cluster control elements, among fuel rods in certain assemblies. In BWRs, the cruciform-type control rods are placed between assemblies. For every "control unit cell," an effective cross section is calculated for the control element in the cell based on the requirement

$$\Sigma_c^{eff} \bar{\phi} V_c = J_c S_c \qquad (5.105)$$

or

$$\Sigma_c^{eff} = \frac{S_c J_c}{V_c \bar{\phi}} \qquad (5.106)$$

where

V_c = volume of unit cell minus volume of control element in it

$\bar{\phi}$ = average flux in the volume V_c

Σ_c^{eff} = the effective absorption cross section in the cell

S_c = the surface area of the control rod

J_c = the average neutron current on the surface of the control rod.

Since the control rod worth is proportional to this effective cross section, Eq. (5.105) demonstrates the well-known fact that the worth of the rod increases with the surface-to-volume ratio.

As an example, the unit control cell for a PWR is shown in Fig. 5.18. If the radius of each control rod is a, the ratio S_c/V_c is given by

$$\frac{S_c}{V_c} = \frac{20 * 2\pi a}{p^2 - 20\pi a^2} \qquad (5.107)$$

For a BWR, the unit cell is shown in Fig. 5.19. In this case, the surface-to-volume ratio is

$$\frac{S_c}{V_c} = \frac{4l}{p^2 - 2cl + c^2} \qquad (5.108)$$

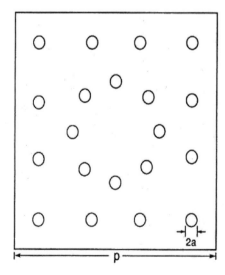

FIGURE 5.18 Unit cell for control rod calculations in a PWR.

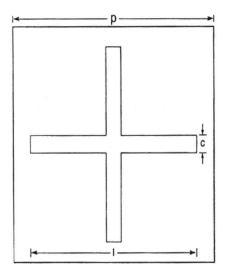

FIGURE 5.19 Unit cell for control rod calculations in a BWR.

Notice that the surface-to-volume ratio is actually the ratio of the control rod perimeter to the cross-sectional area of the rod (unit cell-rod).

As in the case of a central control rod, the diffusion equation is solved in the space outside the control rod and a boundary condition of the type shown in Eq. (5.101) is applied on the surface of the rod. Thus, the flux is obtained as a function of space in the cell. The ratio $J_c/\bar{\phi}$ is then calculated and used in Eq. (5.106) to obtain the effective cross section.

One advantage of this method is the fact that the ratio $J_c/\bar{\phi}$ is, essentially, independent of the composition of the space surrounding the control element. Thus, a very detailed calculation of this ratio can be performed only once and then used for all subsequent fuel depletion conditions.

The third concern of control rod reactivity worth and position in the core has to do with the perturbation of the power distribution caused by the presence of control rods. Consider the axial power profile in a cylindrical reactor with and without a centrally inserted control rod (Fig. 5.20). Without the control rod, the flux and power profiles are, essentially, of the cosine type. With the rod inserted, the flux (and the power) are suppressed considerably in the space occupied by the rod, as a result of which the power peak is moved downward in the core. Since the flux is higher at the bottom half of the core, the fuel is depleted faster at the bottom than at the top. As the control rod is withdrawn, the power peak moves toward the top for two reasons. One, the flux increases as the absorption due to the control rod is removed. Two, fuel with less depletion (relative to the bottom) is exposed to neutrons.

Since the objective is to maintain a power distribution that is as flat as possible and as constant as possible, during the cycle special measures have

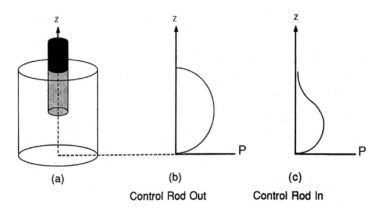

(a) (b) Control Rod Out (c) Control Rod In

FIGURE 5.20 Axial power profile in a cylindrical reactor with and without an inserted control rod.

to be implemented to avoid peaks like those shown in Fig. 5.20. In PWRs, the problem is resolved by using chemical shim for control during operation and inserting in the core only certain control rods. (The primary function of the control rods is to scram the reactor.) In BWRs, the moderator (water) at the bottom half of the core is liquid; at the upper part it becomes steam. Without any control rods, the power at the bottom half would be much higher than that at the upper half of the core. By inserting the control rods from the bottom, the flux and power are suppressed at the bottom half and the overall power distribution becomes more uniform. Obviously, the details of the movement of control rods during a cycle is very much reactor dependent and, to some extent, cycle dependent.

Bibliography

Bell, G.I., and Glasstone, S., *Nuclear Reactor Theory*, Van Nostrand Reinhold (1970).

Computer Methods in Reactor Physics, Greenspan, H., Keller, C.W., and Okrent, D., Eds., Gordon and Breach Science Publishers (1968).

Duderstadt, J.J., and Hamilton, L.J., *Nuclear Reactor Analysis*, John Wiley and Sons (1976).

Duderstadt, J.J., and Martin, W.R., *Transport Theory*, J. Wiley and Sons (1979).

Graves, H.W., *Nuclear Fuel Management*, John Wiley and Sons (1979).

Henry, A.F., *Nuclear Reactor Analysis*, MIT Press (1975).

Lamarsh, J.R., *Nuclear Reactor Theory*, Addison-Wesley (1966).

Lamarsh, J.R., and Baratta, A.J., *Introduction to Nuclear Engineering*, 3rd ed., Prentice Hall (2001).

Lewis, E.E., and Miller, W.F., Jr., *Computational Methods of Neutron Transport*, American Nuclear Society (1993).

Ott, K.O., and Bezella, W.A., *Introductory Nuclear Reactor Statics*, rev. ed., American Nuclear Society (1989).

Rydin, R.A., *Nuclear Reactor Theory and Design*, University Publications (1977).

Spanier, J., and Gelbard, E.M., *Monte Carlo Principles and Neutron Transport Problems*, Addison-Wesley (1969).

Stacey, W., *Nuclear Reactor Physics*, 2nd ed., J. Wiley & Sons (2007).

Weinberg, A.M., and Wigner, E.P., *The Physical Theory of Neutron Chain Reactors*, University of Chicago Press (1958).

Zweifel, P.F., *Reactor Physics*, McGraw-Hill (1973).

References

1. Lamarsh, J.R., *Nuclear Reactor Theory*, Addison-Wesley (1966).

2. Duderstadt, J.J., and Hamilton, L.J., *Nuclear Reactor Analysis*, John Wiley and Sons (1976).

3. Cadwell, W.R., "PDQ-7 Reference Manual," WAPD-TM-678, Bettis Atomic Power Laboratory (1969).

4. "VENTURE: A Code Block for Solving Multigroup Neutronics Problems Applying the Finite-Difference-Diffusion-Theory Approximation to Neutron Transport," ORNL-5062, Oak Ridge National Laboratory (1975).

5. Nguyen, T.Q., Liu, Y.S., Durston, C., and Casadei, A.L., "Benchmarking of the PHOENIX-P/ANC Advanced Nuclear Design System," *Proc. 1988 Int. Reactor Physics Conf.*, Jackson Hole, Wyoming, September 1988.

6. Rhodes, J., Smith, K., and Lee, D. "CASMO-5 Development and Applications," PHYSOR-2006, ANS Topical Meeting, Vancouver, Canada, September 2006.

7. Bahadir, T., Lindahl, S.-O., and Palmtag, S., "SIMULATE-4 Multigroup Nodal Code with Microscopic Depletion Model," presented at Mathematics and Computation, Supercomputing, Reactor Physics and Nuclear and Biological Applications Conference, Avignon, France (2005).

8. Bahadir, T., and Lindahl, S.-O., "SIMULATE-4 Pin Power Calculations," PHYSOR 2006, ANS Topical Meeting, Vancouver, Canada (2006).

9. Yigal, R., *Handbook of Nuclear Reactor Calculations*, Vols. I, II, and III, CRC Press (1986).

10. Larson, B.G., and Lathrop, K.D., "Transport Theory: The Method of Discrete Ordinates," in "Computer Methods in Reactor Physics," H. Greenspan, C.W. Keller, and D. Okrent, Eds., Gordon & Breach Science Publishers (1986).

11. Tomlinson, E.T., Rhoades, W.A., and Engle, W.A., Jr., "Flux Extrapolation Models Used in DOT-IV Discrete Ordinates Transport Code," ORNL/TM-7033, Oak Ridge National Laboratory (1980).

12. "ANISN-W: Multigroup One-Dimensional Discrete Ordinates Transport Code with Anisotropic Scattering," CCC-255, Radiation Shielding Information Center, Oak Ridge National Laboratory (1975).

13. "AMPX-II Modular Code System for Generating Coupled Multigroup Neutron-Gamma Ray Cross Section Libraries from Data in ENDF Format," ORNL-PSR-63, Oak Ridge National Laboratory (1978).

14. "DOT-IV, Version 3, One and Two-Dimensional Transport Code System," RSICCCC-429, Radiation Shielding Information Center, Oak Ridge National Laboratory (1982).

15. McGhee, J.M., et al., *ATTILA User's Manual*, Transpire Inc. (2007).

16. Z. Weiss, "Nodal Equations Derived from Invariance Imbedding Theory," *Nucl. Sci. Eng.*, **48**, 235 (1972).

17. Ancona, A., Becker, M., Berg, M.D., Harris, D.R., Menezes, A., VerPlanck, D.M., and Pilat, E., "Nodal Coupling by Response Matrix Principles," *Nucl. Sci. Eng.*, **64**, 405 (1977).

18. Palmiotti, G., Lewis, E.E., and Carrico, C.B., "VARIANT: VARIational Anisotropic Nodal Transport for Multidimensional Cartesian and Hexagonal Geometry Calculation," ANL-95/40, Argonne National Laboratory (Oct. 1995).

19. Spanier, J., "Monte Carlo Methods and Their Applications to Neutron Transport Theory Problems," WAPD-195, Bettis Atomic Power Laboratory (1959).

20. Scott, R.L., Compiler, "Monte Carlo Method: A Literature Search," TID-35401, Technical Information Service Extension, U.S. Atomic Energy Commission (1959).

21. Briemeister, J.F., Ed., "MCNP—A General Monte Carlo *N*-Particle Transport Code, 4C," LA-13709 (2000). Also MCNP5, LA-UR-03-1987 (2003)

22. Emmett, M.B., "The MORSE Monte Carlo Radiation Code System," ORNL-4972/R2, RSIC-CCC-474, Radiation Shielding Information Center, Oak Ridge National Laboratory (1985).

23. Baur, A., Bourdet, L., Dejonghe, G., Gonnord, J., Monnier, A., Nimal, J.C., and Vergnaud, T., "TRIPOLI-02: A Polyenergetic Monte Carlo Program in 3-D," CEN/Saclay (1980).

24. Petrie, M., and Cross, N.F., "KENO-IV, An Improved Monte Carlo Criticality Program," ORNL-4938, Oak Ridge National Laboratory (Nov. 1975).

25. Ferrari, A., Fasso, A., Ranft, J., and Sala, P.R., "FLUKA: A Multi-Particle Transport Code," CERN 2005-10 (2005).

26. Booth, T.E., "A Sample Problem for Variance Reduction in MCNP," LA-10363-MS, Los Alamos National Laboratory (Oct. 1985).

27. Ozer, O., and Garber, D., "ENDF/B Summary Documentation," ENDF-201, BNL17541, Brookhaven National Laboratory (1973).

28. Honeck, H.C., and Rich, D.R., "FLANGE-II (Version 71-1)—A Code to Process Thermal Neutron Data from an ENDF/B Tape," DP-1278, ENDF-152, Savannah River Laboratory (1971).

29. Mathews, D.R., Koch, P.K., Adir, J., and Walti, P., "GGC-5: A Computer Program for Calculating Neutron Spectra and Group Constants," GA-8871, General Atomic (1971).

30. Henryson, H., II, Toppel, B.J., and Steinberg, C.G., "MC-2: A Code to Calculate Fast Neutron Spectra and Multigroup Cross Sections," ANL-8144, Argonne National Laboratory (1976).

31. "SCALE-3 A Modular Code System for Performing Standardized Computer Analysis for Licensing Evaluation," Vols. I–III, RSIC-CCC-466, Radiation Shielding Information Center, Oak Ridge National Laboratory (1984).

32. SCALE: Special Issue of *Nuclear Technology*, **174**, 125–314 (May 2011).

33. MacFarlane, R.E., "The NJOY Nuclear Data Processing System," LA-12740-M, Vs. 91, NTIS (1994)

34. El-Wakil, M.M., *Nuclear Heat Transport*, American Nuclear Society (1971).

35. Lahey, R.T., Jr., and Moody, F.J., *The Thermal Hydraulics of a Boiling Water Reactor*, American Nuclear Society (1977).

36. Tong, L.S., and Weisman, J., *Thermal Analysis of Pressurized Water Reactors*, 2nd ed., American Nuclear Society (1979).

37. Barry, F.R., "LEOPARD—A Spectrum-Dependent Non-Spatial Depletion Code for the IBM-7094," USAEC, WCAP-3741, Westinghouse Electric Corporation (1963).

38. Breen, R.J., et al., "HARMONY: System for Nuclear Depletion Computation," WAPD-TM-478, Westinghouse Electric Corporation (1965).

39. Nguyen, T.Q., et al., "Qualification of the PHOENIX-P/ANC Nuclear Design System for PWR Cores," WCAP-11596-P-A (June 1988).

40. Fipot, A.J., Van Den Broek, F., Delluassine, A., and Gilissen, R., "Burnable Poison Dispersed in UO_2 Fuel," *Nucl. Eng. Int.* (Apr. 1970).

41. Frogner, B., and Rao, H.S., "Control of Nuclear Power Plants," *IEEE Trans. Automatic Control*, **AC-23**, 3, 405 (1978).

42. Termaat, K.P., and Kema, N.V., "Reactivity Behavior of a Reactor Core Loaded with Gadolinium Poisoned Fuel Assemblies," *Nucl. Technol.*, **38**, 367 (1978).

43. Kodah, Z.H., and Levine, S.H., "Optimized Depletion of Lumped Burnable Poisons in PWRs," *Nucl. Technol.*, **61**, 487 (1983).

44. Galperin, A., Segev, M., and Radkowsky, A., "Effect of Boron and Gadolinium Burnable Poison on the Hot to Cold Reactivity Swing of a PWR Assembly," *Nucl. Technol.*, **75**, 123 (1986).

45. Galperin, A., Segev, M., and Radkowsky, A., "Substitution of the Soluble Boron Reactivity Control System of a PWR by Gadolinium Burnable Poisons," *Nucl. Technol.*, **75**, 127 (1986).

46. Downar, T.J., and Stillman, J.A., "Explicit Burnable Absorber Modeling for PWR Core Reload Design Applications," *Nucl. Sci. Eng.*, **94**, 241 (1986).

47. Cohen, P., and Graves, H.W., Jr., "Chemical Shim Control for Power Reactors," *Nucleonics*, **22**, 5, 75 (1964).

48. H.W. Graves, *Nuclear Fuel Management*, John Wiley & Sons, New York (1979)

Problems

5.1. Write explicitly the multigroup equations for the following conditions: (a) four groups, (b) no upscattering, (c) fissions take place in the last two groups only, and (d) fission neutrons appear in the first two groups only (79% of them in the first group).

5.2. Derive Eq. (5.42) and then show that, with proper definitions, one can write

$$k = \varepsilon \eta \, pf P_{FNL} P_{TNL}$$

5.3. The two-group equations for a cylindrical homogeneous PWR follow. Calculate (a) the value of k and (b) the boron concentration (in ppm) that will make the reactor exactly critical. The reactor dimensions are $H = 3.2$ m and $R = 1.5$ m.

Group Constant	1	2
$\nu\Sigma_f$	0.0	0.33
χ	1.0	0.00
Σ_a	0.012	0.15
D	1.25	0.38
Σ_R	0.035	0.15
$\sigma_{a,B}$	0.0	2250 b

5.4. Prove that the radius of the equivalent unit cell is equal to $R = p/\pi$ for a square cell, and $R = (3/2)^{1/2}p$ for a hexagonal cell [Eq. (5.79)].

5.5. Neutron average cross sections in an eight-group structure are given below. Obtain cross sections for three groups, using the group fluxes and new (broad) group boundaries indicated in the table.

Group	Energy (Upper) (MeV)	Cross Section (b)	Flux ($\times 10^{12}$)	Broad Group Energy Boundaries (MeV)
1	10	1.5	1.3	10
2	6	3.5	1.1	
3	1	6.0	1.2	1
4	0.5	12.0	12.1	
5	0.25	12.0	15.0	
6	0.1	7.0	17.0	0.1
7	0.05	45.0	20.0	
8	1.0×10^{-7}	115.0	55.0	
	Lowest energy $= 1.0 \times 10^{-8}$			

5.6. A cross section is a function of energy that has the form shown below. What is the analytic equation representing this cross section? If the neutron spectrum is of the $1/E$ type [i.e., $\phi(E) \sim 1/E$], what is the average value of this cross section for the energy range shown in the graph?

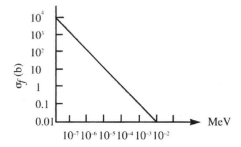

5.7. Calculate the average fission cross section from 1.5 to 3 MeV for the neutron spectrum given below.

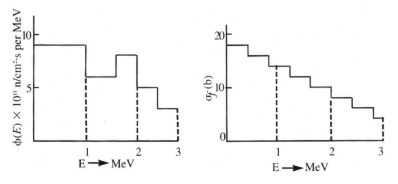

5.8. If the differential scattering cross section is given by the equation $_s\sigma_s = A + B * \cos\theta$, where θ is the scattering angle, show how the angle can be determined in a Monte Carlo program.

5.9. Show that if the value of a variable x is selected by inverting the cdf, $x = F^1(RN)$, the distribution of the x values is given by the function $f(x)$.

5.10. Equation (5.58) gives the representation of the scattering cross section in terms of Legendre polynomials. Determine the physical meaning of the first two coefficients of this series expansion.

5.11. A thermal bare cylindrical reactor with a radius of 1.8 m and height of 3.8 m operates at a power of 1100 MWe with an efficiency of 33%. The reactor is fueled with 95 tons of uranium enriched to 3 wt% in ^{235}U. Assume 200 MeV released per fission and a ^{235}U fission cross section equal to 470 b. What is the maximum of the flux?

5.12. Calculate the mass of ^{239}Pu produced in a reactor operating for a year with an average flux of 1.2×10^{12} n/cm$^2 \cdot$s, loaded with 90 tons of uranium, enriched to 3 wt% in ^{235}U. For cross sections, assume that for ^{238}U, $\sigma_c = 2.1$ b and $\sigma_a = 2.3$ b, and for ^{239}Pu, $\sigma_a = 600$ b and $T_{1/2} = 24,400$ yr.

SIX

IN-CORE FUEL MANAGEMENT

6.1 General Comments

The term *fuel management* is not uniquely defined.[1] It means different things to different people. There are, however, several activities that definitely belong in this area, as given in the following partial list:

1. Supply of materials and services required in the various steps of the nuclear fuel cycle (examples: uranium, conversion services, enrichment services, fabrication, transportation of fresh fuel, disposal of spent fuel, and storage)

2. development, reviews, and evaluation of bids related to contracts that supply materials and services

3. Study of the requirements and design of the fuel needed for successive fuel cycles

4. Operational considerations related to fuel performance in the core

5. Power history of the reactor, that is, operational history of the fuel in the core

6. Core loading pattern

7. Refueling activities

8. Storage and disposal of spent fuel

9. Study of the cost of fuel as one of the cost components for the generation of electricity.

From this list, items 1, 2, 8, and 9 constitute "out-of-core" fuel management activities and are discussed in other chapters of this book. The rest of the activities belong to "in-core" fuel management and are the subject of this chapter.

The main objective of the fuel manager is to minimize fuel costs, thus reducing the cost of generating electricity. The person responsible for this task tries to achieve this objective by altering the parameters that can be changed without violating any of the constraints imposed by safety and operational regulations. Operational constraints include the following:

1. The reactivity of the fuel must be adequate to achieve the scheduled burnup.

2. The core should have adequate reactivity control.

3. Refueling must be scheduled for a period of low demand.

4. Fast neutron flux at the pressure vessel (for PWRs) should be reduced.

The safety constraints are expressed in terms of the values of certain parameters that are not allowed to exceed certain predetermined limits. Examples are:

1. Peak-to-average power ratio

2. Maximum temperature in the core

3. Deviation from nucleate boiling ratio (DNBR)

4. Core reactivity

5. Temperature coefficient of reactivity.

The fuel loading and the power distribution in the core must be such that none of the safety parameters exceeds the prescribed values.

The objective of minimizing fuel costs sounds simple enough, but the factors that determine the "cost" may change over the years. The costs may not be strictly and directly financial. To make this point better understood, a brief history of fuel management objectives and concerns for the U.S. nuclear power industry are discussed here.

Civilian nuclear power started in the United States in the late 1950s under the premise (or should we say *promise*?) of a positive value for the used fuel. The U.S. government had promised the utilities that it would buy from them the plutonium generated in their reactors for use in breeders; thus, the fuel managers carried on their books a future income to be collected from used fuel. There was also an inherent promise by the government to take the used fuel away from the utilities no later than 2 to 5 years after discharge from the core. Based on this understanding, the early plants provided for about 5 years of used fuel storage on site. At that time, the optimization studies of nuclear fuel management were based on the assumption that uranium prices would be stable and low and that reprocessing of the used fuel would also occur at relatively low prices. No particular attention was paid to final fuel burnup.

Around 1970, the U.S. government seemed committed to the reprocessing and recycling of the used fuel. The development of a Generic Environmental Impact Statement for Mixed-Oxide Fuel (GESMO) was set in motion, to be completed by 1976. In 1977 GESMO was almost completed. The Nuclear Fuel Services Company in New York State operated the first private reprocessing plant in the United States from 1966 to 1972. A second commercial reprocessing plant at Barnwell, South Carolina, was almost ready for operation when the new U.S. administration (Carter, 1977) decided not to allow reprocessing in the United States. The newly created U.S. Department of Energy (DOE) was then instructed to initiate a study of new nuclear fuel designs that would achieve burnups of the order of 45,000 to 50,000 MWd/t, a considerable increase from the 30,000 to 33,000 MWd/t achieved by LWR fuel up to that time. The new high-burnup fuel would, presumably, constitute an alternative to reprocessing and recycling for better utilization of uranium resources. The advantage is obvious, at least as far as the quantity of needed uranium is concerned, since the reciprocal of burnup gives t/MWd, that is, mass of fuel per unit energy produced. It was estimated that increasing the burnup from 33,000 to 50,000 MWd/t in PWRs would reduce the mass of yellow cake (U_3O_8) required by less than ~15%, the number of separative work units (SWUs) by 1% to 3%, and the number of discharged assemblies by 40% annually (see also Section 6.4). Another practice implemented by the nuclear utilities, a practice that definitely reduced the number of assemblies discharged per year, was the extension of the fuel cycle from 12 months to 18 to 24 months.

An even better utilization of nuclear fuels could be achieved if plutonium recycling were to be implemented. Of course, plutonium generated in LWRs in the course of their normal operation is partially burned in those same reactors and, in some cases, contributes up to 20% of the plant power.

By 1977, many utilities were hard pressed to find space for storage of their used fuel. The new high-burnup fuel design would certainly help, but its implementation was years away. Because immediate relief for used fuel storage was necessary at certain plants, studies were undertaken by many utilities to determine how to alleviate this problem. Two ideas were considered, and in many plants both were implemented. One was redesigning the existing fuel storage racks in used fuel pools to provide space for more fuel assemblies. The other was an extension of each cycle from 12 to 18 to 24 months. Such an extension resulted in fewer fuel assemblies being used over the life of the plant and, at the same time, reduced the fuel cycle costs, primarily because of the decrease in the average (over plant lifetime) downtime required for refueling. Of course, the higher burnup requires fuel with increased enrichment, which means increased costs for enrichment services.

In 1982, Congress passed the Nuclear Waste Policy Act (NWPA), amended in 1987. In accordance with the NWPA (for which more details are given in Chapter 9), the federal government, through DOE, is obligated to take the used fuel away from the plant, for a fee, and dispose of it properly. More than that, if a utility needs storage space before the government is ready to take the fuel, the NWPA obligates the government to provide interim storage. Thus, as a result of NWPA, storage of used fuel ceased to exist as an issue that affected the fuel cycle.

The NWPA obligated the utilities that own and operate nuclear power plants to pay the government, starting in April 1983, a fee of $0.001/kWh(e) of nuclear-generated electricity. The money accumulated in this fashion (known as the Nuclear Waste Fund) will be used for research and development and all other costs associated with the disposal of the spent fuel. Thus, an expense was officially established for the disposal of spent fuel instead of an income from the sale of plutonium produced in the course of a plant's operation.

As the cost of constructing nuclear power plants increased, and operating experiences accumulated, many people in the nuclear industry started to discuss the possibility of extending the life of a plant beyond its original 40-year license. Any extension would require certification by the U.S. Nuclear Regulatory Commission (NRC) that all safety-related components are sound and will operate properly under normal and abnormal conditions for the extended life.

The primary safety component is the pressure vessel, particularly for PWRs. As a result of neutron bombardment, the steel of a pressure vessel suffers radiation damage (damage directly related to the magnitude of the neutron fluence, particularly the fast neutron fluence). Extension of plant life would require less radiation damage to the pressure vessel, which means, in turn, fewer neutrons bombarding it. How to achieve this objective, namely, the reduction of the number of neutrons leaking out of the core and bombarding the pressure vessel, became a new objective, or constraint, of nuclear fuel management. This issue is known as *low-leakage core management*. The operators of PWRs in the United States achieved this objective and most of them applied successfully for plant life extension and had it approved by the NRC.

In the sections that follow, the means that the fuel manager can call upon to achieve the objective of minimum cost—subject to constraints already mentioned—are presented in detail.

6.2 Multibatch Core Loading

The core of commercial nuclear power plants is made up of fuel assemblies with different initial enrichments. During refueling, only a fraction of the fuel assemblies is removed and replaced by fresh (unirradiated) fuel. The reason for this tactic is the reduced requirements for initial enrichment and reactivity control, for the same burnup (the same energy output), if the core contains more than one batch of fuel. A *batch* is the number of assemblies (with a minimum of one) that enters and leaves the core together as a group;

a batch is composed of the same fuel type and enrichment. Before the advantages and disadvantages of the multibatch core are discussed, the definitions of some of the main concepts involved will be presented.

6.2.1 Burnup, Capacity, and Availability Factors

The burnup (BU) of the fuel over a time period T, expressed in MWd/t or GWd/t, is given by the equation

$$BU\left(\frac{MWd}{t}\right) = \frac{P_0[MWth] * CF * T(days)}{U_M(t)} \tag{6.1}$$

where

P_0 = plant rated power

$U_M(t)$ = mass of uranium in the core, in metric tons

CF = capacity factor, given by

$$CF = \frac{\int_0^T P(t)\,dt}{P_0 * T} \tag{6.2}$$

$P(t)$ = thermal power at time t, during the time period T.

Experience has shown that the final BU is essentially proportional to the initial enrichment of the fuel.

In the definitions given above, the period T is usually taken as 1 year. In the early years, typical capacity factor values were 60% to 70%; after 1980, a continuous improvement process took place, due to more comprehensive operator training, that lengthened the fuel cycle from 12 to 18 to 24 months and reduced the downtime for refueling. This resulted in the average CF value reaching 90% for most plants as of 2011.

A closely related concept is the availability factor (AF), defined as

$$AF = \frac{\text{Time during which the plant was operational in period } T}{T} \tag{6.3}$$

The word *operational* in Eq. (6.3) means operational at any power level above zero. It is obvious that AF > CF. If refueling takes 4 weeks, the maximum value of the availability factor for an annual fuel cycle is AF = 48 weeks/52 weeks = 0.92; for an 18-month cycle, AF = 74 weeks/78 weeks = 0.95.

Another quantity associated with in-core fuel management is the number of effective full-power days (EFPDs), defined as

$$\text{EFPD} = \int_0^T \text{CF}(t)\, dt = \text{CF} * T(\text{days}) \tag{6.4}$$

where the time T is now expressed in days and $\text{CF}(t)$ is the capacity factor at time t and CF is given by Eq. (6.2). Although EFPD has the units of time, it is closely related to the energy generated during the time T. That energy, in MWd, is equal to the product $\text{EFPD} * P_0$. In the ideal case of a plant with a capacity factor equal to 100%, the number of EFPDs in a year would be 365. In reality, with a capacity factor that is close to 80% to 90%, the number of EFPDs in a year is $\sim$300 to 330.

6.2.2 The Reactivity of the Core

The reactivity, ρ, is defined as in Chapter 5:

$$\rho = (k - 1)/k \tag{5.1}$$

where k is the effective multiplication factor. The initial reactivity of fresh fuel is, for all practical purposes, proportional to the fuel enrichment, which, remember, constitutes a major cost component of the nuclear fuel.

The net reactivity of the core is given by

$$\rho_{net} = \rho_{fuel} - \rho_{fp} - \rho_T \tag{6.5}$$

where

ρ_{fuel} = positive reactivity due to the fissile material in the core

ρ_{fp} = reactivity (negative) due to fission products/poisons, primarily Xe and Sm

ρ_T = reactivity (negative) due to temperature effects (Doppler and moderator temperature coefficients).

After the reactor starts operating with fresh fuel, the negative reactivity components due to fission product poisons and temperature effects reach an equilibrium value because fission products reach their saturation value within a few days, and temperature effects are fully present when the reactor is brought to 100% power and the fuel reaches its operating temperature. For this reason, the core reactivity as a function of time, that is, as a function of burnup, shows a quick sharp initial drop (Fig. 6.1) and then, as the fuel is depleted (burned), the positive reactivity of the fuel decreases almost linearly with time.

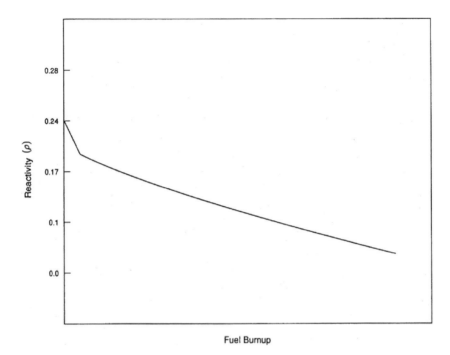

FIGURE 6.1 The core reactivity as a function of burnup.

To operate a reactor over a period of time, called the *fuel cycle*, some positive reactivity (see Table 5.3) is necessary in order to be able to raise the power. Once the desired power is reached, the reactor should be just critical; that is, the net reactivity of the core should be zero. To achieve $\rho = 0$, the positive reactivity of the core, called the *reactivity swing*, has to be compensated for by means of neutron poisons and control rods. A well-designed core is one that has the absolute minimum reactivity swing, because any unnecessary surplus of reactivity creates neutrons that, instead of being allowed to become productive by causing fissions, are removed by neutron poisons through absorption. Obviously, for a fuel cycle length of a year or more, the reactor core must contain enough fissile material to provide a certain amount of excess reactivity.

In PWRs, reactivity control during normal operation is achieved by (1) boron dissolved (as boric acid) in the coolant that flows through the core and (2) the control rods, which are partially withdrawn and are used to shut down the reactor swiftly in emergency situations. At the beginning of a cycle (BOC), when the core is loaded with fresh fuel, the boron concentration in the coolant has a value of ~ 1800 parts per million (ppm) (see Chapter 5). As the fuel is depleted, boron is removed continuously from the coolant, until at the end of the cycle (EOC), its concentration reaches

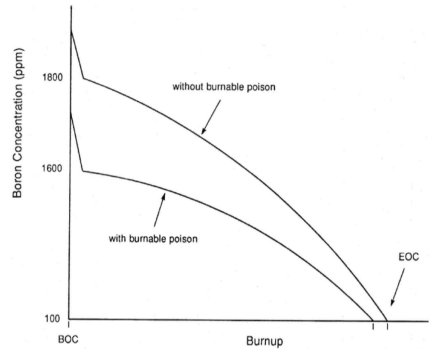

FIGURE 6.2 The boron concentration as a function of burnup.

~100 ppm or less. The change in the boron concentration with time is almost identical to the change in reactivity with increasing burnup (Fig. 6.2). As little boron as possible should be in the core (the less boron in the core, the less boron that has to be removed). To minimize boron concentration in the reactor and still be able to control the reactor, burnable poisons (BPs) are also used.

In BWRs, reactivity control is accomplished by using control rods and fixed BPs. Chemical shim is not used in BWRs for reactor control.

6.2.3 One- and Two-Batch Cores

To show how the multibatch core affects fuel management operations, equations are derived relating the reactivity and final burnup for a multibatch core under the assumption that the relationship between reactivity and burnup is linear. Although the linear relationship is not exactly correct, the conclusions drawn from the derivation are valid, as experience with commercial nuclear plants has shown. (More details about the linear reactivity model are given in Ref. 2.) Before the equations for a multibatch core are derived, it is instructive to look at and compare the one- and two-batch cores.

The following notation is used to designate batch and corresponding burnup:

$BU_N^{(n)}(t)$ = burnup of a batch in an N-batch core, during cycle n, at time t. For each batch in the N-batch core, $n \leq N$

T = length of the fuel cycle, considered constant regardless of the number of batches in the core

$BU_N(T)$ = final burnup of a batch in an N-batch core, after the batch has been in the core for N cycles of equal duration T (total time in the core: $N * T$).

Consider a reactor core that is loaded with one batch of fuel. The reactivity as a function of operational (irradiation) time is given by

$$\rho_1(t) = \rho_1 \left[1 - \frac{BU_1^{(1)}(t)}{BU_1(T)} \right] \tag{6.6}$$

where ρ_1 is the initial reactivity of fuel in a one-batch core and $\rho_1(t)$ is the core reactivity in the one-batch core at time t during the cycle.

Obviously, $\rho_1(T) = 0$ (Fig. 6.3). The value ρ_1 represents the reactivity swing at BOC, that is, ρ_1 is the excess reactivity of the core at BOC, leaving out the initial drop.

Consider next a two-batch core, fueled by two equal fuel batches. Using the same notation as with the one-batch core, the final burnup is $BU_2(T)$. At refueling time, one-half of the core is discharged with burnup equal to $BU_2(T)/2$. The assumption will be made that the total core reactivity, at any

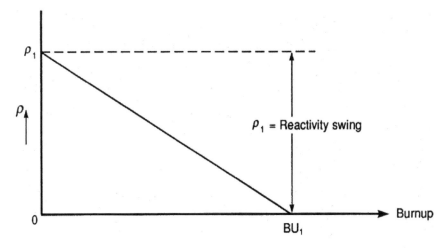

FIGURE 6.3 Reactivity change versus burnup in a one-batch core.

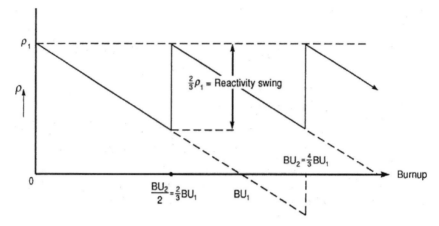

FIGURE 6.4 Reactivity change versus burnup in a two-batch core.

time during the cycle, is equal to the average of the sum of the reactivities contributed by the two batches. This assumption is not exactly right but it represents a very good approximation for the current analysis. For a two-batch core then the reactivity is

$$\rho_2(t) = \rho_1 \frac{\left[1 - \dfrac{BU_2^{(1)}(t)}{BU_1(T)}\right] + \left[1 - \dfrac{BU_2^{(2)}(t)}{BU_1(T)}\right]}{2} \tag{6.7}$$

At refueling time, $\rho_2(T) = 0$, which leads to

$$0 = \rho_1 \frac{\left[1 - \dfrac{BU_2(T)/2}{BU_1(T)}\right] + \left[1 - \dfrac{BU_2(T)}{BU_1(T)}\right]}{2}$$

and after simplification gives the result:

$$BU_2(T) = (4/3)BU_1(T) \tag{6.8}$$

The reactivity swing is now [from Eq. (6.7), setting $t = 0$ at BOC]

$$\rho_2(0) = (2/3)\rho_1 \tag{6.9}$$

These relationships [Eqs. (6.8) and (6.9); also shown in Fig. 6.4] indicate that, by going from a one- to two-batch core, the following two advantages materialize:

1. The final burnup is one-third more than that obtained in a one-batch core, for the same initial reactivity (same initial enrichment).

2. The reactivity swing is now two-thirds of that for the one-batch core, a one-third reduction for the same initial enrichment.

The decrease of the reactivity swing is explained qualitatively as follows. In a two-batch core, the fuel that has been burned has a negative effect on reactivity, relative to the contribution of the fresh fuel (see Fig. 6.4). Thus, the once-burned fuel, which is deficient in fissile content, acts like a neutron "sink" that removes some of the excess neutrons generated by the fresh fuel. In the one-batch core, there is no neutron-deficient fuel to "absorb" neutrons and for this reason external means have to be provided to compensate for all excess reactivity.

6.2.4 The *N*-Batch Core

Consider now an N-batch core fueled by N equal batches, each attaining final burnup equal to $BU_N(T)$. After n cycles, the burnup of a batch in the N-batch core is equal to

$$BU_N^{(n)}(T) = \frac{nBU_N(T)}{N} \bigg|_{n=1,N} \qquad (6.10)$$

Making the same assumption as before, the total core reactivity is given by,

$$\rho_N(t) = \frac{\displaystyle\sum_{n=1}^{N}\left[1 - \frac{BU_N^{(n)}(t)}{BU_1(T)}\right]}{N}\,\rho_1 \qquad (6.11)$$

At refueling time, $\rho_N(T) = 0$, which leads to the expression for the final burnup:

$$BU_N(T) = \frac{2N}{N+1}\,BU_1(T) \qquad (6.12)$$

The values of $BU_N(T)$ as a function of N are given in Table 6.1.

If the only goal were to maximize burnup, the fuel manager would look at Eq. (6.12) and opt for the largest practical number of batches in the core. This approach would not be the correct one, however, because as the number of batches increases so does the frequency of shutdowns for refueling. Since the length of shutdown is almost independent of the batch size (i.e., smaller batches do not necessarily result in faster refueling), the larger the number

TABLE 6.1
Relationship between the Number
of Batches and Final Burnup

Number of Batches	$BU_N(T)/BU_1(T)$
1	1
2	4/3
3	3/2
4	8/5
5	5/3
∞	2

of batches in the core, the smaller the availability and capacity factors become. Relatively quickly, as the number of batches in the core increases, the gains in burnup and reactivity swing due to the increasing number of batches are overshadowed by the reduction in capacity factor. As of early 1990, almost all of the PWRs in operation had three-batch cores and the BWRs had four-batch cores.

The reactivity of an N-batch core at BOC can be obtained from Eq. (6.11) by using the fact that the last batch (fresh) in the core has a reactivity equal to ρ_1. Thus,

$$\rho_N(0) = \frac{\displaystyle\sum_{n=1}^{N-1} \rho_1 \left[1 - \frac{BU_N^{(n)}(T)}{BU_1(T)} \right] + \rho_1}{N} \tag{6.13}$$

If one substitutes the value of $BU_N^{(n)}(T)$ from Eq. (6.10), we get

$$\rho_N(0) = \frac{2}{N+1} \rho_1 \tag{6.14}$$

Figure 6.5 shows the reactivity change with burnup for $N = 1,4$. Again, it is obvious that the initial reactivity swing keeps decreasing as the number of batches increases.

6.3 Fuel Loading Patterns

One of the activities of fuel management mentioned in Section 6.1 is the core loading pattern. The fuel manager has to decide what the "best" pattern of loading the assemblies in the core is so that the constraints imposed on a particular cycle might be satisfied. The safety constraints are always the same and are present for all cycles. Particular cycles, however, may have

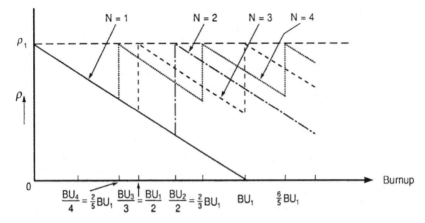

FIGURE 6.5 Reactivity change versus BU in a one- to four-batch core.

special constraints; such as the fuel should achieve a certain burnup or the cycle should have a certain length. Whatever the constraints, the task of finding the optimum pattern is monumental. There are about 200 assemblies in an 1150-MWe PWR and about 650 assemblies in a BWR of corresponding size. Even if one uses 90- or 45-deg symmetry, which deals with only a fraction of the assemblies, it is still a very expensive and time-consuming computer problem to find the optimum pattern.

Many articles have appeared in the literature over the years attempting to solve the so-called "optimization" problem of fuel loading.[3–25] The authors of these articles have used linear programming, dynamic programming, and other methods. Reference 10 gives a brief outline of the topic that is very useful for educational purposes. A very important observation should be made at this point. All of the articles in the literature assume an equilibrium cycle. Theoretically, the equilibrium cycle is reached at the beginning of the N'th cycle, for an N-batch core. After that point in time, all the subsequent reloads look identical and the core loading patterns repeat themselves. Table 6.2 shows the reload-discharge pattern for a three-batch core. The notation for the batch is $b_{i,j}$, where i is the batch number and j equals the periods during which the batch had been in the core at BOC. If $j = 0$, the fuel is fresh.

As seen from Table 6.2, assemblies of the first batch are discharged after producing about one-third of the average energy expected in three cycles. Experience has shown that a better utilization of the fuel is achieved if these partially burned assemblies are reinserted into the core during later cycles. The loading pattern shown in Table 6.2 implies that in a three-batch core, a regularity/equilibrium is reached after the third cycle; after that time the cycles are identical. In reality, there is no equilibrium cycle and no two cycles are exactly alike. The fuel manager may have planned for a cycle

TABLE 6.2
Reloading Pattern for a Three-Batch Core

Batches in Core	Cycle				
	1	2	3	4	5
1	$b_{1,0}$				
2	$b_{2,0}$	$b_{2,1}$			
3	$b_{3,0}$	$b_{3,1}$	$b_{3,2}$		
4		$b_{4,0}$	$b_{4,1}$	$b_{4,2}$	
5			$b_{5,0}$	$b_{5,1}$	$b_{5,2}$
6				$b_{6,0}$	$b_{6,1}$
7					$b_{7,0}$

starting with a certain enrichment, ending with another lower one, and achieving a certain burnup. Behind this plan there is an assumption of a certain power operational history and a certain capacity factor. But many times unplanned deviations from a predetermined schedule occur, for example:

1. At the scheduled shutdown time for refueling, the core has too much reactivity (the capacity factor was lower than expected).

2. The core reaches the lowest reactivity limit before the scheduled shutdown for refueling (the capacity factor was higher than expected).

3. The refueling process has to be done earlier than planned because of defective assemblies.

4. There is a long unforeseen outage, as a result of which the plant has too much reactivity at the scheduled shutdown time. Should the refueling proceed, the core loses (wastes) valuable reactivity in the discharged assemblies. Should refueling be postponed, the next shutdown for refueling might occur at a period of peak demand, that is, outside the range of the allowed refueling "window" (see also Section 6.6).

Any fuel cycle depends on the performance of the previous ones, but the design of the assemblies for the next cycle is completed before the current cycle ends. In fact, the fabricated fuel has to be on site about 1 month before refueling (see Section 6.6). Therefore, an irreversible decision is made before the final condition of the core (enrichment and burnup) is known.

The so-called optimization problem of fuel management is "solved" by assuming an equilibrium cycle. The solution is obtained by forming a functional (that depends on all parameters of interest) and minimizing or maximizing that functional, subject to certain constraints. Since the constraints are not the same for all plants or all cycles for the same plant, no general optimization method has gained dominance in the industry. In all methods, the problem is subdivided into smaller ones. First, use is made of whatever symmetry the core possesses. Usually, this is at least a 90-deg symmetry, and in some cases a 45-deg symmetry, which means that only one-fourth or one-eighth of the core needs to be considered. Second, a guess is made on the condition of the core at shutdown. The guess is based on experience and on the planned operational history for the current cycle. Third, the objectives or performance of the next cycle is decided in terms of expected energy production (i.e., capacity factor and burnup). Again, relevant information (essentially, required enrichment to achieve the desired burnup) is based on experience from the previous cycles of this or other similar plants. Fourth, a decision is made on constraints, both safety and operational ones. With all of this information at hand, the solution proceeds by commencing with a guess about the initial condition of the core loading pattern and by starting the depletion of the fissile materials as the core produces power. The depletion is accomplished by dividing the cycle into a number of time steps and assuming constant flux during each step. At the end of the time step, the new concentrations of the core materials are recalculated and the process is repeated. This calculation is performed using few neutron groups (usually about three) in a diffusion theory code. Pertinent thermal-hydraulic calculations are also performed. Since the changes of the isotopic concentrations over one cycle do not affect the thermal-hydraulic calculations, the latter are performed only once per cycle. At the EOC computation, the performance is evaluated and, based on the objectives and constraints, changes are made to the loading pattern if the optimization is not complete, and the process is repeated again.

The general trend in fuel loading patterns is based on the fact that, drawn from experience, more energy is extracted from the fuel if the ratio of peak-to-average power in the core is as low as possible, that is, if the power distribution in the core is as flat as possible. With this objective in mind, two general schemes had been developed before the low-leakage core strategy became important. The main characteristics of these schemes are discussed in the next section.

6.3.1 OUT-IN Loading

The reactor is divided into N (N = number of batches) concentric annular regions, with each region loaded with a different batch of fuel. The fuel with the highest burnup (lowest enrichment) is placed in the central region. The fresh fuel is placed at the periphery of the core. Batches with intermediate burnup are placed in the regions in between, with proximity to the center of the core being decided based on the amount of burnup (the larger the burnup, the closer to the core center the fuel is placed). Figure 6.6 shows the OUT-IN scheme for a three-batch core. At refueling time, the fuel in the innermost region is discharged and all the other batches are moved toward the center of the core. The fresh fuel is loaded in the outermost region.

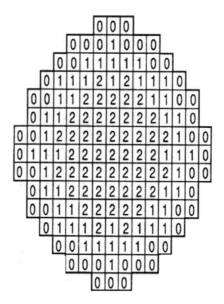

FIGURE 6.6 The OUT-IN refueling scheme. The core is divided into three regions: 0 = fresh fuel; 1 = fuel burned in one previous cycle; 2 = fuel burned in two previous cycles.

The main advantage of this pattern is transfer of the power peak from the center to the outer regions of the core. The peak-to-average power ratio is reduced, however, because the power generated at the outer regions is lower than the peak that would have been present at the center. Two main disadvantages are associated with this scheme: One is the fact that the "burned" fuel generates, at the center of the core, power lower than the average power. The second is the fact that the fresh assemblies at the periphery of the core, by generating high power relative to the average, also produce large numbers of fast fission neutrons, a relatively large fraction of which leaks out of the core. The neutrons leaking out not only represent a loss for the neutronic economy of the core but they also strike the pressure vessel. Because of these disadvantages, especially the second one, the OUT-IN scheme is not used anymore.

6.3.2 Scatter Loading

In this loading scheme, also referred to as a *checkerboard* scheme, the reactor core is divided into many small regions, each consisting of four to six assemblies from different batches (Fig. 6.7). At refueling time, the assemblies with the highest burnup in every such region are discharged and are replaced by fresh ones. The main advantage of this scheme is that it produces a fairly uniform power distribution throughout the core. A second

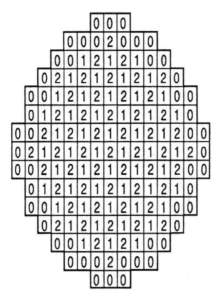

FIGURE 6.7 The scatter (checkerboard) refueling scheme: 0 = fresh fuel; 1 = fuel burned in one previous cycle; 2 = fuel burned in two previous cycles.

advantage is that, with proper placement of the fresh assemblies, it can lead to a low-leakage core. In principle, this strategy would require movement of only the assemblies to be discharged, in which case the downtime for refueling would be reduced. In practice, however, all assemblies are removed from the core to undergo sipping (see Section 4.5).

6.3.3 Low-Leakage Core Loading

A fraction of the neutrons produced by fission in the core escapes and strikes the pressure vessel, thus causing radiation damage. Studies have shown that the neutron flux bombarding the vessel depends very much on the power generated by the peripheral assemblies of the core both in magnitude and shape.[26-28] Figure 6.8 shows the angular distribution of fast neutrons in front of the pressure vessel of a PWR. The two peaks shown in Fig. 6.8 are caused by high-powered assemblies located at the periphery of the core directly across from these peaks. Since the radiation damage of the vessel is decided on the basis of the maximum, not the average, flux, it would be beneficial to reduce the flux, in general, and also flatten the peaks as much as possible. This task is what low-leakage core management is set to accomplish for a PWR. For BWRs, radiation damage to the vessel is less critical because these reactors operate at much lower pressure. The extent of the radiation damage to the pressure vessel is based on the neutron fluence (especially

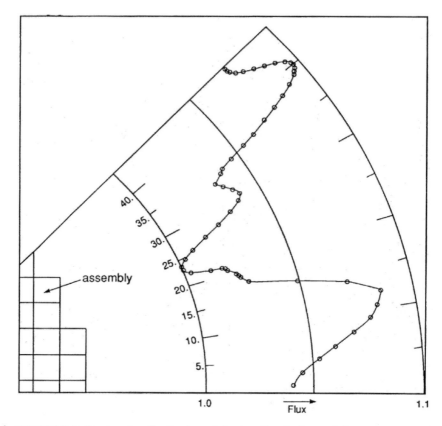

FIGURE 6.8 The angular distribution of the fast flux in front of the pressure vessel of a PWR (relative values shown). Utilizing symmetry, only a 45-deg slice of the horizontal cross section of the core is shown.

fast neutron fluence, $E > 100$ keV) hitting it. The fluence F (n/cm^2) is the integrated neutron flux over operational time:

$$F = \int \phi(t)\, dt \qquad (6.15)$$

Since the time when the pressure vessel radiation damage issue became prominent, many attempts have been made to reduce the neutron flux at the position of the pressure vessel without having to reduce power, and also without violating any safety limits.[29–37] The methods that have been proposed and partially implemented are based on procedures such as these:

1. Placement of only "burned" assemblies at the periphery of the core (Fig. 6.9)

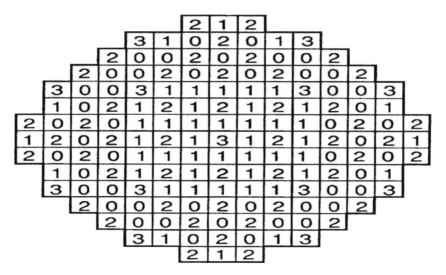

FIGURE 6.9 The low-leakage core refueling scheme: 0 = fresh fuel; 1 = fuel burned in one previous cycle; 2 = fuel burned in two previous cycles; 3 = fuel burned in three previous cycles.

2. Relocation of certain assemblies from positions near critical points (e.g., near welds) to other positions of less importance

3. Replacement of certain peripheral assemblies with stainless steel dummies

4. Placement of attenuating materials, such as steel pads, between the edge of the core and the pressure vessel (Fig. 6.10)

5. The use of gadolinium burnable poison in peripheral elements nearest the pressure vessel.

Figures 6.10, 6.11, and 6.12 show examples of attempts to reduce the fast neutron flux at the pressure vessel.[38] As mentioned, Fig. 6.10 shows the fast flux reduction on the inner surface of the pressure vessel as a result of placing a steel pad on the outer surface of the core barrel. Figure 6.11 presents results of a preliminary study attempting to show the possible reduction of the flux by judiciously placing assemblies at the periphery of the core and controlling their power through burnable poisons. In Fig. 6.12, the numbers referred to as "low-leakage" loading represent the neutron source, that is, power, in assemblies that contain burnable poisons. The low-leakage loading produces lower fluxes, as Fig. 6.11 clearly shows. An additional measure taken to reduce leakage is the use of axial blankets that minimize the number of neutrons escaping through the top and bottom of the core. As explained

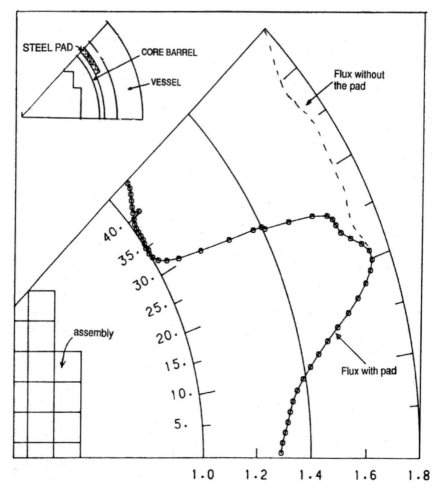

FIGURE 6.10 The fast neutron flux reduction in front of the pressure vessel of a PWR using a steel pad as an attenuating medium. Only relative changes are shown.

in Chapter 4, the axial blanket is formed by replacing the last few inches of the fuel in a fuel rod with pellets of natural or depleted uranium.

The low-leakage core loading helped not only in the reduction of the fast neutron fluence hitting the pressure vessel, but also produced economic benefits.[39] By reducing the neutron leakage, the following benefits were achieved:

1. A reduction in enrichment for the equilibrium cycle between 0.10 and 0.05 wt% ^{235}U

2. An increase in the burnup by 200 to 500 MWd/t.

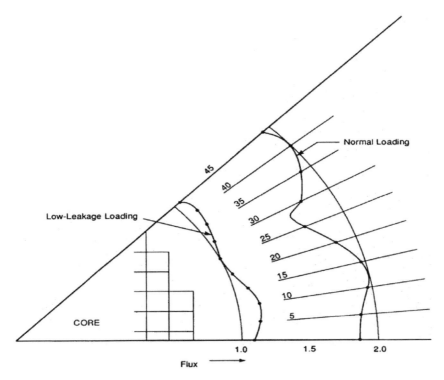

FIGURE 6.11 The fast neutron flux reduction in front of the pressure vessel of a PWR with a low-leakage core loading.

The extent of the benefits depends on the plant type, the size of the core, and the arrangement of the peripheral assemblies. Since, in general, this loading scheme shifts the power generation from the periphery toward the center, means to avoid power peaking have to be provided. One method of avoiding power peaking, as mentioned earlier, is the use of burnable poisons (see also Chapter 4). No method has been formulated that applies to every reactor. Obviously, each utility and plant are somewhat unique and respond to issues, such as that of pressure vessel integrity, according to their own needs, constraints, and the age of the plant.

6.3.4 Gas-Cooled Reactor Fuel Loading

The gas-cooled nuclear reactors have quite a different design compared to the LWRs (see also Sections 1.4, 1.5, and 4.7.1). The differences come from the use of a gas instead of a liquid (helium instead of H_2O) for a coolant, and the use of graphite instead of H_2O as a moderator.

The gas turbine modular helium-cooled reactor (GT-MHR) created by General Atomics is designed to produce 600 MWth of power per module

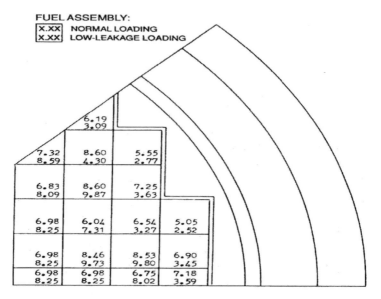

FIGURE 6.12 The neutron source, by assembly, for normal and low-leakage loading. The numbers represent 10×10^{12} n/cm$^3 \cdot$s.

and use the Brayton cycle. The core will consist of 102 columns of hexagonal graphite fuel elements stacked 10 elements high to form an annular core, as shown in Fig. 6.13. The fuel consists of small spheres, known as TRISO-coated particles and having a diameter of about 650 to 850 microns

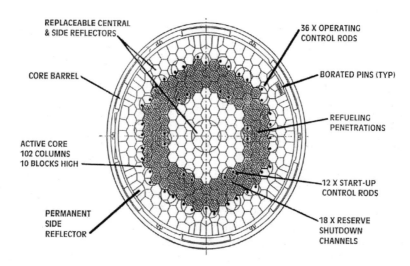

FIGURE 6.13 A cross section of the GT-MHR reactor core.

that are encapsulated inside the graphite blocks (see Figs. 4.9 and 4.10). Graphite blocks (without fuel) surround the core and serve as reflectors both in the axial and radial directions. There is a central reflector as well, which gives the core its annular shape.

Another gas-cooled reactor (see Section 4.7.1), whose development is of potential interest, is the pebble bed reactor. In this design, the fuel is made in the form of spheres (pebbles) with an approximate diameter of 60 mm. The pebbles are "thrown" into the reactor vessel and form an almost spherical core. The helium gas coolant percolates through the pebbles and removes the heat generated in the core. One intriguing feature of this reactor is the possibility for on-line refueling.

6.4 Extended Burnup and Longer Fuel Cycle Length

When the nuclear industry started in the United States, the norm for LWRs was a 12-month fuel cycle and a discharge burnup of about 30,000 MWd/t. Starting in the mid-1980s and continuing through today, the U.S. nuclear utilities switched to an 18-month cycle (and a few use a 24-month cycle); typical fuel burnups reached about ~50,000 MWd/t with the goal of reaching ~60,000 MWd/t. The interest in higher burnup started in the early 1970s when it seemed that the price of uranium would follow the trend of oil and skyrocket. Because the nuclear industry did not expand as expected, uranium prices declined for a few years, instead of increasing. As mentioned in Section 6.1, in 1977 the U.S. government banned reprocessing and recycling. Because of that decision, the interest in extended burnup received new impetus as a means to achieve better utilization of the nuclear resources and the accompanying reduced fuel costs. All of the aspects surrounding higher burnup and longer fuel cycles[40-44] are examined in detail next.

6.4.1 Effect of Extended Burnup on Fuel Performance

To attain higher burnup, the initial enrichment of the fuel has to be increased in order to provide the extra reactivity needed for the extended burnup. Assemblies with higher enrichment produce higher power and may cause power-peaking effects. It has been shown,[45] however, that these effects can be handled without severe penalties.

Two neutronic effects due to the extended burnup are decreased control rod worth and greater reactivity response to coolant temperature changes. The reduction of the control rod worth is the result of the presence in the core of a larger plutonium mass and a larger fission product inventory. The plutonium tends to increase the fast-to-thermal flux ratio. Since the control rods absorb mainly thermal neutrons, a reduction of the thermal neutron population reduces their effectiveness. The response of the core reactivity to coolant temperature is the result of the higher enrichment and of the larger fission product inventory. This increased sensitivity of the core is useful during transients that heat up the primary coolant loop; it is detrimental during transients that tend to cool it down rapidly. Management schemes have been developed that mitigate these effects. One such method is the low-leakage loading (Section 6.3.3).

With respect to the mechanical-chemical performance of the fuel, extended burnup may introduce problems of cladding corrosion, dimensional stability, fission gas release, and fuel failure as a result of pellet/cladding interaction (PCI) (see Chapter 4). The new fuel, developed with the express goal of achieving burnups up to 50,000 MWd/t, was designed in such a way as to avoid failure, especially through PCI. A pure zirconium lining has been used on the inside surface of the cladding to increase resistance to PCI. In addition, graphite coatings, annular pellets, large-grain fuel, and changes in dimensions to better accommodate fission gases and fuel rod expansion have been incorporated in these new fuel designs. Improved burnable poisons have also been introduced into these new fuels to better handle the reactivity swing.

A considerable amount of the LWR fuel has been taken to burnup of nearly 50,000 MWd/t without significant failures.

6.4.2 Effect of Extended Burnup on Uranium and Enrichment Needs

As the discharge burnup increases, higher initial enrichment is required, but the number of SWUs is about constant because the mass of uranium needed decreases (Fig. 6.14). This effect should not be surprising since, by definition, the inverse of burnup is mass of uranium needed per unit of energy produced. The number of assemblies decreases as the burnup increases for the same energy produced.

6.4.3 Other Effects Due to Higher Burnup

The reduced uranium requirements result in reduced mining, milling, conversion, and fabrication operations, which, in turn, result in fewer environmental effects, accidents, and radiation exposure to workers and the public and, of course, reduced fuel costs.

6.4.4 Effects Due to Fuel Cycle Length

Longer fuel cycles are considered along with extended burnup. Most commercial nuclear plants in the United States have already switched from a 12- to an 18-month cycle. Longer cycles offer the following advantages:

1. Fewer licensing submittals as a result of fewer refuelings

2. Plant availability increase and corresponding capacity factor increase

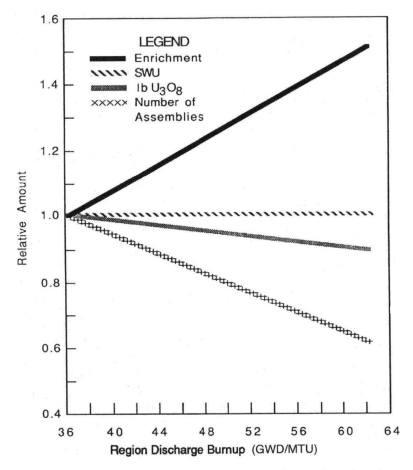

FIGURE 6.14 The changing of enrichment, SWUs, uranium, and number of assemblies as a function of burnup.[40]

3. Reduced need for replacement power during refueling shutdowns (This is probably the most important savings resulting from longer fuel cycles, especially for utilities that have to purchase the power because they do not have adequate reserve capacity in their own system.)

4. Reduced radiation exposure to operating personnel.

Note that the economics of longer versus shorter fuel cycles is not the same for all PWRs or all BWRs. Each plant and each utility is unique. In general, however, one can make the statement that fuel cycles longer than 12 months will save money, particularly for those utilities that have to purchase replacement power during the refueling of their nuclear plant. The replacement power cost is a significant component of the savings equation. In the United States,

TABLE 6.3
Economics of a 24-Month Cycle Relative
to a 12-Month Cycle*

Increased fuel costs		$ 4.7 \times 10^6
Savings due to:		
Replacement power cost	$8.5 \times 10^6	
Refueling labor	$1.5	
Fuel design/licensing	$0.2	$10.2
Net gain		$ 5.5

*For a 950-MWe PWR.[34]

where the replacement cost is important, there is a definite trend toward longer cycles. In other countries (e.g., France) the 12-month cycle is preferred, because there is no power purchased from another utility or from a more expensive plant during shutdown for refueling. One example of the costs and savings involved is given in Table 6.3.

There is an intricate relationship among the following factors as shown in Fig. 6.15: enrichment (number of SWUs), mass of uranium, burnup, fuel cycle length, and fuel cost. Consider, for example, burnup of 38 GWd/t. An increase in cycle length from 12 to 18 months results in a decrease of 11% in U_3O_8 [(4.6 − 4.15)/4.15; data in GWd/t taken from Fig. 6.15] and a decrease of 18% in SWU requirements [(7.5 − 6.35)/6.35; Fig. 6.15]. If, however, one decides to reach a burnup of 48 GWd/t with the 18-month cycle, the decreases are 10% in U_3O_8 [(4.85 − 4.4)/4.4; Fig. 6.15] and 14% in SWUs [(7.25 − 6.35)/6.35; Fig. 6.15]. What these numbers indicate is that the savings in SWUs and uranium do not change by the same amount as burnup and cycle length.

The sensitivity of the fuel cost to burnup and cycle length is shown in Fig. 6.16. The lines of Fig. 6.16 should be interpreted in the following manner: Consider an improvement in the reactor design that saves 0.1% in initial enrichment. Examples of things that would improve the cycle economics are better cladding, more efficient fuel core loading, and improved burnable poisons. If the achieved burnup is 41 GWd/t, the savings in fuel cost are as follows:

1. 2.15% for a 12-month cycle

2. 2% for a 18-month cycle

3. 1.8% for a 24-month cycle.

For the storage racks in the used fuel storage pool, to hold the fuel with the higher enrichment (need for the higher burnup), modifications are usually necessary. The NRC requires the k of the stored fuel to be 0.95 or less. To accomplish this additional safety factor, additional boron carbide or boral

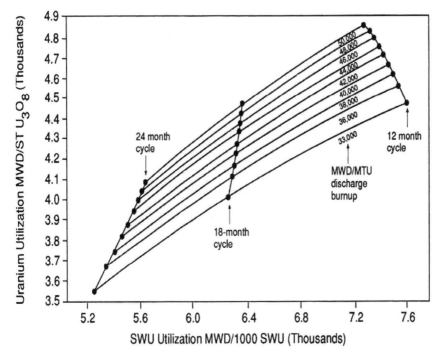

FIGURE 6.15 Uranium and SWU utilization as a function of cycle length and burnup. Consider a burnup of 38 GWd/t. An increase in cycle length from 12 to 18 months results in a decrease of 11% in U_3O_8 [(4.6 − 4.15)/4.15] and an decrease of 18% in SWU requirements [(7.5 − 6.35)/6.35]. (Courtesy of Westinghouse.)

sheets attached to the racks are frequently necessary (see Chapter 9 for additional information).

The changes in discharge burnup for BWRs and PWRs for the period 1980 to 2000 are shown in Figs. 6.17 and 6.18, respectively. Up to this time (2011) utilities have used fuel enriched to less than 5% in ^{235}U. To reach burnup of 60,000 MWd/t or more, the enrichment must be greater than 5%.

6.4.5 The Effect of NWPA on Extended Burnup

Before the Nuclear Waste Policy Act went into effect, it was necessary to add, as an advantage from an extended burnup, the benefit from the reduction in the number of spent fuel assemblies. Because less spent fuel means less mass of radioactive wastes to be disposed of, the disposal cost would be less for the utility if, as expected before the NWPA, the government would impose a disposal fee per kilogram. According to the NWPA, however, the government charges the utilities a standard fee of 1 mill/kWh(e) for fuel discharged after April 7, 1983. (For fuel discharged before that date, a fixed

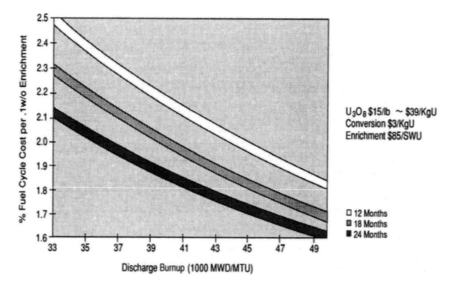

FIGURE 6.16 Fuel cycle cost sensitivity to enrichment change as a function of burnup. Assuming an improvement in reactor design saves 0.1% in initial enrichment and the burnup is 41 GWd/t, the savings in fuel cost are ~2% for an 18-month cycle and ~1.8% for a 24-month cycle. (Courtesy of Westinghouse.)

fee per kilogram will be charged; see Chapter 9.) The imposition of a standard fee negates the incentive to reduce the amount of spent fuel, except perhaps for the benefit accrued by the reduction in the amount of space required to store it. In fact, the imposition of a standard fee amounts to an

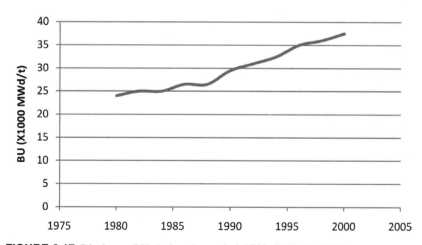

FIGURE 6.17 Discharge BU during the period 1980–2000 for BWRs.

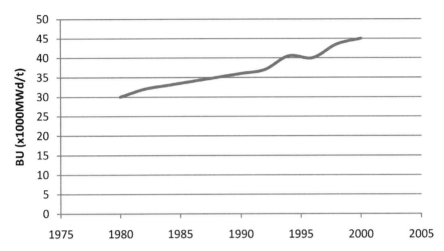

FIGURE 6.18 Discharge BU during the period 1988–2000 for PWRs.

increase in the disposal cost as burnup increases. Assuming a 32% thermal efficiency and an average burnup of 33,000 MWd/t, the 1 mill/kWh(e) is equivalent to $253/kgU. If the burnup increases to 48,000 MWd/t, the corresponding cost becomes $368/kgU (see Problem 6.1).

6.4.6 Fuel Cycle Stretchout (Coastdown)

There are times when, at the end of a scheduled shutdown for refueling, it is advantageous for the utility to delay refueling for a certain period of time. This may happen, for example, when an unexpectedly long shutdown in the middle of the cycle moves the scheduled EOC to a time of high demand (e.g., midwinter or midsummer). In such cases, the operator of the plant may desire to "stretch out" the cycle in order to refuel the plant at a more convenient time. Stretchout is achieved by taking advantage of the fact that, in today's LWRs, a change in the temperature of the core changes multiplication factor k, the reactivity of the core.

At EOC, the reactivity of the core, with all control rods as well as soluble poisons out, is essentially zero. Suppose that the decision is made to start operating the reactor at a power lower than its designed power, which also means lower operating temperature. As a result of the lower temperature, three effects tend to increase the reactivity of the core:

1. The LWRs are fueled with UO_2, a material with a negative Doppler coefficient amounting to 1% to 1.5% of the reactivity at full power. If the temperature is reduced, the Doppler effect is also reduced. Such a reduction amounts to the addition of positive reactivity in the core.

2. The equilibrium concentration in the core of the fission poison Xe increases with power. Therefore, reduced power also changes the negative reactivity contribution due to xenon.

3. The third component of positive reactivity added to the core is the result of the density change of the coolant. Today's LWRs are "under-moderated," that is, an increased amount of moderator would increase the reactivity. When the temperature of the core decreases, the density of the water moderator increases, which is equivalent to adding more moderator in the core. Again, the core reactivity increases.

It is possible, therefore, to introduce positive reactivity into the core by operating at a lower power level, thereby extending the length of the cycle. Obviously, such a decision is made when it is better to continue operating at a reduced power level rather than shutting down the plant immediately.

The stretchout extends the cycle and produces more energy, but it also increases the burnup of the fuel. As a result, the reactivity (i.e., the enrichment) of the fresh fuel that will be used during the next cycle has to be increased because the fuel already burned and kept in the core for the next cycle has decreased enrichment.

6.5 Burnup Measurement Techniques

Several burnup measurement techniques have been proposed and are used. A summary is given below, taken primarily from Refs. 46 and 47.

1. *Direct measurement.* This technique is used when the fuel is still in the reactor. It is performed by using in-core flux probes, ion chambers for gammas and fission chambers or flux wires for neutrons. Best accuracy achieved is 2%.

2. *Indirect measurement.* This type of measurement is made after the fuel is discharged from the core. It is based on the measurement of certain parameters, called burnup indicators, that have a known correlation with burnup. Examples are:

(a) *Activity of ^{137}Cs 662-keV gamma ($T_{1/2} = 30$ years).* The advantage using this Cs isotope is the fact that it is a fission product with an almost equal yield from U and Pu and its half life is relatively long. The disadvantage is that it is an absolute measurement; therefore, the gamma measurement has to be done very carefully (known detector geometry, efficiency, etc). The correlation is

$$BU = a + bA(^{137}Cs) \qquad (6.16)$$

where a and b are calibration constants and $A(^{137}Cs)$ is the measured ^{137}Cs activity.

(b) *Measurement of the activity ratio $A(^{134}Cs)/A(^{137}Cs)$.* This method offers the advantage that it is a relative measurement. The disadvantages are that the use of this ratio is limited by the 2.2-year half life of ^{134}Cs, thus it can only be used with relatively fresh fuel and the correlation with BU depends on ^{235}U enrichment and power rating. The correlation is

$$BU = c(e,r) + d(e,r) * [A(^{134}Cs)/A(^{137}Cs)] \qquad (6.17)$$

where c and d are calibration constants, e is the enrichment, and r is the power rating.

(c) *Measurement of the activity ratio (using gammas)* $R_0 = A(^{106}Ru)\,A(^{137}Cs)/[A(^{134}Cs)]^2$. The advantages of this method are that it is a relative measurement, and that it is almost independent of enrichment and power. The disadvantage is that it can be used for relatively fresh fuel because of the short half life of ^{106}Ru (1.02 years). The correlation is

$$BU = a\exp[b\ln(R_0)] \qquad (6.18)$$

with a and b being calibration constants.

6.6 Refueling Activities

Refueling of nuclear power plants is generally guided by two major requirements: It should take place during the proper refueling "window" and it should be completed as quickly as possible. Since a nuclear power plant, like any large complicated plant, also needs maintenance that can best be performed when the plant is shut down, the refueling activities are not only those strictly related to the discharge of the spent fuel and the insertion of the new fuel, but also all the necessary maintenance tasks.

The refueling "window" mentioned above is a time of low demand when the nuclear plant can be shut down without putting undue pressure on the reserves of the utility. All utilities that own nuclear power plants operate them as base load plants; that is, they operate them at the maximum possible power all the time. For load following, a utility utilizes smaller fossil plants. The reason for this mode of operation is the large size of the nuclear plants and their relatively low cost to operate. Every nuclear utility would like to shut down a nuclear plant at a time when there are adequate reserves and there is no need to buy replacement power. The period of low demand, the refueling window, is not the same for all utilities. It depends on the region of the country that the company serves and on what fraction of its total capacity the nuclear plant represents.

Utilities in the Midwest, for example, face two peak load demands—one in the summer and one in the winter. There are two refueling windows. The first is from about the first of March to the first of May, and the second is from about mid-September to mid-October. Keeping in mind that refueling takes about 25 days, it is obvious that these periods do not coincide with either the hot summer or the cold winter days. For utilities serving the southern regions of the United States, there is only one peak demand, during the summer, and the refueling window lasts from about the first of October to the first of April.

The ability to shut down and complete refueling during the best window is more critical for a small utility that owns only one nuclear power plant, which represents a considerable fraction of its generating capacity, than for a large company that operates many large plants (nuclear and fossil) for which the shutdown of one generating facility is easier to handle.

If the reactor can be refueled on-line, that is, without having to shut down, there is considerable flexibility in the refueling planning. The only example of a commercial reactor for which on-line refueling is practiced is the CANDU, a heavy-water-moderated, natural-uranium-fueled reactor developed by Canada.

6.6.1 Planning for a Refueling Outage

Planning for the outage is extremely important. Just how important becomes obvious if one remembers that the 24-h income from a 1200-MWe plant is about $800,000 to $1,000,000. Thus, even hours count since the loss of income per hour is from $33,000 to $42,000. The loss of income is particularly painful if the utility has to buy replacement power from another company.

For a successful outage, the utility ought to:

1. Establish an outage organization with a single person in charge at least 6 months before shutdown.

2. Maintain, at all times, an inventory of outstanding tasks to be performed.

3. Prepare as soon as possible the master list of tasks that have to be done during the next refueling.[48]

Every item on the list is examined for:

1. The possibility of deferral

2. Relative priority

3. The number of other tasks affected by it

4. The need for off-site expertise and equipment

5. The need for contingency preplanning, particularly for critical items.

Of the items in the master list, the most important ones are those that affect what is called the *critical path*. The critical path is the path that will take the plant from shutdown to startup in a minimum amount of time, resulting in the shortest outage. Critical tasks are those that may lengthen the critical path. Examples are:

1. Tasks that involve a large fraction of the plant, as a result of which they require considerable planning to determine the proper job sequence

2. Tasks that have significant delay potential themselves or that involve other tasks that depend on them.

Many methods have been developed for the determination of the critical path. One of them, described briefly here, is the critical path method (CPM); another, also used frequently, is called the program evaluation and review technique (PERT).[49]

Consider planning for the refueling of a reactor. All of the activities that have to be performed are identified by a letter or a number (see Fig. 6.19). For example, number 10 may indicate reactor vessel head removal, number 20 may mean opening a steam generator, number 30 may be fuel removal, number 80 may be reintroducing fuel back into the core, etc. The number above each circle in Fig. 6.19 indicates the time it takes, in weeks, to complete the corresponding activity. The arrows indicate the sequence in which each operation must be performed. For example, the reactor vessel head must be removed prior to fuel removal. Having two or more arrows originating from one activity means that those tasks may be performed in parallel. For example, activities 20 and 30 may both start after 10 is completed.

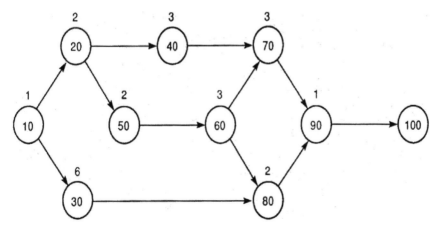

FIGURE 6.19 A typical CPM diagram. The numbers inside the circles indicate activities; the numbers outside the circles indicate the time it takes, in weeks, to complete that activity.

As shown in the figure, there are several options or paths that may lead to the final activity shown (100). From Fig. 6.19, the following paths are identified:

Path A: 10–20–40–70–90–100; total time required is 10 weeks.

Path B: 10–20–50–60–70–90–100; total time required is 12 weeks.

Path C: 10–20–50–60–80–90–100; total time required is 11 weeks.

Path D: 10–30–80–90–100; total time required is 10 weeks.

For this example, path B is the critical path because any slippage in any of the activities encountered along this path will cause a delay in reaching activity 100. Path B may be the longest in terms of actual time span, but it represents the minimum time in which *all* tasks can be completed, without waiting between any two activities.

To speed up the refueling outage, extra workers are hired for that purpose. The manager of the outage asks (and requires answers to) such questions as:

1. How many extra workers will we need?

2. How many workers can we employ in an efficient manner?

3. Are plans in place to train the workers?

4. How long does the training last?

5. Do we have the necessary equipment (mock-ups) for training?

6.6.2 Reload Fuel Procurement

The activities necessary to design, fabricate, and have the fuel transported on-site start about 2 years before the plant is shut down for refueling. They involve not only the fuel management group of the utility but also the fuel fabricator, the company that converts the U_3O_8 to UF_6, the provider of enrichment services (in the United States this is the USEC; see Chapter 3), the group that reviews the fuel design, and the NRC, which licenses the new fuel. The detailed list of activities is presented in Table 6.4, in chronological order, assuming refueling begins on February 1, 2013, as an example. This is also shown in Fig. 6.20.

Some utilities have in-house capability to perform all the tasks necessary for the design and safety analysis of the reload fuel; others prefer to hire outside persons or organizations to do the work for them. Because a utility may realize several and considerable benefits by performing all work in-house, the Electric Power Research Institute (EPRI) has developed a methodology for the complete analysis required for reload fuel. This work by EPRI, known as the Reactor Analysis Support Package (RASP), is explained in Ref. 50.

TABLE 6.4
A List of Refueling Activities

Task	Date at Which Activity Occurs; Batch Is Loaded on 2/1/2013
1. U_3O_8 supply.	2/1/11
2. Utility notifies conversion supplier about UF_6 requirements.	9/1/11
3. Utility notifies fuel fabricator of tentative batch requirements.	6/1/11
4. Preliminary fuel cycle analysis begins.	5/1/11
5. Utility adjusts UF_6 amount previously asked for from conversion supplier.	3/1/11
6. Fuel design review begins.	7/1/11
7. Fuel fabricator completes tentative fuel design.	8/1/11
8. Utility notifies fuel fabricator about final fuel design.	10/1/11
9. Fuel fabricator completes final fuel design.	12/1/11
10. Utility notifies DOE about SWUs required.	12/1/11
11. UF_6 is delivered to enrichment plant.	2/1/12
12. Enriched UF_6 is delivered to fuel fabrication plant.	6/15/12
13. Delivery of fuel to site is completed.	12/1/12
14. Fuel fabricator submits specifications for physics startup tests.	12/15/12
15. Plant is shut down; refueling starts.	2/1/13

6.6.3 Reload Fuel Design Activities

The major requirements for the new reload fuel are (1) to satisfy the energy requirements of the cycle and (2) to operate within the technical specifications of the plant. The new fuel design activities have as a goal the determination of the enrichment and number of assemblies for the new batch, and

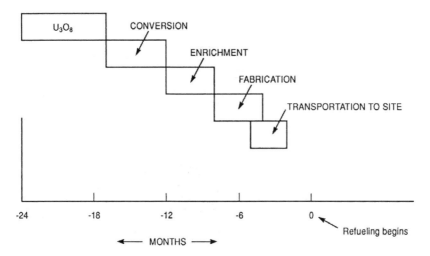

FIGURE 6.20 The reload fuel procurement activities calendar.

the actual mechanical design of the new assemblies and the core loading pattern. This proceeds along the following steps[51]:

1. Determine cycle operational and safety requirements.

2. Develop a preliminary core design that includes number of assemblies, old and fresh; enrichment; and loading pattern.

3. Identify the values of key safety parameters used in the Final Safety Analysis Report (FSAR).

4. Determine the values of the key safety parameters for the new cycle.

5. Confirm the applicability of the FSAR accident analysis. If applicability is not possible because of changes in the new fuel, the issue should be reexamined.

6. Identify technical specification changes required.

7. Finalize core design.

8. Write reload safety document.

6.6.4 Licensing the Reload Fuel

The licensing requirements for reload fuel are given in the Code of Federal Regulations, specifically, in 10 CFR 50.59 (Ref. 52). Explanatory guidelines for following Ref. 52 are given in NEI 96-07 (Ref. 53). In fuel reload, two operating cycles are involved: the upcoming cycle, called the *reload cycle*, and the *reference cycle* to which the reload fuel is compared. The reference cycle is the cycle with the most up-to-date safety information, information that has been approved by the NRC. In most cases that is the current operating cycle.

If the reload fuel and the procedures planned for it are conservative relative to the reference cycle, the utility may proceed without specific authorization by the NRC. If there are any changes, then the utility must address the implications for safety from the new fuel and/or new procedures by following 10 CFR 50.59.c (Refs. 52, 53) and apply for an amendment to its operating license. A safety analysis report is prepared that must include the following:

1. Calculations that support the safety review of the new core

2. Identification of differences between the fresh fuel and the fuel remaining in the core

3. Discussion of any changes in operating philosophy, from the previous or the reference cycle

4. A core loading map showing the position of and identifying all assemblies, old and new

5. Mechanical design characteristics for all fuel (pellet size, cladding, gaps, materials, etc.)

6. Previous operating experience with similar fuel

7. Nuclear characteristics of the core (moderator temperature coefficient of reactivity, Doppler coefficients, peaking factors, control rod worths, control rod drop parameters, delayed neutron fractions, prompt neutron lifetime, boron worth for PWRs, standby liquid control system worth for BWRs, control rod bank insertion limits for PWRs)

8. Details of the thermal-hydraulic design (core thermal power, coolant flow, coolant pressure in the core, core inlet enthalpy of coolant, limiting fuel assembly parameters, local peaking factors, DNBR, linear heat generation rate, etc.)

9. Analysis of postulated transients and accidents (including rod withdrawal, moderator dilution, loss-of-coolant flow, stuck rods, loss of electric power, steamline rupture, steam generator tube failure, fuel handling accident, loss-of-coolant accident)

10. Startup tests (including control rod performance, comparison between measured and calculated moderator temperature coefficients, check of core symmetry by comparing the readings of detectors at symmetric positions, reactivity coefficients, projected burnup, power level, temperatures, pressures, etc.).

6.6.5 Refueling Outage Tasks

No two refueling outages are identical in any one plant or in different plants because maintenance activities are an essential part of the tasks performed during shutdown for refueling, and it is highly unlikely that maintenance activities will be identical for two different shutdowns. However, the actual refueling activities follow a certain pattern and they take a certain time to perform. There is enough experience at this time, for both BWRs and PWRs, to make possible the enumeration of the major activities and their approximate duration. The reader should keep in mind that activities may overlap.

One may divide the tasks into seven categories, in terms of the time period in which they are performed:

1. *Shutdown activities prior to reloading operations:* Examples of activities during this period for BWRs are cooldown, de-inerting, and drywell and vessel disassembly; for PWRs, containment servicing, crane preparation, refueling pool cleaning, transfer canal preparation, and removal of the reactor vessel head insulation.

2. *Unloading the fuel:* In LWRs, although only a fraction of the core is discharged at every refueling, the whole core is unloaded because (a) all assemblies are inspected for leaks, (b) work needs to be performed inside the pressure vessel (inspection, repair, replacement of internals), and (c) the safety requirements are quite different depending on whether or not fuel is present inside the vessel. The average time it takes to remove one assembly from the core to the spent fuel pool is about 20 min. Therefore, moving 180 assemblies requires about 60 h.

3. *Fuel inspection (sipping):* All assemblies that will go back into the core must be inspected for leaks, that is, the fuel must undergo *sipping*. The time it takes for sipping depends on the method and on the number of assemblies that failed. Sipping may be done concurrently with unloading the fuel (see Section 4.4.5).

4. *Work on in-vessel (internals) and ex-vessel equipment:* These activities vary considerably from refueling to refueling and from plant to plant and cycle to cycle.

5. *Reloading the fuel and closing the vessel:* Same as in item 2 above, minus the time for inspection.

6. *Equipment inspections and repair before startup tests:* Examples are reactor coolant pump work, main turbine work, steam generator maintenance, and reconnection of instrumentation. These activities fall under maintenance but they are listed here because they are performed, to some extent, during every refueling (see Section 6.6.6).

7. *Startup tests:* These are tests required before the reactor reaches 100% of its design power. Examples are reactor coolant heatup, reactor criticality, turbine generator on-line, and various tests to verify nuclear and thermal-hydraulic parameters at various power levels.

The downtime for refueling LWRs in the United States has decreased continuously. The average time for refueling has gone down from 83 days in 1989 to about 30 in 2010, with some plants completing refueling in less than 30 days (the minimum reported is 17 days). This considerable improvement in performance, translating into better capacity factors and therefore reduced generating costs, is due primarily to the establishment of a better management team responsible for the refueling outage; secondarily, it is due to accumulated experience (learning curve). This improvement in performance of U.S. nuclear power plants during the period 1980–2000 resulted in additional electricity generation that would have required 27 new 1000-MWe plants; that is, without this improvement electric utilities would have to build 27 GWe of new generating capacity to satisfy U.S. electricity needs.

6.6.6 Maintenance Activities

As mentioned at the beginning of Section 6.6, in addition to the refueling itself, the outage is used to complete other tasks generally referred to as maintenance tasks. Maintenance has to do with the following activities being applied to components of equipment or whole pieces of equipment: modification, repair, inspection and testing, replacement, and cleaning.

For a complicated entity like a nuclear power plant, it is not possible to make up a list of all the maintenance tasks, in part, because no two plants are exactly alike. However, because the major components are the same in all PWRs and all BWRs, a rather comprehensive, but not all-inclusive, list can be written that applies to LWRs only. The tasks listed below are not performed at every outage:

1. *Reactor vessel:* In-service inspection, studs inspection and/or replacement, O-ring inspection and/or replacement, flange cleaning, internals cleaning, removal of debris

2. *Steam generators:* Bundle flush, foreign object search, tube inspection, U-bend heat treatment, tube plugging check, blowdown isolation valve inspection

3. *Reactor coolant pumps:* Seal and motor inspection, seal replacement, block valve replacement, rotating assembly (impeller/shaft) inspection by radiography

4. *Turbine-generator (TG):* TG inspection, turbine rotor replacement, turbine motor replacement, turbine valve overhaul, generator crawl-through inspection, generator retaining rings inspection, generator exciter inspection and/or replacement

5. *Control rods (CR):* CR drive mechanism inspection and/or replacement, inspection for wear, examination of control rod blades

6. *Pressurizer:* Nozzle inspection and/or replacement

7. *Moisture separator reheater:* Relief valve inspection, tube bundle inspection and/or replacement

8. *Reactor coolant system:* Cleanup to reduce activity

9. *Containment:* Containment integrity test (PWRs), drywell leak test (BWRs)

10. *Fuel handling system:* Inspection, testing

11. *In-core instrumentation:* In-core detector replacement (PWRs), traversing in-core probe drives (BWRs)

12. *Ex-core instrumentation:* Inspection, testing, and/or replacement

13. *Diesel generators:* Inspection and testing

14. *Service water system:* Piping inspection

15. *Valves:* Motor-operated valve actuators and electromagnetic relief valves

16. *Residual heat removal system:* Inspection of core spray, inspection of pumps and motors

17. *Cooling tower:* Inspection and possible overhaul, if cooling towers are used.

An excellent review of nuclear power plant maintenance activities appears in Ref. 54. An outage management benchmarking guideline was prepared by EPRI.[55] Finally, there is an effort under way for on-line maintenance,[56] with obvious advantages for refueling: The refueling outage duration will definitely be shortened if there is no maintenance to be performed.

6.7 Radiation Exposure to Personnel

Refueling activities are the major source of radiation exposure to personnel at nuclear power plants. Although the annual limit of exposure for radiation workers is 50 mSv (5 rem), the operators of nuclear plants are required to follow the "as low as reasonably achievable" (ALARA) principle, as a result of which the average exposure to personnel over a year has continuously declined from about 7 person-Sv (700 person-rem) for PWRs and 10 person-Sv (1000 person-rem) for BWRs in 1981 to about 0.6 person-Sv (60 person-rem) for PWRs and 1.2 person-Sv (120 person-rem) in BWRs in 2010; the trend is shown in Figs. 6.21 and 6.22. There is a continuous effort in nuclear power plants all over the world to follow such practices so that the average exposure to workers will be minimized. For LWRs, experience has shown that proper control of the water coolant chemistry may reduce the radiation dose considerably.[58]

In LWRs, most of the radiation dose is a result of radioactive materials that are removed by the chemical action of the water flowing through the core and from the assemblies and the other internals of the pressure vessel. These materials, generally referred to as *crud*, have been activated by neutrons in the core and, once entered into the coolant, they circulate with it. In PWRs, the crud is retained in the primary loop unless there is a leak in one of the steam generator tubes. In BWRs, the crud will reach the turbine. Two cobalt isotopes are the primary source of radiation: ^{60}Co, produced by the (n, γ) reaction with ^{59}Co, and ^{58}Co produced by the (n, p) reaction with ^{58}Ni.

In PWRs, experience has shown that there is considerable reduction in the radiation field if the pH of the water in the primary loop is kept at 6.9 or higher and the lithium concentration is kept between 2 and 7 ppm. There was some concern when this approach was first applied about the effect of lithium on enhanced oxidation of Zircaloy and the intergranular stress corrosion

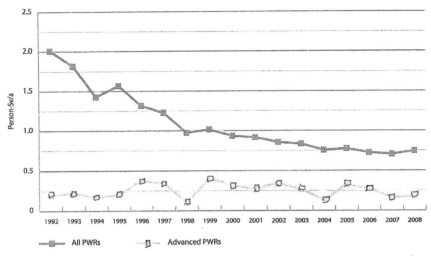

Source: OECD/NEA Information System on Occupational Exposure (ISOE), 2008.

FIGURE 6.21 Average annual collective dose trends for PWRs.[57]

cracking of Inconel. Tests performed by EPRI showed that a lithium concentration of 2 to 7 ppm and a pH value from 6.9 to 7.4 cause no problems.

In BWRs, there is no unanimity about the best method for water chemistry control. General Electric uses injection of zinc oxide into the feedwater

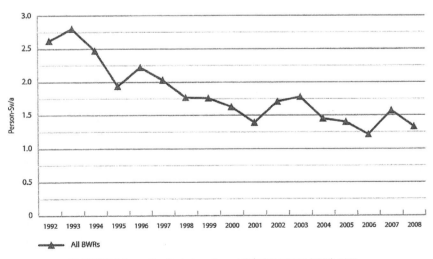

Source: OECD/NEA Information System on Occupational Exposure (ISOE), 2008.

FIGURE 6.22 Average annual collective dose trends for BWRs.[57]

in the range of 5 to 15 ppb. The Japanese adopted this method to maintain the Ni/Fe ratio at 0.2 ppb, either by bypassing the condensate system or by iron injection.

Bibliography

Driscoll, M.J., Downar, T.J., and Pilat, E.E., *The Linear Reactivity Model for Nuclear Fuel Management*, American Nuclear Society (1990).

Fuel Management and Handling, British Nuclear Energy Society (1995).

Graves, H.W., *Nuclear Fuel Management*, John Wiley & Sons (1979).

The Nuclear Fuel Cycle, P.D. Wilson, Ed., Oxford University Press (1996).

Silvennoinen, P., *Nuclear Fuel Cycle Optimization*, Pergamon Press (1982).

Silvennoinen, P., *Reactor Core Fuel Management*, Pergamon Press (1976).

References

1. Mingle, J.O., "In-Core Fuel Management via Perturbation Theory," *Nucl. Technol.*, **27**, 248 (1975).

2. Driscoll, M.J., Downar, T.J. and Pilat, E.E., *The Linear Reactivity Model for Nuclear Fuel Management*, American Nuclear Society (1990).

3. Wall, I., and Fenech, H., "The Application of Dynamic Programming to Fuel Management Optimization," *Nucl. Sci. Eng.*, **22**, 285 (1965).

4. Stover, R.L., and Sesonske, A., "Optimization of BWR Fuel Management Using an Accelerated Exhaustive Search Algorithm," *J. Nucl. Energy*, **23**, 673 (1969).

5. Fagan, J.R., and Sesonske, A., "Optimal Fuel Replacement in Reactivity Limited Systems," *J. Nucl. Energy*, **23**, 683 (1969).

6. Suzuki, A., and Kiyose, R., "Application of Linear Programming to Refueling Optimization for Light Water Moderated Power Reactors," *Nucl. Sci. Eng.*, **46**, 112 (1971).

7. Sauar, T.O., "Application of Linear Programming to In-Core Fuel Management Optimization in Light Water Reactors," *Nucl. Sci. Eng.*, **46**, 274 (1971).

8. Naft, B.N., and Sesonske, A., "Pressurized Water Optimal Fuel Management," *Nucl. Technol.*, **14**, 123 (1972).

9. Motoda, H., Herczeg, J., and Sesonske, A., "Optimization of Refueling Schedule for Light Water Reactors," *Nucl. Technol.*, **25**, 477 (1975).

10. Levine, S.H., "In-Core Fuel Management Educational Module," *Nucl. Technol.*, **53**, 303 (1981).

11. Colletti, J.P., Levine, S.H., and Lewis, J.B., "Iterative Solution to the Optimal Poison Management Problem in Pressurized Water Reactors," *Nucl. Technol.*, **63**, 415 (1983).

12. Ahnert, C., and Aragones, J.M., "Fuel Management and Core Design Code Systems for PWR Neutronic Calculations," *Nucl. Technol.*, **69**, 350 (1985).

13. Maldonado, G.I., Turinsky, P.J., and Kropaczek, D.J. "Employing Nodal Generalized Perturbation Theory for the Minimization of Feed Enrichment During Pressurized Water Reactor In-Core Nuclear Fuel Management Optimization," *Nucl. Sci. Eng.*, **121**, 312 (1995).

14. Moore, B.R., and Turinsky, P.J., "Higher Order Generalized Perturbation Theory for Boiling Water Reactor In-Core Fuel Management Optimization," *Nucl. Sci. Eng.*, **130**, 98 (1998).

15. Shatilla, Y.A., Little, D.C., Penkrot, J.A., and Holland, A., "In-Core Fuel Management with Biased Multiobjective Function Optimization," *Nucl. Technol.*, **130**, 282 (2000).

16. Karve, A.A., and Turinsky, P.J., "FORMOSA-B: A Boiling Water Reactor In-Core Fuel Management Optimization Package," *Nucl. Technol.*, **131**, 48 (2000).

17. Ziver, A.K., et al., "Multicycle Optimization of Advanced Gas-Cooled Reactor Loading Patterns Using Genetic Algorithms," *Nucl. Technol.*, **141**, 122 (2003).

18. Jose-Ortiz, J., and Requena, I., "An Order Coding Genetic Algorithm to Optimize Fuel Reloads in a Nuclear Boiling Water Reactor," *Nucl. Sci. Eng.*, **146**, 88 (2004).

19. Turinsky, P.J., "Nuclear Fuel Management Optimization: A Work in Progress," *Nucl. Technol.*, **151**, 3 (2005).

20. Yamamoto, A., et al., "Reduction in Workload of BWR In-Core Fuel Shuffling by New Optimization Methods," *Nucl. Technol.*, **154**, 318 (2006).

21. Popa, F., "The PEARLS^{TM} Loading Pattern Search Tool in Practice," *Proc. Advances in Nuclear Fuel Management (ANFM-IV)*, Hilton Head, South Carolina, April 12–15, 2009.

22. Fukao, A., "Minimum Shuffling Model in the BWR Loading Pattern Optimization Code FINELOAD-3," *Proc. Advances in Nuclear Fuel Management (ANFM-IV)*, Hilton Head, South Carolina, April 12–15, 2009.

23. Yilmaz S., Kvaall G., and Sutton S., "Advanced ePROMETHEUS™ Fuel Cycle Optimization Tool," *Proc. Advances in Nuclear Fuel Management (ANFM-IV)*, Hilton Head, South Carolina, April 12–15, 2009.

24. Sato, H., Tojo, M., Iwamoto, T., and Elam, J., "Development of a New GNF Shuffling Sequence System EPIMETHEUS," *Proc. Advances in Nuclear Fuel Management (ANFM-IV)*, Hilton Head, South Carolina, April 12–15, 2009.

25. Alim, F., Yilmaz, S., Ivanov, K., and Levine, S.H., "Genetic Algorithms to Automatically Optimize PWR Fuel Management Calculations," *Proc. Advances in Nuclear Fuel Management (ANFM-IV)*, Hilton Head, South Carolina, April 12–15, 2009.

26. Tsoulfanidis, N., et al., "Calculation of Neutron Energy Spectra in the Core and Cavity of a PWR (ANO-1)," EPRI NP-3776, Electric Power Research Institute (Dec. 1984).

27. Tsoulfanidis, N., et al., "Neutron Energy Spectra in the Core and Cavity of the ANO-2 PWR," EPRI NP-4238, Electric Power Research Institute (Sep. 1985).

28. Tsoulfanidis, N., "Neutron Energy Spectra in the Core and Cavity of the McGuire-1 PWR," EPRI NP-5622, Electric Power Research Institute (Feb. 1988).

29. Guthrie, G.L., McElroy, W. N., and Anderson, S.L., "A Preliminary Study of the Use of Fuel Management Techniques for Slowing Pressure Vessel Embrittlement," NUREG/CR-2345, 4, HEDL-TME 81-36, R5, Hanford Engineering and Development Laboratory (Oct. 1982).

30. Franklin, D., and Marston, T., "Investigating the Flux Reduction Option in Reactor Vessel Integrity," EPRI NP-3110-SR, Electric Power Research Institute (May 1983).

31. Cokinos, D., Aronson, A.L., Carew, J.F., Kohut, P., Todosow, M., and Lois, L., "Pressure Vessel Damage Fluence Reduction by Low-Leakage Fuel Management," *Trans. Am. Nucl. Soc.*, **45**, 594 (1983).

32. Todosow, M., Aronson, A.L., Carew, J.F., Kokinos, D., Kohut, P., and Lois, L., "Pressure Vessel Fluence Reduction Through Selective Fuel Assembly Replacement," *Trans. Am. Nucl. Soc.*, **45**, 595 (1983).

33. Southworth, F.H., "Experience with Low-Leakage Fuel Management," *Trans. Am. Nucl. Soc.*, **46**, 93 (1984).

34. Spetz, S.W., "B&W Experience with Low-Leakage Fuel Management," *Trans. Am. Nucl. Soc.*, **46**, 94 (1984).

35. Ankney, R.D., Casedei, A.L., and Stucker, D.L., "Westinghouse Experience with Low-Leakage Fuel Management," *Trans. Am. Nucl. Soc.*, **46**, 97 (1984).

36. Chang, Y., and Sesonske, A., "Optimization and Analysis of Low-Leakage Core Management for Pressurized Water Reactors," *Nucl. Technol.*, **65**, 292 (1983).

37. Fenech, H., and Tsai, K., "Fluence Reduction of Nuclear Reactor Pressure Vessels by Fuel Management Strategies," *Ann. Nucl. Energy*, **13**, 85 (1986).

38. Aguilar, O., "Fuel Loading for a Low-Leakage Core in a Pressurized Water Reactor," MS Thesis, University of Missouri–Rolla (Aug. 1986).

39. Frank, F.J., and Scherpereel, L.R., "Fuel Cycle Cost Reduction Through Westinghouse Fuel Design and Core Management," *Trans. Am. Nucl. Soc.*, **50**, 101 (1985).

40. Scherpereel, L.R., and Frank, F.J., "Fuel Cycle Cost Considerations of Increased Discharge Burnups," *Nucl. Technol.*, **56**, 106 (1982).

41. Ho, A.L.B., and Sesonske, A., "Extended Burnup Fuel Cycle Optimization for Pressurized Water Reactors," *Nucl. Technol.*, **58**, 422 (1982).

42. Bernstein, I., Greacen, J.S., Matzie, R.A., and Miller, D.D., "An Evaluation of Pressurized Water Reactor Frequent Refueling," *Nucl. Technol.*, **56**, 516 (1982).

43. Spetz, S.W., "Options and Trade-offs for In-Core Fuel Management," *Trans. Am. Nucl. Soc.*, **56**, 115 (1988).

44. Anderson, C.K., "Extended Cycle Length Economics," *Trans. Am. Nucl. Soc.*, **56**, 116 (1988).

45. "Licensing Assessment of PWR Extended-Burnup Fuel Cycles," R.A. Matzie, Ed., CEND-381, Combustion Engineering (1981).

46. Christensen, A.S., "Radiometric Instrumentation for Spent Fuel Monitoring," DOE/RIO-0472, Rev. 0, Topical Report, U.S. Department of Energy (Aug. 1996).

47. NUREG/CR-6998, "Review of Information for Spent Nuclear Fuel Burnup Confirmation," U.S. Nuclear Regulatory Commission (2009).

48. Edwards, D.W., "Outage Management: A Case Study," *Nucl. News* (Dec. 1975).

49. Kerzner, H., *Project Management: A Systems Approach to Planning, Scheduling, and Controlling*, 3rd ed., Chap. 12, Van Nostrand-Reinhold (1989).

50. *Reactor Analysis Support Package (RASP)*, Vol. 10: *Guidelines for Developing a Reload Licensing Capability*, EPRI NP-4498, Electric Power Research Institute (Aug. 1988).

51. "Westinghouse Reload Safety Evaluation Methodology," S.L. Davidson and W.R. Kramer, Eds., WCAP-9273-NP-A, Westinghouse Electric Corporation (July 1985).

52. *Code of Federal Regulations*, Title 10, "Energy," Part 50, "Domestic Licensing of Production and Utilization Facilities," Chap. 1, U.S. Nuclear Regulatory Commission (10 CFR 50).

53. "Guidelines for Implementation of 10 CFR 50.59," NEI 96-07, Revision 1, Nuclear Energy Institute (Nov. 2000).

54. Plant Maintenance Special Sections, *Nucl. News*, pp. 45–73 (Dec. 1988) and pp. 37–62 (Oct. 2009).

55. "Outage Management Benchmarking Guideline," EPRI Technical Report 1004383, Electric Power Research Institute (2003); see also *Nucl. News*, pp. 33–55 (Apr. 2009) and pp. 43–60 (Apr. 2011).

56. "Guidance for Developing and Implementing an On-Line Maintenance Strategy," EPRI Technical Report 1009708, Electric Power Research Institute (2004).

57. *NEA News*, **28**, 2 (2010)

58. Health Physics Special Section, *Nucl. News*, pp. 47–84 (July 1988).

Problems

6.1. Prove that if a utility pays 1 mill/kWh(e) for disposal of used fuel, it is equivalent to $253/kgU. Assume a burnup of 33,000 MWd/t and an average thermal efficiency of 32%.

6.2. A utility is given the choice of paying 1.2 mill/kWh(e) for a used fuel disposal fee or $300/kgU at 35,000 MWd/t burnup and 32% efficiency. Which choice is more economical?

6.3. The initial enrichment of uranium in LWRs is 3% and the final (at discharge after 3 years in the core) is 0.8%. Based on these numbers, calculate the average thermal neutron flux in an LWR.

6.4. What are the availability and capacity factors for a reactor that had the power history shown below?

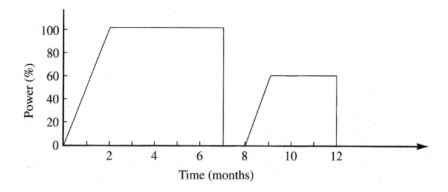

6.5. Calculate the EFPD for the operating history shown below.

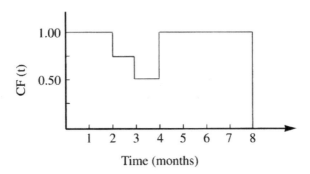

Time (months)

6.6. A nuclear power plant uses 87 tons of uranium in its core. The first core consists of three equal batches with enrichments of 2.5%, 2.9%, and 3.1%. For subsequent cycles, the reactor uses batches with enrichments equal to 2.6% and 3.2% in alternate years. One-third of the core is discharged each year and is replaced by new fuel. Assume a 30-year lifetime and 0.2% tails during the life of the plant. Calculate:

(a) The number of SWUs needed for the first core, the number of SWUs every year after the first cycle, and the total SUWs over the life of the plant.

(b) The amount of U_3O_8 and UF_6 needed for the first core, every year after, and the total U_3O_8 and UF_6 over the life of the plant. Give your result in metric tons of uranium, UF_6, and U_3O_8.

(c) Assume the following prices and calculate the cost of the first core and the cost of the fuel per year for the life of the plant.

U_3O_8: $65.00/kg

Conversion: $7/kg; 0.5% loss

SWU price: $105

Fabrication/transportation: $250/kg; 0.8% loss

6.7. Is it possible for the availability and capacity factors to be equal? Explain your answer. Take into account the real operating conditions of a reactor.

6.8. A nuclear power plant operated for a year with a 69% capacity factor. What is the burnup of the fuel if the core contains 95 tons of uranium and has been designed to produce 1200 MWe with a 32% efficiency? What will be the average burnup, over the life of the plant, if one-third of the core is replaced every year? Assume a 30-year life for the plant and a constant capacity factor and efficiency.

SEVEN

REPROCESSING AND RECYCLING

7.1 What Is Reprocessing and Recycling?

Fresh LWR fuel consists of UO_2, enriched to 3% to 4.5% in ^{235}U. The used nuclear fuel contains most of the original ^{238}U, about one-third of the original ^{235}U, a certain amount of plutonium, almost all of the fission products, and transuranics (TRU, elements with $Z > 92$).

Reprocessing is the operation of recovering the uranium and plutonium isotopes from the used fuel, while the rest (cladding, fission products, TRU, contaminated chemicals) becomes high-level radioactive waste (HLW), to be disposed of in accordance with the Nuclear Waste Policy Act (see Chapter 9).

Recycling refers to the introduction of the uranium and plutonium that was recovered from the reprocessing of used fuel back into a fission reactor for additional energy production. Reactor fuel made from recycled uranium and plutonium will be a mixture of UO_2 and PuO_2 and is known as mixed-oxide fuel (MOX). The MOX can be used in the current generation of LWRs, as a supplement to the fuel fabricated using fresh unirradiated uranium, or it can be used as a fuel in breeder reactors.

7.2 An Historical Perspective

The civilian nuclear industry started on the premise of a closed nuclear fuel cycle, which requires recycling; recycling, of course, is impossible without reprocessing. In 1976 with the completion of the Generic Environmental Impact Statement for Mixed-Oxide Fuel study[1] (see Section 6.1), the United States was ready to implement recycling. During that same year, however, in the midst of a presidential campaign, weapons proliferation issues surfaced and soon dominated the nuclear debate. *Weapons proliferation* refers to the possibility for a country or for a terrorist group to divert enough uranium and/or plutonium from a reprocessing plant to make a nuclear weapon.

232

It is not clear why the proliferation issue became so dominant in 1976. The number of nations with declared weapons capabilities remained small—the United States, the United Kingdom, the Soviet Union (now Russia), France, and China. Certain international efforts were aimed at nonproliferation, the most prominent ones being those of the International Atomic Energy Agency, created in 1957, and the Treaty on the Nonproliferation of Nuclear Weapons (NPT), signed by most nations in 1968. Some of the countries that did not ratify the NPT are China, India, Pakistan, and Israel. In 1974, India shocked the world by announcing a successful nuclear explosion. Although the Indian government said that the purpose of the experiment was the peaceful use of nuclear explosives, the fact that the capability for the production of nuclear weapons was there and, more important, that materials and facilities used in this program had been provided to India for peaceful purposes (research and the generation of electricity) made the world aware that the connection existed between civilian nuclear power and nuclear weapons.

In October 1976, President Gerald Ford announced that reprocessing and recycling of uranium and plutonium should not proceed unless the risks of weapons proliferation were reduced to an acceptable level. He also said that the United States should no longer regard reprocessing as a necessary and inevitable step in the nuclear fuel cycle. Further, it was stated that nonproliferation issues must take precedence over economic interests. President Jimmy Carter, who succeeded Ford, followed the same line and went further by deferring reprocessing and recycling indefinitely. (Note that the reprocessing discussed here refers to reprocessing of civilian used fuel. The U.S. government reprocessed nuclear fuel for many years for defense-related activities.)

President Carter initiated two studies related to the relationship between nuclear power and weapons proliferation issues—one domestic, the other international. In the United States, the government funded the Nonproliferation Alternative Systems Assessment Program (NASAP); at the instigation of President Carter, the international community launched the International Nuclear Fuel Cycle Evaluation (INFCE). Both studies[2-4] began in 1977 and ended in 1980.

The objective of NASAP was to study all nuclear fuel cycles and offer recommendations for the development of nuclear power systems and institutions that, as much as possible, would be proliferation resistant. The degree of proliferation resistance is based on the difficulty of obtaining weapons-grade materials (uranium enriched to more than 20% in ^{235}U or more than 12% in ^{233}U, or plutonium in any amount). The most important conclusions[4] of NASAP are as follows:

1. There is no nuclear fuel cycle that is 100% proliferation proof; that is, there is no technical fix to make any nuclear cycle proliferation proof.

2. Improvements in technical aspects (safeguards technology such as better detection capabilities of nuclear materials) and institutional ones

(ratification and commitment to international treaties, international control of enrichment facilities and of used fuel, etc.) can increase proliferation resistance.

3. The once-through fuel cycle is the most proliferation resistant because material directly usable for weapons is never produced at any time during the cycle.

Alternatives proposed by NASAP to the once-through cycle included advanced converters, recycling of LWR fuel, the introduction of the light water breeder reactor (LWBR), or the fast breeder reactor (FBR), with the FBR being the first choice. The alternatives mentioned above should be introduced to correct imbalances in the supply and demand equation for uranium fuel. NASAP projected that such imbalances would not occur until about the year 2010 and also stated that establishment of confidence in the current supply of materials and services for civilian nuclear power is a major step in generating a nonproliferation environment. Of the options mentioned by NASAP, the U.S. nuclear industry chose to follow fuel cycles that would lead to increased burnup.

The INFCE report studied fewer possible cycles than NASAP, but it dealt more generically with the question of how the international community could reconcile nonproliferation issues with vital energy needs. Sixty-six countries and five international organizations participated in this study, including then-Soviet-bloc nations but not China. The major findings of INFCE were as follows:

1. The misuse of civilian nuclear facilities for the production of weapons, although possible, is neither the easiest nor the most efficient way to achieve such an objective.

2. Plutonium recycling in LWRs could result in uranium savings in the range of 35% to 40% (see Section 7.5.1; the true number is closer to 20%). However, there is no economic incentive to implement such a plan under the present political and regulatory barriers.

3. In the long run, there is no essential difference in the degree of proliferation resistance between the once-through cycle and others such as plutonium recycling in LWRs and FBR fuel cycles. (This conclusion is the major difference between NASAP and INFCE. NASAP concluded that there is a difference between the LWR once-through cycle and all others that involve reprocessing.)

4. The use of nuclear power is considered an "inalienable right" of all countries and represents a viable electricity supply option in many developing countries.

5. International safeguards agreements can offer a considerable reduction in proliferation risk and should be an integral part of the world civilian nuclear power industry.

INFCE agreed with NASAP that confidence in the adequate, uninterrupted supply of materials and services to the countries with civilian nuclear power programs by the countries that offer these materials and services is a very important step toward reducing the proliferation risk.

In 1981, the Reagan administration lifted the ban on reprocessing and directed the U.S. Department of Energy to study the feasibility of commercial reprocessing in the United States. Because there are no commercial breeder reactors and because recycling of uranium and plutonium in LWRs does not offer any advantages [and, one should add, the MOX fuel has not been licensed yet by the U.S. Nuclear Regulatory Commission (NRC); only a few test assemblies have been inserted in a PWR], no effort has been made by any industrial firms in the United States to plunge into a reprocessing venture.

7.3 Why Consider Reprocessing and Recycling?

Reprocessing is necessary to extract from the irradiated nuclear fuel useful nuclides that are contained in it. Obviously, reprocessing without recycling (e.g., for weapons activities) is feasible, but not the other way around. In that context, the discussion that follows addresses the need for recycling nuclear fuel for the generation of electricity by nuclear power reactors. Reprocessing for weapons needs is not addressed at all.

Recycling of plutonium and uranium in connection with breeder reactors is not questioned. Recycling is imbedded in the very concept of a breeder, which produces more fuel than it consumes and reintroduces (recycles) the bred fuel to itself or to other reactors.

Recycling of plutonium and uranium in LWRs is not necessary, but it could be used if it offered advantages relative to the once-through cycle. Potential advantages of recycling are the reduction in the amount of uranium to be mined, the reduction of the number of separative work units (SWUs), and the reduction in the amount of used fuel to be stored. It is not clear if recycling results in an overall reduction in the quantity of HLW to be disposed; however, the composition of the HLW will be different, especially if the TRU is removed and burned in reactors. Potential disadvantages of recycling are the need for reprocessing and the risks reprocessing entails relative to weapons proliferation.

There is no doubt that recycling of uranium and plutonium represents a better utilization of nuclear fuels than the once-through fuel cycle. Let us define the nuclear resources utilization as the ratio

$$U = \frac{(mass\ of\ fuel\ consumed)}{(mass\ of\ resource\ used)} \tag{7.1}$$

where, in the case of reactors using uranium, the denominator is the mass of natural uranium fed into the system (as feed to the enrichment plant or directly loaded into the reactor). In the once-through cycle, Eq. (7.1) takes the form

$$U = \frac{M_f}{FF * M_l} \qquad (7.2)$$

where

M_f = mass of fuel consumed

M_l = mass of fuel loaded into the core

FF = feed factor [Chapter 3, Eq. (3.6)].

■ **Example 7.1:** What is the value of uranium utilization for an LWR that uses 4% enriched fuel in a once-through fuel cycle and burns it to 50,000 MWd/t? Assume enrichment tails equal 0.2%.

Answer: Using Eq. (3.6) with x_p = 4%, x_w = 0.2%, and x_f = 0.711%, one gets FF = 7.436. The mass of fuel that was fissioned can be related to the energy produced, given the energy per fission. Assuming 200 MeV per fission and a capture-to-fission ratio equal to 0.169 (^{235}U, thermal neutrons), the result[5] is 1.23 g of ^{235}U consumed per MWd. Therefore, the uranium utilization is

$$U = (50 \text{ MWd/kg})(1.23 \text{ g/MWd})/(7.436 \times 1000 \text{ g/kg}) = 0.0083 \ (0.8\%) \quad ■$$

Uranium utilization increases dramatically if the reactor is a breeder. Then, one can show that U is given by[5]

$$U = \frac{\dfrac{M_f}{M_l}}{\left[\dfrac{M_f}{M_l}\right](1 - \gamma) + \gamma} \qquad (7.3)$$

where γ is the fraction of fissile and fertile materials lost during reprocessing and fuel fabrication. The value of γ is ~0.02. The value of M_f/M_l, assuming 80,000 MWd/tHM[a] for breeder reactor fuel, is equal to

$$\frac{M_f}{M_l} = 80,000 \text{ (MWd/tHM)} * 1.23 \text{ (g/MWd)} * 1.0 \times 10^{-6} \text{ (tHM/g)} = 0.098$$

---

[a] When only uranium fissions in the core, burnup is expressed in terms of MWd/t. If other isotopes also fission, as is the case if plutonium is also present in the core, the burnup is expressed in terms of MWd/tHM (megawatt-day per ton heavy metal).

Therefore, Eq. (7.3) gives

$$U = 0.098/[0.098(1 - 0.02) + 0.02] = 0.84 \, (84\%)$$

No units are shown in the calculation of U because all of the quantities involved are ratios.

Thus, a breeder reactor fuel cycle has the capability to extract from the nuclear fuel more than 80 times the energy that becomes available by burning it in an LWR using the once-through cycle. Between the level of utilization achieved by an LWR in a once-through cycle [Eq. (7.2)] and that reached by a breeder reactor [Eq. (7.3)], there is a range of continuously increasing uranium utilization attained by reactors through their conversion capabilities. In the once-through cycle (in which used fuel is stored, not reprocessed and recycled), improved utilization is accomplished by increasing the burnup of the UO_2 fuel in LWRs.

As explained in Chapters 4 and 6, the goal for fuel burnup (BU) is to exceed 50,000 MWd/t. The most important benefits from increased BU are as follows:

1. Less uranium needs to be mined, hence the LWR era can be extended.

2. Less fuel is used, hence storage requirements for used fuel are reduced.

3. The cycle length becomes longer, hence the plant availability and capacity factors increase because of less frequent refueling.

4. With recycling, uranium utilization is further improved, with additional benefits from reduction in the uranium mass and SWUs needed.

Calculations of uranium and SWU savings as a result of recycling of uranium and plutonium are presented in Sections 7.5.2 and 7.5.3.

On what grounds should the decision to proceed with reprocessing and recycling be made? Economic? Uranium utilization? Other? The answer is not unique. It depends on the conditions prevailing in a particular country. The United States' decision in 1976 not to reprocess was based almost entirely on weapons-proliferation risks; since 1981, reprocessing has not been forbidden. However, with the current electricity demand; the prices of uranium, enrichment, fuel fabrication, and disposal; and the regulatory climate, recycling in the United States is not considered economical. The major component of the cost of nuclear power is construction costs, a component that has nothing to do with uranium price and availability, which are the major arguments for recycling.

In Western Europe and in Japan, the conditions are such that recycling of plutonium and uranium offers some advantages. As a result, these countries have strong, comprehensive reprocessing and recycling programs and have already accumulated considerable experience (see Section 7.4.7).

Although the U.S. civilian nuclear power program utilizes the once-through fuel cycle, discussion of recycling and reprocessing is important because (1) other countries in the world use recycling, (2) it is quite probable that reprocessing and recycling will be employed in the United States in the future as well, and (3) uranium and plutonium from weapons dismantlement will be used as fuel in LWRs.

7.4 Reprocessing

7.4.1 General Comments

A reprocessing operation consists of the following major steps:

1. Mechanically chop the used fuel assembly into small pieces.
2. Dissolve the parts from step 1 in nitric acid.
3. Use solvent extraction to separate into streams containing the products of interest and the wastes.
4. Convert U-nitrate to UO_2 and Pu-nitrate to PuO_2.
5. Handle the waste, mostly HLW, appropriately.

The details of carrying out the various processes differ from plant to plant, but the general flow of the operation is based on the five steps listed above. Because of the first two steps, the method is referred to as the *chop and leach* system.

The liquid wastes generated by the reprocessing operation constitute HLW. When the first reprocessing plants were set up, there was no specific plan for the final disposal of these, mostly liquid, HLWs. They were just stored on site for the most part. With the passage of the two congressional acts dealing with radioactive wastes (see Chapters 9 and 10), the handling of the wastes is considered an integral part of any reprocessing operation. The HLW, as well as any low-level waste produced, will have to be treated and disposed of in accordance with these acts and their amendments.

The first reprocessing operations were set up for the extraction of plutonium needed for the U.S. weapons program. Many methods for plutonium separation were considered, but solvent extraction was selected as the most suitable. Different solvents were used in the United States and other countries. In 1951, a plant began operation in Hanford, Washington, that employed a well-known industrial solvent called *hexone* for the reduction and oxidation of plutonium. The process became known as REDOX. The British had developed a slightly different process, called BUTEX, named after the solvent used (butex di-butoxy-diethyl-ether). Both REDOX and BUTEX suffered from chemical engineering–type problems. To avoid those problems, a new process was developed in the United States that became known as PUREX (Pu-U recovery extraction).

Large reprocessing plants based on the PUREX process started operating in 1954 at Savannah River, and in 1956 at Hanford. As far as it is known, all reprocessing plants in the world employ variations of the PUREX process.[6,7] The recent debate over proliferation issues brought forward many ideas for more proliferation-resistant reprocessing processes.[8–12] A reprocessing plant that is properly designed recycles chemicals and other materials used—to the maximum extent possible—to reduce costs and the amount of wastes leaving the plant.

7.4.2 The PUREX Method of Reprocessing

PUREX uses a solvent called TBP (tri-n-butyl phosphate) and liquid-liquid extraction principles, combined with oxidation-reduction chemical reactions (Fig. 7.1). After the fuel is chopped, it is dissolved in nitric acid. The heavy elements go into solution, leaving behind the cladding. The nitric acid solution,

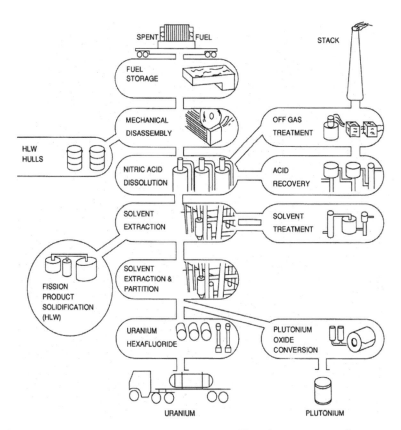

FIGURE 7.1 The PUREX reprocessing process. Chopping, storage, and recovery of material are batch processes; the solvent extraction requires continuous operation.

which contains the uranium and plutonium, is processed through a solvent extraction process that separates fission products and TRU elements from the uranium and plutonium. After that, uranium and plutonium are separated by using a chemical that reduces plutonium to an organic-insoluble state but not the uranium. More details about PUREX are given in Ref. 13.

When the fuel dissolves into the nitric acid, gases such as ^3H, krypton, xenon, iodine, CO_2, nitrogen oxides, and steam are released. The gases are directed to a gas-treatment system where some are stored for later treatment and/or release, and others are recycled (nitrogen oxides again become nitric acid). Effective tritium containment is always questionable. It should be mentioned that a reprocessing plant has an elaborate ventilation system and operates under negative pressure.

The uranium is first recovered as uranyl nitrate $[UO_2(NO_3)2.6H_2O]$, which is subsequently converted into UF_6 if it is to be sent to an enrichment plant. Plutonium is recovered first as nitrate $[Pu(NO_3)_4]$, which is later converted into oxide (PuO_2).

7.4.3 The Pyrometallurgical Method of Reprocessing

A reprocessing method developed by scientists at Argonne National Laboratory may replace PUREX in the future. As of 2011, pyroprocessing was still under research and development. Instead of a solvent extraction, the recovery of uranium and plutonium from irradiated fuel is achieved by a pyrometallurgical process based on an electrorefining operation.[14,15] The first step of this operation is the dismantling of the fuel assemblies and removal of the cladding. The second step is dissolution of the fuel into a molten halide salt, and the third step is the electrorefining of this liquid mixture. The molten fuel is dissolved in cadmium and placed in a crucible with a molten salt as the electrolyte. For selective removal of uranium, a low-carbon steel shaft is used as the cathode. Only uranium is deposited on the cathode because chemical reactions with the halide prevent the deposition of plutonium. For removal of uranium and plutonium together, a cadmium cathode is utilized.

The recovery of uranium and plutonium by this process is a one-step operation, done at a temperature of $\sim500°C$. The method has the added advantage that the actinides follow the U-Pu mixture, thus offering two additional benefits. First, the new MOX fuel is highly radioactive and, therefore, extremely hazardous to would-be thieves or saboteurs. Second, the radioactive wastes left behind (essentially only fission products) decay faster than the actinides; for this reason, the number of years during which these wastes are dangerous to man is considerably smaller than with the actinides included.

7.4.4 Proliferation-Resistant Processes

All of the so-called "proliferation-resistant" reprocessing proposals have as a common element the nonseparation of the reprocessing streams into pure plutonium (especially ^{239}Pu) or weapons-grade uranium. Instead, the streams of the solvent extraction process are mixtures of fissile elements and others (fission products and transuranics). Thus, the argument goes, the would-be thief or saboteur would have to do additional work before the material is ready to be used for the manufacturing of a nuclear explosive. Clearly, none of the methods can be 100% proliferation proof (see also Section 7.2).

Many processes, studied by various groups, have been proposed, with names like CIVEX,[8] APEX,[9] coprocessing,[10] or just proliferation resistant.[11,12] The term *spiking* is used in some proposals and refers to the mixing of the fissile materials with nuclides having high specific activity, resulting in a material that is so radioactive or reaches such high temperatures that it is practically impossible to handle. The CIVEX process, for example, spikes the plutonium with fission products (gamma emitters). Another spiking agent that has been considered is ^{238}Pu, an alpha emitter. Calculations show that the addition of 5% of ^{238}Pu to fissile materials having the concentration needed for a nuclear weapon will create a surface temperature of about 875°C. Since the melting point of plastic explosives is ~200°C, it would be impossible to bring together the fissile material with a conventional explosive to trigger the mixture and achieve a nuclear explosion of relatively high explosive yield; such a device will "fizzle" and is called a dirty bomb.

7.4.5 Materials Accountability of Reprocessing Plants

Two types of accountability/safety are imposed on reprocessing plants. One is to avoid criticality anywhere in the stream of the operation; the other is safeguards accountability.

Avoidance of criticality is obvious. The facility should be designed in such a way that criticality is physically impossible under any possible concentration of fissile material. One way to achieve this goal is to use containers that result in neutron leakage–prone geometries. One possible design is shown in Fig. 7.2.

Safeguards accountability is the result of a government's ratification of and adherence to the NPT. As a result, civilian reprocessing plants operating in countries that ratified the NPT are subject to international safeguards inspection and control. It is interesting to note that, as far as criticality is concerned, a design is used to ensure that an unknown amount of fissile material does not accumulate in a certain location; but as far as safeguards are concerned, the aim is at making sure that an unknown amount of material is not removed from the system.

In all reprocessing plants, very strict rules apply for the accountability of all fissile inventory at all times. From the practical point of view, it is impossible to have 100% accountability at all times. The difference between the book inventory and a physical inventory is referred to as *MUF* (material

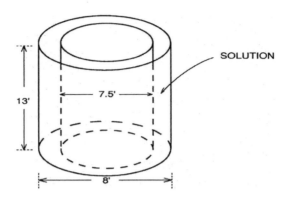

FIGURE 7.2 A sketch of a container to be used in a reprocessing plant for the avoidance of criticality. The solution is stored in the space between the two cylinders.

unaccounted for). No fixed value is assigned to MUF, but every plant should be able to justify its current MUF value, using statistical methods.[16]

7.4.6 Reprocessing Experience in the United States

Reprocessing experience in the United States consists primarily of defense-related reprocessing operations using the PUREX process.

Of the private (commercial) reprocessing plants constructed in the United States, only one, the Nuclear Fuel Services (NFS) Plant at West Valley, New York, ever operated. The NFS plant operated from 1967 until 1972 and reprocessed 600 tons of used nuclear fuel. Uranyl nitrate $[UO_2(NO_3)2.6H_2O]$ was returned to the Atomic Energy Commission (the precursor to the NRC) and was converted to UF_6, that is, its quality was good enough for conversion. Some uranium metal was also produced for government programs. Plutonium stored at the plant was in the form of $Pu(NO_3)_4$.

In 1972, NFS closed the plant to incorporate modifications that would make it commercially viable and satisfy newly established federal regulations. NFS was planning to expand the capacity to 750 ton/yr and add facilities that would convert the uranyl nitrate to UF_6 and plutonium nitrate to PuO_2, and also handle the radioactive wastes in such a way that they would be ready for shipment to and disposal in a federal repository. But, in 1976 NFS announced its decision not to reopen the plant because it represented an uneconomical venture.

General Electric Company constructed a reprocessing plant at Morris, Illinois. A construction permit was granted in 1967 and the plant was scheduled to start operating in 1971. But because of technical problems (e.g., repairs in high-radiation areas could not be performed by remote control) and the lack of a pressing need for reprocessing, the Morris plant never began operation. It is now used as a used fuel storage facility.

Allied-General received a construction permit to build a reprocessing plant at Barnwell, South Carolina, which was supposed to be the first truly commercial reprocessing plant in the United States. When it was ready for operation, it would have had facilities to convert the recovered uranium into UF_6 and plutonium nitrate to PuO_2 and facilities to handle the radioactive wastes. The company applied for an operating license and the hearings for the license continued until 1976. When President Carter announced an indefinite ban on reprocessing, the NRC terminated the licensing proceedings. Financial considerations precluded the use of the facility even for storage of used fuel—the tax write-off to Allied-General outweighed any potential income from used fuel storage.

7.4.7 Reprocessing Experience Outside the United States

Reprocessing activities are more prevalent in Western Europe and Japan than in the United States. Russia and China also have reprocessing plants, but very little relevant information exists in the open literature on this subject. For this reason, activities in these two countries are not discussed further.

France is the most active Western European nation in the area of reprocessing. The French reprocess used nuclear fuel and recycle the Pu as MOX, which they burn in their LWRs. When their two breeder reactors, PHENIX and SUPERPHENIX, were operating, reprocessing was necessary for their fuel as well.

The first reprocessing plant in France was constructed at Marcoule and was designated as UP-1 (Usine de Plutonium 1); it was commissioned in 1958 and was initially dedicated to defense activities, which ended in 1994. UP-1 reprocessed used nuclear fuel from gas-cooled graphite reactors (Electricité de France [EdF] owned and operated six such reactors) until its closing in 1997. The experience gained at UP-1 was used in the construction of the second plant at La Hague facility, designated UP-2; UP-2 was commissioned in 1966 and continued, originally, the reprocessing of metallic fuel from gas-cooled reactors (GCRs). In the early 1970s, UP-2 was modified in order to reprocess used fuel from LWRs (by that time France had abandoned GCRs in favor of PWRs). It was also planned for UP-2 to reprocess fuel from abroad. The initial design capacity of UP-2 was 400 thM/yr. In the 1980s, another reprocessing plant was built, designated UP-3, with the purpose of exclusively reprocessing foreign fuel. UP-3 started operations in 1990 and was entirely financed by the countries that were planning to have their fuel reprocessed by it. At about the same time, another reprocessing plant was designed and built, implementing the advanced technologies used in UP-3. This plant, designated UP-2-800, started operating in 1994 with an initial capacity of 800 thM/yr; later its capacity was increased to 1000 thM/yr.

The British started reprocessing at Windscale in 1952 in a plant designated as B-204, with a second plant beginning operation in 1964 (B-205). Initially, only metallic fuel was reprocessed, but in 1969, after appropriate modifications, oxide fuel was also handled. From 1969 until 1973, B-204 reprocessed about 100 tons of oxide fuel. Modifications were completed in 1976, allowing an increase of capacity by a factor of 3.

The experience at Windscale was so satisfactory that the United Kingdom decided to build a plant at Sellafield to reprocess irradiated fuel from thermal reactors. The plant, known as THORP (Thermal Oxide Reprocessing Plant), was completed in 1994 and started operating in 1997. It was designed for a final capacity of 1200 ton/yr. During its first 10 years of operation, the plant was scheduled to reprocess 7000 tons of used nuclear fuel, most of it coming from abroad. In 2005, THORP developed a major radioactive leak. Although the leak was contained within the plant and posed no danger to the workers or the public, operations were halted. At the time of the accident, 6000 tons of used fuel had been reprocessed at THORP. As of 2011 there were conflicting reports about the future of THORP in terms of whether it would continue to operate or be shut down.

Belgium has the Eurochemic plant, a small demonstration facility built by the 13 members of the Nuclear Energy Agency of the Organisation for Economic Co-operation and Development. This plant cannot be considered a full-size commercial facility because of its limited capacity and its mission to reprocess a wide variety of fuels.

Japan has two reprocessing plants. There is an experimental pilot plant at Tokai Mura with a capacity of 300 thM/yr. Construction started in 1971, and it produced the first Pu in 1977. It was transformed into an experimental facility in October 2006.

The commercial-size plant is located at Rokkasho. Construction started in 1993 and the first active test was performed in 2006. The plant has a design capacity of 800 thM/yr. To date, 425 tons of LWR used fuel have been processed. The Rokkasho plant includes a vitrification facility for treatment of liquid HLWs.

India is operating several reprocessing plants. The most important ones are the plant at Kalpakkam with a 100 thM/yr capacity, which started up in 1998, and the plant at Tarapur, also with a 100 thM/yr capacity and a 2011 start-up date. Another plant is under construction at Kalpakkam.

7.5 Plutonium and Uranium Recycling in LWRs

7.5.1 Materials Flow with Recycling

The once-through fuel cycle is not actually a cycle but an open-ended process. One starts with natural uranium, which is enriched to 3% to 5% in ^{235}U and then fabricated into fuel assemblies. In the reactor, it produces energy at the rate of 40,000 to 50,000 MWd/tU of fuel. It is then discharged and stored as used fuel. With recycling, the used fuel is reprocessed and the uranium and plutonium are recovered (Fig. 7.3). The plutonium is sent to a

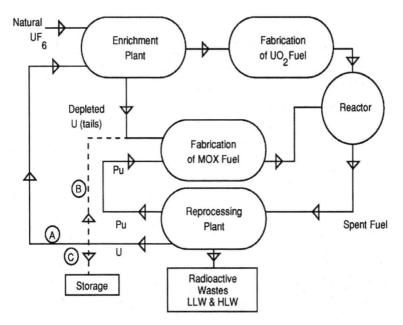

FIGURE 7.3 Materials flow in a nuclear fuel cycle with recycling of uranium and plutonium. The reprocessed uranium may be reenriched (line A), used for MOX fuel fabrication (line B), or stored (line C; the most likely option for this reprocessed U).

fuel fabrication facility, where it is made into MOX fuel along with uranium that may be coming from two sources: The first is depleted, unirradiated uranium from the tails of the enrichment process; the second is uranium recovered from the used fuel (line B in Fig. 7.3). The uranium recovered from the used fuel may be sent to the enrichment plant (line A in Fig. 7.3), where together with fresh uranium ore it is enriched and then sent to a fuel fabrication plant (UO_2 fuel), or it may be simply stored. The most likely option for the reprocessed uranium is storage. With recycling, the reactor core will consist of a mixture of UO_2 and MOX fuel.

7.5.2 Natural Uranium Savings Due to Uranium and Plutonium Recycling

The following notation will be used in developing the equations for uranium savings:

x_p = enrichment of fresh fuel (weight fraction)[b]

x_w = tails (weight fraction)

[b] Usually, enrichment is expressed in weight percent. In this section only, enrichment is expressed as a weight fraction in order to simplify the form of Eqs. (7.4) to (7.14).

x_s = enrichment of uranium in used fuel (weight fraction)

x_f = amount of ^{235}U in uranium feed (weight fraction)

p = fissile Pu to ^{235}U neutronic equivalence (0.8 g ^{235}U per 1 g Pu)

fPu = mass of fissile plutonium

s = kilograms of fPu recovered per kilogram of used fuel

u = kilograms of used fuel per kilogram of fresh fuel

M = kilograms of enriched uranium needed per refueling

FF = feed factor, with feed being natural uranium [see Ch. 3, Eq. (3.6)]

FF_s = feed factor with feed being uranium recovered from used fuel

SF = SWU factor for natural uranium being enriched [see Eq. (3.11)]

SF_s = SWU factor for uranium from used fuel being enriched.

The savings in natural uranium due to plutonium recycling is calculated first. Consider 1 kg of uranium fuel with enrichment x_p. That kilogram contains x_p kg of ^{235}U. If we desire to replace this fuel with MOX consisting of plutonium and uranium tails, it is necessary to calculate the mass of plutonium that establishes the following equivalence:

$$x_p \text{ (kg of } ^{235}\text{U)} \quad \leftrightarrow \quad x_w \text{ kg of } ^{235}\text{U in uranium tails}$$
$$+ \left[(x_p - x_w)/p \right] \text{ (kg } f\text{Pu mass)}$$

(natural uranium fuel) (MOX)

If natural uranium is used as feed, FF kg of natural uranium are needed for every kilogram of fuel enriched to x_p in ^{235}U. Therefore, if one fabricates MOX fuel,

$$(x_p - x_w)/p \text{ kg of } f\text{Pu save } FF \text{ kg of natural uranium}$$

That is, the savings is $FF/(x_p - x_w)/p$, or

$$\frac{FF * p}{x_p - x_w} \text{ (kgU saved/kg} f\text{Pu)} \tag{7.4}$$

Because the amount of Pu in used fuel is s(kg fPu/kg used fuel), the U saved per kilogram of fuel discharged is

$$\frac{s * FF * p}{x_p - x_w} \text{ (kgU saved/kg of fuel discharged)} \tag{7.5}$$

or, since the used fuel contains u kg of uranium per kilogram of fresh fuel, we have

$$\frac{u * s * FF * p}{x_p - x_w} \text{ (kgU saved/kg fuel initially charged in the reactor)} \tag{7.6}$$

Dividing by FF (kilograms of natural uranium feed per kilogram of fresh fuel), the result is

$$\frac{u * s * p}{x_p - x_w} \text{ (kgU saved/kg natural U feed)} \tag{7.7}$$

If losses in fabrication, ℓ_f, and in reprocessing, ℓ_r, are included, Eq. (7.7) takes the following form:

$$(1 - \ell_r)(1 - \ell_f) \frac{u * s * p}{x_p - x_w} \tag{7.8}$$

■ *Example 7.2:* What is the savings in uranium feed if plutonium recycling is practiced under the following fuel specifications? Neglect fabrication and reprocessing losses.

$x_p = 0.038$ (3.8%)

$x_w = 0.002$ (0.2%)

$u = 0.93$

$p = 0.8$ g ^{235}U/g fPu

$s = 6.5$ g fPu/kg of used fuel

Answer: Using Eq. (7.7), the savings are

$$(0.93 * 0.0065 * 0.8)/(0.038 - 0.002) = 0.134 = \sim 13\%$$

Notice that in using Eq. (7.7) or (7.8), there is no need to show units since all of the numerical quantities involved are ratios.   ■

Consider next uranium recycling as well; that is, the uranium recovered from the used fuel is sent back to the enrichment plant as feed. This uranium contains a fraction x_s of ^{235}U. For the LWR fuels used today, the value of x_s is between 0.6% and 0.8%. Since natural uranium contains 0.711% ^{235}U, uranium from used fuel with $x_s > 0.711$ is better than natural feed for enrichment.

If the enriched uranium introduced into the core is M kg, the mass of uranium in the used fuel is $u * M$. This mass of uranium will produce, if used as feed in an enrichment plant,

$$(u * M)/FF_s \text{ kg of enriched uranium}$$

Using natural uranium as feed, one would need

$$(u * M/FF_s) * FF \text{ kg of natural U} \tag{7.9}$$

to produce the same kilograms of enriched fuel. The amount of uranium given by Eq. (7.9) represents the savings from M kg of fuel charged to the reactor. The savings per mass of natural uranium feed is

$$\frac{(u * M * FF)/FF_s}{M * FF} = \frac{u}{FF_s} = \frac{u(x_s - x_w)}{x_p - x_w} \tag{7.10}$$

If losses in reprocessing, ℓ_r, in conversion, ℓ_c, and in fabrication, ℓ_f, are included, Eq. (7.10) takes the following form, where typical values for all losses $\ell_i | i = c, r, f$ are less than 1%:

$$(1 - \ell_r)(1 - \ell_c)(1 - \ell_f) \frac{u(x_s - x_w)}{x_p - x_w} \tag{7.11}$$

The total natural uranium savings from Pu and U recycling is (without losses in reprocessing, etc.)

$$\text{Natural U savings} = \frac{u * s * p}{x_p - x_w} + \frac{u(x_s - x_w)}{x_p - x_w} \tag{7.12}$$

If losses are included, Eq. (7.12) takes the form

$$\text{Natural U savings} = (1 - \ell_r)(1 - \ell_f) \frac{u * s * p}{x_p - x_w}$$

$$+ (1 - \ell_r)(1 - \ell_f)(1 - \ell_c) \frac{u(x_s - x_w)}{x_p - x_w} \tag{7.13}$$

■ *Example 7.3:* What is the total uranium savings from plutonium and uranium recycling, assuming that the used fuel contains 0.8% ^{235}U? The rest of the data needed are the same as in Example 7.2.

Answer: Using Eq. (7.10), the savings due to uranium recycling alone is

$$0.93(0.008 - 0.002)/(0.038 - 0.002) = 0.155 = \sim 15\%$$

The total savings is

$$0.134 + 0.155 = 0.289 = \sim 29\% \quad ■$$

The equations presented in this section for uranium savings do not take into account the effect of the lighter isotopes ^{232}U, ^{234}U, and ^{236}U that are present in used fuel. All of these isotopes are neutron absorbers (see Section 7.7).

7.5.3 SWU Savings Due to Uranium and Plutonium Recycling

Assuming M kg of fresh fuel are needed, the number of SWUs required is equal to $M * SF$. Utilizing recycling of plutonium and uranium, one needs MF kg of natural uranium feed, where

$$MF = M * FF \left[1 - \frac{u * s * p}{x_p - x_w} - \frac{u(x_s - x_w)}{x_p - x_w} \right] \tag{7.14}$$

In Eq. (7.14) and the rest in this section the equations used do not include the losses from conversion, reprocessing, etc., because the losses are small; the losses are shown correctly in Eqs. (7.8), (7.11), and (7.13). The amount of uranium given by Eq. (7.14) will produce MF/FF kg of fresh enriched fuel, consuming in the process $(MF/FF)SF$ SWUs. To this number, one should add the number of SWUs needed to enrich the uranium recovered from the used fuel, which is equal to $[(u * M)/FF_s]SF_s$. The total number of SWUs is, therefore,

$$MF * SF/FF + u * M * SF_s/FF_s$$

The SWU savings, as a fraction of the number needed without recycling, is

$$\frac{M * SF - \left(MF * \dfrac{SF}{FF} + u * M * \dfrac{SF_s}{FF_s} \right)}{M * SF} \tag{7.15}$$

which after some algebra becomes

$$\text{SWU savings} = \frac{u}{x_p - x_w}\left[s * p + (x_s - x_w)\left(1 - \frac{SF_s}{SF}\right)\right] \qquad (7.16)$$

■ *Example 7.4:* What is the SWU savings, as a result of plutonium and uranium recycling, using the data of Examples 7.2 and 7.3?

Answer: The SWU factors are [see Eq. (3.11)] $SF = 6.090$ and $SF_s = 5.467$. Using Eq. (7.16),

$$\left(\frac{0.93}{0.038 - 0.002}\right)\left[0.0065 * 0.8 + (0.008 - 0.002)\left(1 - \frac{5.467}{6.090}\right)\right]$$

$$= 0.15 = 15\% \quad ■$$

Because of the presence of ^{232}U, ^{234}U, and ^{236}U in recycled uranium (see Section 7.7), it is very likely that the reprocessed uranium will not be used, especially in LWRs. In that case, the savings equation based on recycling Pu alone becomes

$$\text{U savings} = \text{SWU savings} = \frac{u * s * p}{x_p - x_w} \qquad (7.17)$$

7.6 Characteristics of a Reactor Core with MOX Fuel

When a fraction of an LWR core, normally fueled with UO_2, is replaced by MOX fuel, many characteristics of the core will change because of the different physical, chemical, and neutronic properties of the MOX fuel relative to UO_2. During the past 20 years, many papers appeared dealing with the use of MOX fuel in LWRs as well as in breeder cores.[17-25] In general, the results of test assemblies irradiated in LWRs or in fast reactors, like the Experimental Breeder Reactor II (EBR-II) or the Fast Flux Test Facility, show that mixtures of UO_2 and PuO_2 behave in much the same way, physically and chemically, as pure UO_2. The potential differences are minimized by replacing only a fraction of the UO_2 with MOX fuel. Much closer attention, however, must be paid to the neutronic differences between UO_2 and MOX fuels.

There are two reasons for the neutronic differences. One is that the MOX fuel contains not one but many plutonium isotopes with relative concentrations that depend on the origin of the plutonium (recycled from LWR fuel or recovered from an FBR blanket), the time period during which the plutonium was stored, and whether or not the plutonium was recycled one or more times. For example, the relative concentrations[25] of plutonium that was burned to 33,000 MWd/t, reprocessed 3 years after discharge, and then stored

TABLE 7.1

Values of Important Neutronic Parameters
for ^{235}U and ^{239}Pu

Parameter	^{235}U	^{239}Pu
σ_a (2200 m/s)	682 b	1019 b
(Spectrum average)	430 b	915 b
σ_f (2200 m/s)	584 b	748 b
(Spectrum average)	365 b	610 b
η (2200 m/s)	2.07	2.11
(Spectrum average)	2.07	1.90
β (delayed neutron fraction)	0.0065	0.0021
l (neutron lifetime)	47 μs	27 μs

for 2 years are 1.8% ^{238}Pu, 58.3% ^{239}Pu, 23.3% ^{240}Pu, 11% ^{241}Pu, and 5.6% ^{242}Pu. If it is burned in a subsequent cycle, again to 33,000 MWd/t, this discharged fuel would have the following approximate composition: 2% ^{238}Pu, 46.4% ^{239}Pu, 27.4% ^{240}Pu, 16.3% ^{241}Pu, and 7.9% ^{242}Pu. Notice that the fraction of fissile plutonium (^{239}Pu plus ^{241}Pu) is 69.3% in LWR-reprocessed fuel, but it becomes 62.7% after it is irradiated one more time. Obviously, for LWRs only the two fissile isotopes are useful; the others act as neutron poisons. This reduction of fissile plutonium, as irradiation increases, is well known to weapons designers and is one of the reasons why the civilian nuclear fuel cycle is proliferation resistant to a certain extent.

The second reason for the differences between UO$_2$ and MOX fuel comes from the values of important neutron parameters like cross sections, neutrons emitted per fission, etc. Table 7.1 provides the values of the most important parameters for core neutron physics.

The changes of the absorption and fission cross sections and of η, as a function of neutron energy, are shown in Figs. 7.4, 7.5, and 7.6. Beyond the energy region shown by these figures, there is a significant overlap of resonance structure in uranium and plutonium isotopes that complicates the neutronic calculations. Let us examine now, one by one, the significance of the values for the parameters shown in Table 7.1.

As a result of the larger absorption cross section of ^{239}Pu in the thermal region, the reactivity worth of the control rods and of dissolved boron (in PWRs) is reduced. To ameliorate this effect, one should place MOX rods away from control rods. The higher fission cross section of ^{239}Pu will tend to produce power peaks. One way to avoid this effect is to place the MOX rods away from the water gap (where the thermal flux is high).

The fact that the average value of η is less for ^{239}Pu than for ^{235}U makes the former worth less (in the neutronic sense) than the latter. The existence of many resonances in ^{239}Pu cross sections causes larger reactivity changes, due to the temperature-caused Doppler effect, than those of ^{235}U. Both of these effects would require more fissile plutonium mass than with

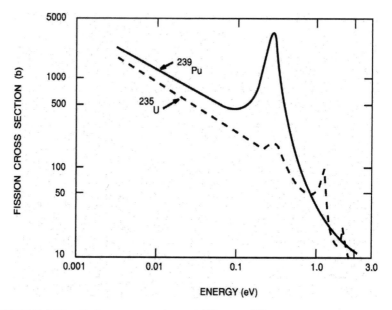

FIGURE 7.4 The fission cross sections of ^{235}U and ^{239}Pu, as a function of energy, for $E < 3$ eV.

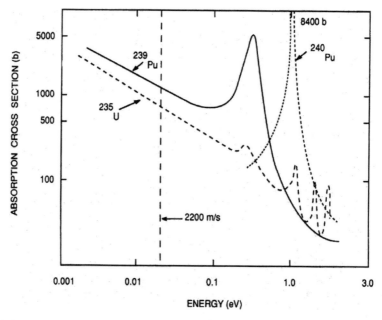

FIGURE 7.5 The absorption cross sections of ^{235}U and ^{239}Pu, as a function of energy, for $E < 3$ eV. Part of σ_a for ^{240}Pu is also shown.

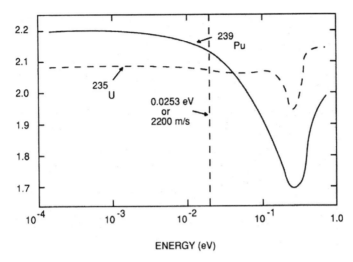

FIGURE 7.6 The value of η for ^{235}U and ^{239}Pu as a function of neutron energy.

UO_2 fuel to obtain the same excess reactivity in the core. Luckily, the reactivity decrease with burnup is slower in MOX fuel than in UO_2. In fact, the difference is such that, to achieve the same burnup, one needs less excess reactivity with MOX than with UO_2 fuel.

The lower value of the delayed neutron fraction β is of concern for the safe operation of the reactor. A lower value for β means that it takes less reactivity to reach prompt criticality. The main method of alleviating this potential problem is to limit the amount of MOX in the core. The difference in prompt neutron lifetimes causes similar kinetics concerns.

In France, the decision has been made (1) to restrict the amount of MOX in the core to no more than 30% to ensure kinetics safety and (2) to place the MOX rods, within an assembly, in two or three zones with different enrichments. The French report three enrichments as shown in Table 7.2. This type of zoning results in the flattening of the power distribution.

7.7 Problems with Recycled Uranium

The problems encountered in recycling reprocessed uranium stem from three isotopes that, although present in relatively small concentrations, present adverse effects when handling such uranium. These isotopes are ^{232}U, ^{234}U, and ^{236}U. Table 7.3 gives half lives and other information regarding these and other isotopes found in reprocessed uranium and plutonium.

Uranium-234 is a tiny fraction of natural uranium. During enrichment, ^{234}U follows the ^{235}U; therefore, with repeated enrichments the fraction [^{234}U/(total U)] increases. Also, ^{234}U has higher specific activity than either ^{238}U or ^{235}U, but the main problem is its ability to absorb neutrons.

TABLE 7.2
Enrichments of Fissile Plutonium Fuel Rods within the Same Assembly

	Enrichment	
Zone	Fissile Pu (%)	Total Pu (%)
Exterior	3.60	5.20
Intermediate	5.05	7.30
Central	6.05	9.40

Uranium-232 is a daughter of ^{236}Pu, which, in turn, is produced by the chain shown in Fig. 7.7. Uranium-232 is also a neutron absorber.

Plutonium-236 decays, first to ^{232}U, and then through successive alpha decays becomes ^{208}Tl, which, with a half life of 3.1 min, emits a penetrating gamma with energy 2.6 MeV.

Uranium-236 is produced by the n-γ reaction with ^{235}U and electron capture (EC) in ^{236}Np. Its main problem is its neutron-absorbing ability. An environmentally troublesome isotope, because of its long half life, is ^{237}Np ($T_{1/2} \sim 2 \times 10^6$ yr); in addition to the path shown in Fig. 7.7, ^{237}Np is also produced by the reaction ^{238}U$(n,2n)$ ^{237}U $\rightarrow$ ^{237}Np.

The presence of these three isotopes makes the reprocessed uranium more difficult to handle and also, more importantly, necessitates the reenrichment of such uranium to a ^{235}U fraction higher than that required with natural uranium feed. Because of these difficulties, the use of reprocessed uranium in LWRs is questionable.

7.8 Problems with Recycled Plutonium

Problems with recycled plutonium come from the relatively increased activity of all of the isotopes involved and, more importantly, from the change

TABLE 7.3
Troublesome Isotopes in Reprocessed U and Pu

Isotope	Total Half Life (yr)	Spontaneous Fission Half Life (yr)	Undesirable Features
^{232}U	72	8×10^{13}	γ-radiation
^{234}U	2.45×10^5	2×10^{16}	n-absorber
^{236}U	2.39×10^7	2×10^{16}	n-absorber
^{236}Pu	2.85	3.5×10^9	Leads to ^{232}U, heat
^{238}Pu	86.4	4.9×10^{10}	n-source (spont. fiss.)
^{240}Pu	6,580	1.4×10^{11}	n-absorber, n-source (spont. fiss.)
^{242}Pu	3.79×10^5	7×10^{10}	n-absorber, n-source (spont. fiss.)
^{241}Am	458	2×10^{14}	γ-radiation, n-absorber

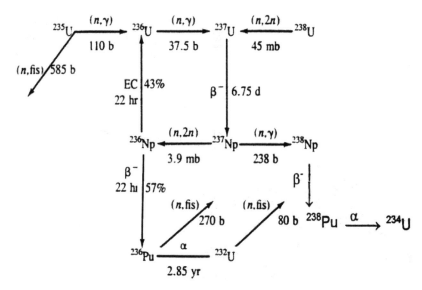

FIGURE 7.7 Production modes of the most important isotopes encountered with recycled uranium.

with time of the relative isotopic composition of such plutonium. This change is, of course, due to the different half lives of the isotopes involved. Another minor problem is the difference in isotopic composition of plutonium originating from a breeder reactor versus that from an LWR. Figure 7.8 shows the chain of TRU elements formed in a fission reactor fueled with uranium; Fig. 7.9 shows the buildup of the main plutonium isotopes as a function of burnup.[26]

One isotope, ^{236}Pu and its decay scheme, was already mentioned in Section 7.7. One of the most bothersome isotopes, ^{208}Tl, is several decay steps away from ^{236}Pu and for this reason it is not important in freshly purified plutonium. It builds up, however, with age. Plutonium with just 50 ppb of ^{236}Pu would produce a dose rate of 1.5 mrem/h behind 0.5 in. of lead after 1 year.[19] The concentration of ^{236}Pu depends, of course, on the irradiation history of the fuel and its age. In any case, the typical concentration is of the order of 20 to 100 ppb.[23]

Plutonium-238 is produced through the reaction $(^{237}$Np $+ n)$ and the subsequent beta decay of the ^{238}Np. It is a strong heat source because of alpha emission. If the concentration of ^{238}Pu is considerable, its neutron emission (from spontaneous fission) may present a problem. Plutonium-240 is a neutron source because of its spontaneous fission. It is also a neutron absorber.

A daughter of ^{241}Pu, ^{241}Am, is, through its own daughters, a source of many gamma rays and also a neutron absorber. Over time, stored plutonium

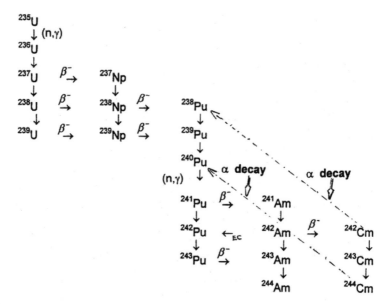

FIGURE 7.8 The chain of TRU elements formed in a fission reactor fueled with uranium.

loses its fissile potential because ^{241}Pu decays into ^{241}Am. Plutonium coming from LWR fuel irradiated to typical burnups of 35,000 MWd/t must be utilized no later than 3 years after discharge. Otherwise, because of the ^{241}Am buildup, purification is necessary before it can be used in MOX fuel for LWRs.

Details about the use of recycled Pu are given in a five-volume report produced by NEA/OECD[26] titled *Physics of Pu Recycling* and in a companion report[27] titled *Management of Separated Pu—The Technical Options*.

7.9 Experience with MOX Fuel Used in LWRs

In the United States, experience with MOX fuel comes from testing programs that were flourishing before 1976. In the course of these tests, MOX assemblies have been irradiated in the EBR-II and in several LWRs. The objectives of those experiments were to verify the values of physical and neutronic properties during irradiation and to check, after discharge, the condition of the fuel and also measure its isotopic composition. With the change in government policy in 1976–1977, MOX-related activities lost importance. Even after the government declaration in 1981 that reprocessing would be allowed, there was no incentive for the private sector in the United States to consider recycling. Today there are plans to place MOX assemblies manufactured with weapons Pu (see next section) in some LWRs.[28]

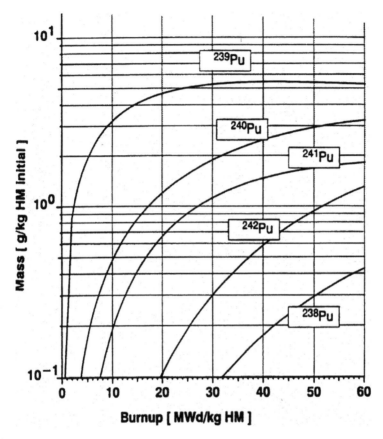

FIGURE 7.9 The buildup of Pu isotopes as a function of burnup in a PWR with initial enrichment of 4%. (Courtesy of NEA/OECD.[26])

France, more than any other country, is using MOX in its LWRs. When it became apparent in the 1980s that the breeder program had stalled, the decision was to make MOX and load it into the operating PWRs. Implementation of this decision was helped by the fact that reprocessing capacity was available (see Section 7.4.7). Reprocessing and nuclear electricity generation were completely owned by the French government (EdF); for this reason the decision and its implementation were relatively easy tasks. An additional reason given by the French for reprocessing and recycling of the LWR used fuel is their decision not to place intact LWR used assemblies in a geologic repository; their plan is for the repository to accept vitrified HLW. A MOX fabrication facility, called MELOX, was constructed in Marcoule with a capacity of 115 ton/yr; MELOX started operating in 1995 and delivered the first MOX assemblies to EdF in 1996.

In Germany there also was strong commitment to reprocessing and recycling of LWR used fuel until 1998. Then, the newly elected government came to power with the promise to shut down all nuclear power plants. The shutdown date was not firm and no plants were shut down until 2011. After the Fukushima accident in Japan in 2011, the German government announced that all its nuclear plants would be shut down by 2022.

Belgium was active in MOX development and use from the very beginning, in cooperation with France. The two countries manufactured MOX assemblies in two small plants, one in Cadarache, France (started in 1970; capacity 15 ton/yr), and the other in Dessel, Belgium (started in 1973; capacity 35 ton/yr). A decision to use MOX in two LWRs was made in 1993.

In the United Kingdom, British Nuclear Fuel Limited (BNFL) constructed the Thermal Oxide Reprocessing Plant (THORP) and started preliminary tests in 1994. BNFL built a commercial-size plant for the fabrication of MOX assemblies, next to THORP, called the Sellafield MOX Plant (SMP), now owned by the Nuclear Decommissioning Authority (NDA). The SMP was placed next to THORP for security reasons. Used fuel will enter THORP and MOX assemblies will leave SMP. The SMP was completed in 1997; it had agreements to make MOX for Germany and Japan. In 2011, as a result of the Fukushima accident, contracts with both countries fell through and NDA decided to close SMP.

In Switzerland, considerable experience exists with MOX assemblies. The Swiss, like most of the Europeans, believe in the benefits of reprocessing and recycling. There are no plans, however, to construct reprocessing plants in Switzerland. The Swiss plan to use the reprocessing services of Belgium and France.

In Japan, MOX demonstration assemblies have been loaded into BWR and PWR reactors. The MOX assemblies were manufactured in France; Japan also has an agreement with Belgium for making MOX assemblies.

China is also interested in MOX fuel fabrication and use. In 2010, it was announced that China has signed an agreement with Belgium for MOX fuel fabrication.

7.10 Recycling/Burning of Minor Actinides

Minor actinides (MAs) are the TRU elements except Pu that are generated in used nuclear fuel after successive neutron absorptions and decays (see, e.g., Fig. 7.8). The MAs include Np, Am, Cm, Bk, Cf, Es, and Fm. The most important ones are Np, Am, Cm, and Cf.

The suggestion to recycle the MAs has more to do with the disposal of HLW (see Chapter 9) than with improvements in the fuel cycle. Among the MAs are some isotopes with relatively long half lives that, if left in the HLW, will dictate the design and constraints for a geological repository. On the other hand, if MAs are recycled and burned, the isotopes left in the

HLW for eventual disposal will have much shorter half lives, thus shortening considerably the number of years during which radioactive releases from the repository will be of concern.

The burning or transmutation of MAs is based on the ability of fast neutrons to split them by fission into lighter and short-lived isotopes. The neutron absorption cross section decreases with neutron energy for many MAs. However, the ratio of fission to capture increases; therefore, with sufficiently high neutron energy, it may be possible to destroy by fission most of the MAs exposed to such a neutron spectrum.[28–31] A fast neutron spectrum may become available either from a fast nuclear reactor or an accelerator-driven subcritical (ADS) system. In an ADS system protons are accelerated to ~800 to 1000 MeV, hit a target, and create fast (MeV) neutrons by spallation reactions. The accelerator is surrounded by a blanket that forms the subcritical reactor; the blanket contains the MAs along with some fissile material.[32,33] The fast neutrons generated by the spallation reactions are transported into the blanket where they destroy the MAs by fissioning them. There is considerable global interest in ADS systems.[33]

7.11 Factors Affecting Implementation of Reprocessing and Recycling

Whether or not reprocessing and recycling will be implemented depends on many factors: technical (performance of MOX fuel both from the neutronics and materials points of view), economic, nuclear resources utilization, weapons proliferation issues, ecological concerns, etc. Because of the presence of these numerous and diverse issues and the different weights given to them by different countries, there is no clear answer to the question "Should reprocessing and recycling be implemented?" and for this reason only a discussion of the factors involved is offered here, not a clear recommendation.

In the once-through cycle, the cost of nuclear fuel consists of three main components: the cost of the U_3O_8, the cost of enrichment, and the cost of fabrication. With recycling, two major changes are introduced. One is the cost of reprocessing and the other the cost of fabrication of MOX assemblies. Not only fabrication but also transportation of the MOX fuel will cost considerably more than that of the LWR once-through fuel. The transportation cost of MOX fuel will increase considerably because special casks are needed to transport both the LWR used fuel (see Chapter 9) and the MOX assemblies themselves. There is no reliable cost estimate for reprocessing and MOX fuel fabrication except for the cost of the casks. There are various reasons for this: (1) No commercial reprocessing plant has been recently built and operated (especially in the United States); (2) for existing plants, the contracts that define prices are not made public; and (3) costs depend on all the assumptions made (size of the plant, construction cost, cost of money,

TABLE 7.4

Best Estimates of Prices for Nuclear Fuel Activities*

Activity	Once–Through Cycle	With Recycling (Use of MOX)
Uranium (U_3O_8)	$155/kgU	$155/kgU
Conversion	$10/kgU	$10/kgU
SWU price	$110	$110
Reprocessing	—	$1000/kgHM
Fabrication[a]	$200–300/kgU	$600/kgHM
Transportation	—	$400/kgHM

* In 2011 dollars.
[a] In the United States, fabrication and transportation costs are combined.

vitrification of HLW included or not). Studies have been performed and their results vary wildly. A 1994 study by OECD/NEA[34] gives a reprocessing cost range of $620 to $1220/kgHM, depending on the cost of money (discount rate; see Chapter 8). Another more recent study[35] from 2003 gives the cost of reprocessing as $370 to $585/kgHM. Best price estimates/guesses for 2011 are given in Table 7.4.

The dismantlement of nuclear weapons as a result of the agreement between the United States and the former Soviet Union to reduce the number of nuclear weapons has made available large amounts of highly enriched uranium (HEU) and weapons-grade plutonium (which is primarily ^{239}Pu). What to do with these nuclear materials in order to avoid accidents that may affect humans and their environment is the subject of debate among the countries that have produced them.

For the HEU from dismantled weapons, a consensus has been reached to blend it with depleted uranium and make it into low-enriched uranium that is usable as a fuel in LWRs. This program called "Megatons-to-Megawatts" started in 1993 and Russian HEU has been received by the United States and converted into LWR fuel. The Megatons-to-Megawatts program is beneficial in two ways. First, HEU that might be misused is safely disposed of. Second, this HEU becomes fuel that generates electricity.

For the weapons-grade Pu, the United States and Russia signed an agreement in 2000 to dispose of 34 tons of such Pu by making MOX fuel with it. Based on that agreement, the United States is building a MOX fabrication plant at the Savannah River Laboratory in South Carolina with completion planned for 2016. There is a plan under way to use that MOX fuel in Tennessee Valley Authority–operated reactors.[36] MOX made from weapons plutonium is "cleaner" in a certain sense. Table 7.5 gives the approximate composition of MOX fabricated from used nuclear fuel and from weapons-grade plutonium.

TABLE 7.5
Composition of MOX Fuel

Isotope	Fresh UO$_2$	Used LWR Fuel	MOX from Recycled LWR Fuel	MOX from Weapons Pu
^{238}U	96%	93%	91%	95%
^{235}U	4	1	<1	<1
Fission products	0	5	0	0
Pu, average in assembly	0	1	9	4.3
^{238}Pu	0	1	1	0
^{239}Pu	0	57[a]	57	94
^{240}Pu	0	27	27	5
^{241}Pu	0	8	8	<1
^{242}Pu	0	7	7	≪1

[a] Percentage of ^{239}Pu out of total Pu.

Bibliography

Advanced Separation Techniques for Nuclear Fuel Reprocessing and Radioactive Waste Treatment, K.L. Nash and G.J. Lumetta, Eds., Woodhead Publishing (2011).

Advances in Nuclear Science and Technology, Vol. 25, J. Lewins and M. Becker, Eds., Plenum Press (1997).

Committee on Separations Technology and Transmutation Systems, U.S. National Research Council, *Nuclear Wastes: Technologies for Separations and Transmutation*, National Academies Press (1996).

Encyclopedia of Chemical Processing and Design, Vol. 65: *Waste: Nuclear Reprocessing and Treatment Technologies to Wastewater Treatment*, J.J. McKetta, Ed., Marcel Dekker (1998).

"Spent Fuel Reprocessing Options," TECDOC-1587, International Atomic Energy Agency (2008).

References

1. NUREG-0002, "Final GESMO Report," U.S. Nuclear Regulatory Commission (Aug. 1976).

2. "Nuclear Proliferation and Civilian Nuclear Power—Report of the Nonproliferation Alternative Systems Assessment Program," USDOE/NE-001, U.S. Department of Energy (June 1980).

3. "International Nuclear Fuel Cycle Evaluation Report," INFCE/PC/2/9, Atomic Energy Agency (Jan. 1980).

4. Spiewak, I., and Barkenbush, J.N., "Nuclear Proliferation and Nuclear Power: A Review of the NASAP and INFCE Studies," *Nucl. Safety*, **21**, 6, 691 (1980).

5. Lamarsh, J.R., and Baratta, A.J., *Introduction to Nuclear Engineering*, 3rd ed., p. 195, Prentice Hall (2001).

6. "La Hague: French Face Bright Prospects for Commercial Oxide Fuel Reprocessing," *Nucl. News*, p. 58 (Nov. 1978).

7. Taylor, R.J., Hudson, P.I., and Philipps, C., "The Development of Oxide Fuel Reprocessing," presented at IAEA Symp. Back End of the Nuclear Fuel Cycle—Strategies and Options, Vienna, May 1987.

8. "CIVEX: Solution to Breeder/Diversion Dilemma," *Nucl. News*, p. 32 (Apr. 1978).

9. Steinberg, M., Powell, J.R., and Takahashi, H., "APEX Nuclear Fuel Cycle for Production of LWR Fuel and Elimination of Radioactive Waste," *Nucl. Technol.*, **58**, 437 (1982).

10. Polereskin, M., Kok, K.D., and Madia, W.J., "Coprocessing—An Evaluation of Chemical Reprocessing Without Pu Separation," *Nucl. Technol.*, **41**, 149 (1978).

11. Asquith, J.G., and Grantham, L.F., "A Low-Decontamination Approach to a Proliferation Resistant Fuel Cycle," *Nucl. Technol.*, **41**, 137 (1978).

12. Eschbach, E.A., "Some Pu Recycle Program Fuel Cycles Having Reduced Proliferation Characteristics," *Nucl. Technol.*, **41**, 168 (1978).

13. Benedict, M., Pigford, T., and Levi, H., *Nuclear Chemical Engineering*, 2nd ed., McGraw-Hill Book Company (1981).

14. PYRO 2006 Special Issue, *Nucl. Technol.* (May 2008).

15. PYRO 2008 Special Issue, *Nucl. Technol.* (Sep. 2010).

16. Jaech, J.L., "Statistical Methods in Nuclear Material Control," U.S. Atomic Energy Commission (1973).

17. Deonigi, D.E., "The Value of Pu Recycle in Thermal Reactors," *Nucl. Technol.*, **18**, 80 (1973).

18. Brite, D.W., "Pu Fuel Technology, Part I: Pu Fuel Fabrication," *Nucl. Technol.*, **18**, 87 (1973).

19. Smith, R.C., Faust, L.F., and Brackenbush, L.W., "Pu Fuel Technology, Part II: Radiation Exposure from Pu in LWR Fuel Manufacture," *Nucl. Technol.*, **18**, 97 (1973).

20. Brown, C.L., Davenport, L.C., and Oden, D.R., "Pu Fuel Technology, Part III: Nuclear Criticality Safety Considerations in LWR $(Pu,U)O_2$ Fuel Fabrication," *Nucl. Technol.*, **18**, 109 (1973).

21. Uotinen, V.O., Leonard, B.R., Jr., and Liikala, R.C., "The Neutronics of Pu Recycling," *Nucl. Technol.*, **18**, 115 (1973).

22. Freshley, M.D., "UO_2-PuO_2—A Demonstrated Fuel for Pu Utilization in Thermal Reactors," *Nucl. Technol.*, **18**, 141 (1974).

23. Edlund, M.C., "Physics of the U-Pu Fuel Cycle in PWR's," *Trans. Am. Nucl. Soc.*, **24**, 508 (1976).

24. Gambier, G., "The Different Ways of Using Pu in PWR's," *Trans. Am. Nucl. Soc.*, **34**, 385 (1980).

25. Laurence, L.A., "Performance of High Pu Weight Fraction MOX Fuel," *Trans. Am. Nucl. Soc.*, **44**, 256 (1983).

26. *The Physics of Pu Recycling*, Vols. 1–5, Nuclear Energy Agency, Organisation for Economic Co-operation and Development (1995).

27. "Management of Separated Pu—The Technical Options," Nuclear Energy Agency, Organisation for Economic Co-operation and Development (1997).

28. Makaiyama, T., Yoshida, H., and Ogawa, T., "Minor Actinide Transmutation in Fission Reactors and Fuel Cycle Considerations," *Proc. Specialists Mtg.*, Obninsk, Russia, TECDOC-693, International Atomic Energy Agency (1993).

29. Taiwo, T.A., Kim, T.K., Stillman, J.A., Hill, R.N., Salvatores, M., and Finck, P.J., *Nucl. Technol.*, **155**, 34 (2006).

30. Mayer, M.K., Hayes, S.L., Carmack, W.J., and Tsai, H., "The EBR-II X501 Minor Actinide Burning Experiment," INL/EXT-08-13835, Idaho National Laboratory (2008).

31. *Actinide and Fission Product Partitioning and Transmutation: 11th Information Exchange Meeting*, San Francisco, California, November 2010; http://www.oecd-nea.org/pt/iempt11/index.html.

32. Rimpault, G., et al., "General Synthesis Report of the Different ADS Design Status. Establishment of a Catalogue of the R&D Needs," DEN/CAD/DER/SPRC RT 2010 SPRC/LEDC/10-2, CEA-Rapport Technique DEN (2010).

33. MEGAPIE, Paul Scherrer Institut Web site, http://megapie.web.psi.ch.

34. "Reprocessing Costs," Nuclear Energy Agency, Organisation for Economic Co-operation and Development (1994); www.new.fr/html/ndd/reports/efc.

35. Haire, M.J., "Nuclear Fuel Reprocessing Costs," *Proc. Advances in Nuclear Fuel Management III*, Hilton Head, South Carolina, American Nuclear Society (2003).

36. Mastilovic, M., "Potential for Using MOX Fuel Derived from U.S. Nuclear Weapons in TVA's Reactors," *Proc. World Nuclear Fuel Cycle 2011*; www.wnfc.info/proceedings/2011/presentations/mick_mastilovic.pdf.

PROBLEMS

7.1. What is the value of uranium utilization in LWRs, for a once-through fuel cycle, if the fuel achieves a burnup of 45,000 MWd/tU? Assume enrichment of fuel is 3.2% and tails are equal to 0.28%.

7.2. Repeat Problem 7.1 for a breeder reactor. Assume $\gamma = 0.02$.

7.3. What is the savings in natural uranium if both uranium and plutonium are recycled in LWRs, assuming the following: 3% enriched fuel with 0.22% tails, 0.78% ^{235}U in spent fuel, 6.9 g fPu/(kg of spent fuel), 0.90 kg of spent fuel recovered/kg of fresh fuel, 0.8 Pu-^{235}U equivalence.

7.4. What are the SWU savings for the conditions given in Problem 7.3?

7.5. Discuss the effects of losses in conversion, fabrication, and reprocessing by performing the calculations of Problems 7.3 and 7.4 twice, first with and then without including losses.

7.6. Which of the following two alternatives is more expensive?

    (a) Unirradiated uranium is used for fabrication of UO_2 fuel, enriched to 3.9% in ^{235}U. Assume tails are 0.25%, conversion loss 0.5%, and fabrication loss 0.8%.

    (b) Fresh fuel is used for 20% of the core as in (a). The rest of the fuel is made up with recycled plutonium and tails of 0.25%. Assume 0.8 Pu-^{235}U equivalence.

Prices: uranium: $45/kg; conversion: $4.50/kgU; SWU cost: $85/ SWU; fabrication cost of unirradiated fuel: $210/kgU; reprocessing costs: $750/kgHM; fabrication and transportation of MOX fuel: $400/kgHM; cost of tails: $10/kg; and MOX fabrication loss: 0.8%.

7.7. At what reprocessing price would the two alternatives of Problem 7.6 cost the same?

7.8. Calculate the price of natural uranium, as a function of reprocessing cost, above which it is more economical to recycle spent fuel rather than to use only natural uranium as feed. Give the result in the form of a graph having reprocessing cost as the abscissa and uranium price as the ordinate. Assume the following costs: conversion: $4/kg; SWU cost: $80/SWU; fabrication cost of unirradiated fuel: $210/kg; and fabrication and transportation cost of MOX: $400/kg.

    Assume 0.6% loss in conversion, 0.7% loss in fabrication, and 1% loss in reprocessing. The Pu-^{235}U equivalence is 0.8, and the tails are 0.21%. The enriched fuel is 3%. The irradiated fuel contains 95% of the original uranium, 0.795% ^{235}U, and 6.5 g of plutonium per kilogram of fuel. The cost of the tails is one-fifth of the price of natural uranium. The MOX fuel (equivalent to the 3% fuel) will consist of plutonium plus uranium tails. Assume that the reprocessed uranium is in the form of UF_6.

7.9. Repeat Problem 7.8 under the assumption that only plutonium will be recycled. The rest of the data are as stated in Problem 7.8.

7.10. Calculate the cost of nuclear fuel ($/kgU) based on the cycle shown below. All of the Pu in the spent nuclear fuel is reprocessed and recycled and the difference is made up with fresh uranium. Use the prices of Table 7.4. Assume 0.6% loss in conversion, 0.7% loss in fabrication, 1% loss in reprocessing, Pu-^{235}U equivalence 0.8, fuel enrichment 3.3%, tails 0.21%, and 0.90 of original uranium is still in the spent fuel. In addition, the spent fuel contains 7 g fPu/kg spent fuel, and 0.79% ^{235}U; cost of tails is one-tenth of the cost of fresh UF_6. The reprocessed uranium and plutonium come out as oxides. (The UO_2 needs to be converted to UF_6 before it is enriched.)

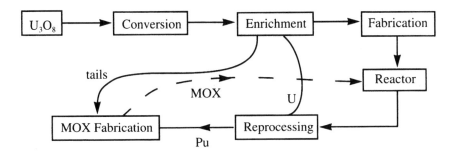

7.11. Repeat the calculations of Problem 7.10 with the assumption that the reprocessed uranium goes into storage.

EIGHT

ELECTRIC UTILITY AND NUCLEAR POWER ECONOMICS

8.1 General Comments and Definitions

8.1.1 Capital and Business Activities

To start a business and continue to operate it, money is needed, that is, capital. In many business ventures, both public and private, this capital frequently involves millions of dollars and raising that much money is often a problem. Capital is often obtained from such sources as private investors, lending agencies, endowment funds, and banks. In the case of private companies, the capital ultimately comes from individuals, whereas for public corporations, funds come from borrowing or by taxation. Quite naturally those who supply the capital are interested in its efficient or wise use because they expect some benefit or monetary reward for the use of their money and, unless the capital is used wisely, the company will go out of business and most if not all of the capital will be lost. For this reason, financial managers and engineers are required to plan and account for the utilization of capital, so as to ensure its most effective use.

8.1.2 The Engineer's Role in Business

Every business venture that involves the design, construction, and marketing of a new project or product requires a balanced economic and engineering analysis in order to increase the probability of its success. If engineering is given greater importance, at the expense of economics, chances are that the project or product may be sound from the engineering point of view, but it may be expensive and therefore unable to compete in a marketplace driven by competition in a free enterprise environment. If, on the other hand, economics is stressed at the expense of sound engineering principles, the final design may appear to be inexpensive but it also may not be a good one; for example, it may be unsafe and, thus, can cost more in the long run for its construction and/or operation.

Engineers commonly take part in the conception of new ideas and projects that require the eventual expenditure of large sums of capital before they reach the marketplace (consider, e.g., the billions of dollars needed for the construction of a nuclear power plant). Because the engineers are the persons most likely to understand the technical requirements of a project, they are very frequently called on to conduct studies combining the technical and financial details of a proposed project. In addition, engineers must consider social, political, ethical, and environmental consequences as well as the aesthetic values of the proposed project. A sound managerial decision will be based on the results of an engineering and financial analysis.

Engineers are called on to make evaluations and help management arrive at decisions about the prudency and soundness of the investment being recommended. To be successful in that task, the engineer must possess a sound technical background but also some basic knowledge of economics to be able to find the proper balance between the technical and financial requirements of a project. Although the objective of this chapter is to discuss the most important financial/economic concepts the engineer may encounter as a professional, it is just an introduction to the topic. The Bibliography lists publications that provide more detail about this topic.

8.1.3 Financial Terms

In discussing economics and business activities, certain terms appear frequently. The terms defined below will be used in this and subsequent chapters:

Assets—those things of value that are possessed by a corporation or business (cash, land, buildings, equipment, etc.).

Investment—money (capital) used for a business venture.

Rate of return or return on investment—annual net profit/capital investment.

Interest—money paid for the use of borrowed money; usually, this charge is expressed as an interest rate over a certain period of time, usually a year.

Equity capital—capital owned by a business or company using it (see also "Stocks" below).

Debt capital—borrowed money. To use debt capital, a company must pay a use charge (interest). For debt capital, the interest is the only benefit received by the owner of the capital (see also "Bonds" below).

Stocks—shares of the company sold to investors. A stockholder is a part owner of the company, with a voice in managing the company proportional to the number of stock shares that he or she owns.

Dividend—the return on investment to the stockholder. At certain time periods (once a year or more frequently), the company pays the stockholder a certain amount of money per share (called the dividend) in recognition of the profit made by the company. The dividend may be only a fraction of the return per share for each payment period, because the company may elect to retain earnings for growth of equity capitalization in the company. During lean times, when a dividend has been established as an amount expected by the shareholder, the dividend may exceed the earnings per year, per quarter, or whatever period is used, and be a "return of capital," essentially reducing the value of each share. The worth represented by all of the outstanding stock represents the equity capital of the company.

Bonds—issuing bonds amounts to borrowing money for a business venture. Bonds are issued not only by businesses but also by governments. A bond with a maturity of N years represents a promise by the entity selling the bond to pay the owner of the bond a certain amount of money (the interest) every accounting period (usually a year), and return the full amount at the end of N years. Paying the bondholders is a financial obligation that comes before paying the stockholders. A dividend to the stockholders may be skipped but not the interest owed to bondholders. Thus, a bond is a more secure investment relative to a stock. Because the risk in a stock investment is higher than that of a bond, the rate of return for stocks is higher than that for bonds. The amount of money owed in the form of debentures represents the debt capital of the company. There are several types of debt capital, which may even include a firm lease contract. In fact, short-term loans of 3 to 5 years arc ideal for nuclear fuel expenses and tap a source of capital that long-term bonds do not attract.

Depreciation—a charge recorded every accounting period against the company's revenue in order to recover the original investment in plants and equipment (see Section 8.1.5).

Direct costs—money paid directly for materials and services.

Indirect costs—usually the interest on borrowed money, return on investment, taxes, and other costs associated with the time value of money (see Section 8.1.6). These are also called fixed charges. However, for a utility company the indirect costs are usually considered to be the costs the utility incurs when building a new plant or project. In this case it involves their own employee costs, the architect/engineer fees, licenses, and other expenses not paid by the contractor.

8.1.4 Business Taxes

Companies, like individuals, have to pay federal, state, and local taxes. Federal taxes on corporations are based on the net earnings of the company. Net earnings are defined as gross revenues minus operating expenses, state and local taxes, charges for depreciation, and interest paid to bondholders. The federal tax rate of corporate income is always a lively topic for discussion in the halls of the U.S. Congress. Corporate tax rates change from time to time, based on political and economic reasons. As of 2011, the corporate rates were 15% to 35% (notice the plural "rates"; there is more than one rate, depending on type of corporation and income). State corporate taxes vary from state to state, both in terms of the rate and the net earnings; they range between 2% and 12%. Local taxes, mostly property taxes, are levied by local authorities (the city or county where the business is physically located) and are determined on the basis of the assessed valuation of a company's plant and equipment. Usually, the assessment is a fraction of the initial cost of the assets being taxed or of their current replacement cost.

8.1.5 Depreciation

Plants and equipment have finite lifetimes. If a company is to continue operating, it must make provisions for the replacement of assets that are no longer economically useful to operate (equipment) or to use (buildings). This need for replacement of assets is recognized not only by the businessman but also by those who levy taxes. The term *depreciation* defines the process of charging a certain amount of money, during every accounting or other time period, for the purpose of recovering the investment lost by wear and tear on the assets being depreciated. There are two types of depreciation: book depreciation, which represents the money set aside by the company for the replacement of an asset at the end of its life, and tax depreciation, which is whatever amount the Internal Revenue Service (IRS) and state and local tax authorities will allow to be subtracted before earnings are taxed. Tax depreciation is a permissible cost recovery method that makes possible the return of lost value to the company and appears as a noncash expense in the cash flow of the corporation. Book depreciation practices are not too different from tax depreciation practices (see Ref. 1 for details). Tax depreciation is used throughout this chapter unless otherwise indicated.

The IRS and state taxing agencies allow many types of depreciation methods to be used. Regardless of the method, however, the total tax related to the depreciated asset is the same (over the life of the asset). What the different depreciation methods change is the distribution of taxes in time. A brief discussion of the most common methods follows.

Straight-Line Method of Depreciation: This is the simplest way of handling depreciation. Let:

B = original cost of the item (the basis for depreciation)

N = probable life of the depreciated asset (in years)

S = salvage (scrap) value of the asset

D_n = depreciation charge for year n.

Then

$$D_n = (B - S)/N|n = 1, N \qquad (8.1)$$

Thus, using this method of depreciation, each year the book value of the asset is decreased by the constant amount D_n.

Sum-of-the-Years' Digits (SYD): This method depreciates the asset faster during the early years of its life. The amount of money representing the depreciation per time period is given by

$$D_n = \frac{N - n + 1}{[N(N + 1)]/2} (B - S)|n = 1, N \qquad (8.2)$$

Double Declining Balance (DDB): This is a variation of the SYD method. Again, depreciation is faster during the early years. In this case, the fraction depreciated per time period is

$$\frac{2}{N}\left(1 - \frac{2}{N}\right)^{n-1} \qquad (8.3)$$

The amount of money representing the depreciation per time period is given by

$$D_n = \frac{2}{N}\left(1 - \frac{2}{N}\right)^{n-1} B \qquad (8.4)$$

Note that in the DDB method, the fraction D_n multiplies the value of the asset without subtracting the salvage value.

Regardless of the method used, the total amount of depreciation allowed can never exceed the amount $\$(B - S)$. In the straight-line and SYD methods, this condition is satisfied for any N. This is not the case, however, for the DDB method. Depending on the number N, we may reach N years without having exhausted all of the depreciation allowed; or we may reach total depreciation equal to $\$(B - S)$ for $n < N$. If after N periods the total amount depreciated is going to be less than $\$(B - S)$, a company may switch to the straight-line depreciation method so that the total depreciation is equal to $\$(B - S)$. Such a switch is usually made when the depreciation given by the DDB method is less than that calculated by the straight-line method. In the opposite case, depreciation stops when the total amount reaches $\$(B - S)$.

Accelerated Cost Recovery System of Depreciation (ACRS) or Modified Acceleration Cost Recovery System (MACRS): The Economic Recovery Act of 1981 introduced the ACRS system of capital recovery, and the 1986 Tax

TABLE 8.1

An Example of Three Depreciation Methods for an Asset with
$B = \$10,000$ and $S = \$1000$

Year	Straight Line Fraction of Depreciation	D_n ($)	Sum-of-the-Years' Digits Fraction of Depreciation	D_n ($)	Double Declining Balance Fraction of Depreciation	D_n ($)
1	0.1	900	0.182	1638	0.200	2000
2	0.1	900	0.164	1476	0.160	1600
3			0.145	1305	0.128	1280
4			0.127	1143	0.102	1024
5			0.109	981	0.082	820
6			0.091	819	0.066	660
7			0.073	657	0.052	520
8			0.055	495	0.042	420
9			0.036	324	0.034	338
10	0.1	900	0.018	162	0.034	338
	1.0	$9000	1.0	$9000	0.9	$9000

Reform Act modified it to MACRS. The basis of ACRS and MACRS is (1) classification of all assets subjected to depreciation into "property class lives" and (2) assumption that the salvage value is zero. After the asset is classified, the depreciation schedule is determined from tables provided by the IRS.[1] Both ACRS and MACRS represent accelerated methods of depreciation (similar to DDB).

Note that the depreciation allocated per year depends on the type of asset, the date of purchase, and the depreciation method followed. (More information on depreciation is given in Refs. 1 through 3.)

As an example of the use of these depreciation methods, consider an asset with a lifetime of 10 years, $B = \$10,000$, and $S = \$1000$. Table 8.1 shows the values of D_n per year, assuming purchase of the asset on the first day of the year. In the DDB case, a switch is made to the straight-line method after the first 8 years because the application of the DDB method would not give a total depreciation equal to $9000 in 10 years; this switch to the straight-line method is allowed to obtain the correct total in 10 years.

8.1.6 The Time Value or the Present Worth of Money

Money is a valuable commodity because it may generate more money. The simplest example we can give is as follows. If you have $P today and put it in a savings account for a year at $i\%$ per year interest rate, a year later you will have $\$(P + iP)$. Individuals or organizations are willing to pay the interest when they borrow money because they can invest those same funds and generate a profit greater than the interest they have to pay. The bank that paid $iP as interest to the person above will not keep the $P in a vault but will probably lend it to another person or organization at an interest rate $j > i$, or invest it in some other way, and expect to see a rate of return again greater than $i\%$ per year.

This simple discussion shows that money not only produces more money if properly invested, but that the timing of availability of funds is also important. One dollar today, either as income or as an expense, is not worth one dollar a year from now. It should be pointed out that the change of the value of money discussed at this point has nothing to do with the change in purchasing power due to inflation.

Because the value of money changes over time, the economic evaluation of a project that lasts many years cannot be done properly without (1) agreeing on a date on which the economic balance should be established and (2) computing all the funds involved, revenues or expenses, for that same date. This "transfer" in time of the equivalent value of money leads to the concept of the "present worth" or "time value" of money.

By shifting the value of money through time by the present-worth concept, the entire cash flow model can yield equivalent cost at any specific time in the history of a project. Thus, this method provides an average cost picture for any desired time period.

The present worth is the equivalent value at the start of a reference year, or any specific date, of an amount of money required at the end of some future year. The present worth factor (PW) is expressed by the following equation:

$$PW = \frac{1}{(1 + i)^n} \tag{8.5}$$

where i is the interest rate (in fraction/year) and n is the number of years (or, generally, time periods). Another way of illustrating the use of the PW factor is:

$$\left[\begin{array}{c} \text{Present worth of a $P payment or} \\ \text{investment to be made } n \text{ years from now} \end{array} \right] = \$P * PW = \$ \frac{P}{(1 + i)^n}$$

$$\left[\begin{array}{c} \text{Present worth of a $P payment or} \\ \text{investment made } n \text{ years ago} \end{array} \right] = \$P/PW = \$P(1 + i)^n$$

One obvious way to see the PW concept is this: If you have to pay $P amount n years into the future, you can put $P/(1 + i)^n$ into a savings account today and have $P n years later to make the payment.

■ **Example 8.1:** What is the present worth of $1000 to be given as a down payment for a car 5 years from now? Assume $i = 9\%$.

Answer: The present worth of this money is $1000/(1.09)^5 = $1000 * 0.65 = $650.   ∎

∎ *Example 8.2:* What is the present worth of a $3000 down payment made 10 years ago to buy a house? Assume again $i = 9\%$.

Answer: The present worth of this money is $3000(1.09)^{10} = \$3,000 * 2.37 = \$7102.$ ∎

Interest calculated based on a year, as the unit of time, is said to be compounded annually if the interest is added to the principal yearly. If the interest is calculated over a time unit different from a year, the factor $(1 + i)^n$ becomes $(1 + i/m)^{m \cdot n}$, where m is the number of time periods per year. If $m = 12$, the interest is compounded monthly. In some cases, an effective interest rate, i_e, is defined based on the condition

$$(1 + i_e)^n = (1 + i/m)^{m \cdot n} \tag{8.6}$$

which leads to

$$i_e = (1 + i/m)^m - 1 \tag{8.7}$$

Carrying it to the extreme of $m \to \infty$, we can obtain the equivalent interest rate for "continuous compounding" by requiring

$$(1 + i)^n = \lim_{m \to \infty} (1 + i_e/m)^{m \cdot n} = \exp(i_c n)$$

Therefore, as $m \to \infty$,

$$i_c = \ln(1 + i) \tag{8.8}$$

∎ *Example 8.3:* If the annual interest rate is 12%, what is (a) the effective interest rate for monthly compounding and (b) the equivalent interest rate for continuous compounding?

Answer: (a) Using Eq. (8.7), the effective interest for monthly compounding is

$$i_e = (1 + 0.12/12)^{12} - 1 = 0.1268 = 12.68\%$$

(b) The continuous compounding effective interest rate from Eq. (8.8) is

$$i_c = \ln(1 + 0.12) = 0.113 = 11.3\%$$ ∎

Related to the idea of the present worth of money is the method of repayment of borrowed money. Four general methods are used:

1. Pay principal plus interest in one payment at the end of the period for which the loan was made. If the principal is P, the interest rate i, and the loan period N years, the borrower will pay at the end of N years the total sum F equal to:

$$F = \$(1 + i)^N P \tag{8.9}$$

2. Pay only the interest at the end of every year. Then, at the end of year N, pay the principal plus interest for the last year. The total amount paid in this case is

$$F = \$(1 + iN)P \tag{8.10}$$

3. Use N equal payments to repay principal plus interest. This method, called *amortization*, is favored in home loans. The total amount paid in this case is

$$F = \left[\frac{i(1 + i)^N}{(1 + i)^N - 1} P \right] N \tag{8.11}$$

The quantity in the brackets is the payment/year.

4. Repay the principal with N equal payments, but also pay the interest of the unpaid balance at the end of each year. The total amount paid in this case is

$$F = \$\left[1 + i \frac{(N + 1)}{2} \right] P \tag{8.12}$$

Assuming a loan of $10,000 for 5 years at 8%, the amounts paid under the four plans are shown in Table 8.2. Although the actual amounts paid are different and plan 4 seems to be the least expensive, we can show (see Problem 8.5) that the equivalent present-worth amounts are equal to that of plan 1 in all cases, provided that both the lender and the borrower expect the same rate of return i.

TABLE 8.2
Amounts Paid under Four Payment Plans
for Repayment of Loan of $10,000

Plan	Amount
1	14,663
2	14,000
3	12,523
4	12,400

8.2 The Electric Utility as a Business

8.2.1 Main Financial Characteristics of Utilities

Public utilities that provide services such as water, gas, electricity, and telephone to an entire population of the region where they are allowed to operate enjoyed monopoly status before the U.S. Congress introduced deregulation legislation in the 1970s. To provide government services, public property such as streets, highways, and air space became available to the government and the right of "imminent domain" was granted to allow it to acquire property where and when needed.

The "one utility per region" concept was adopted in order to avoid competing companies having to build duplicate facilities in the same area, resulting in more expensive service to their customers. In addition, duplicate facilities might even be environmentally unsound.

In return for their monopoly status, utilities are expected to:

1. Operate within the regulatory constraints dictated by the federal, state, and local governments (see Section 8.2.3).

2. Expand to meet the growth of the community or its service area. This requirement is enforced by the appropriate regulatory agency. Because of their monopoly status, utilities must render service when demanded.

3. Keep abreast of technical developments in their field that would permit a reduction in cost to the customers. This requirement exists both to maintain public goodwill and to satisfy the regulatory agency.

By 2011, some of the utilities in every U.S. state had been completely deregulated (e.g., telephone companies). As for electric companies, they have been deregulated in some states (19 states in 2011), but not in all. Details about this new economic environment introduced by deregulation are discussed in Section 8.2.3.

To raise the money needed for its construction program, an electric utility relies on investors who are willing to buy its stocks and bonds. The ratio of stocks (equity) to bonds (debt) is about one. For other industries, this ratio is much bigger than one. Utilities are allowed to operate with such a high debt-to-equity ratio because of their financial stability. For the same reason, investors are easily found to buy utility bonds and stocks. Utilities must rely on a large proportion of new capital, as borrowed money, for expansion because very little of their earnings may be kept as a result of a ceiling on earnings imposed, usually, by the regulatory agencies. Electric utilities may be investor owned, publicly owned, cooperatives, or nationalized.

The relatively large construction program makes an electric utility a very capital-intensive business, which may be demonstrated in two ways. First, the average U.S. industrial company has about $16,000 invested per employee. For a typical electric utility, the corresponding figure is four to five times this value. Second, for manufacturing companies, the ratio of net worth to revenues is less than one. For an electric utility, this ratio is about three.

The costs of an electric utility are divided into three areas with the following approximate percentages:

1. Generation, 60% (construction, fuel, operation and maintenance)

2. Transmission, 10%

3. Distribution, 30%.

8.2.2 The Cash Flow Statement

A company's financial statement or cash flow indicates, in general, the sources of incomes and expenses and their interrelationships. Cash flow can be explained with the help of the diagram shown in Fig. 8.1. Note that, although companies use various types of cash flow statement, Fig. 8.1 is useful because it shows most of the items and practices involved, especially for electric utilities.

The total revenue (also known as gross income) is the total income from the sale of the product and/or services of the company. Expenses for fuel,

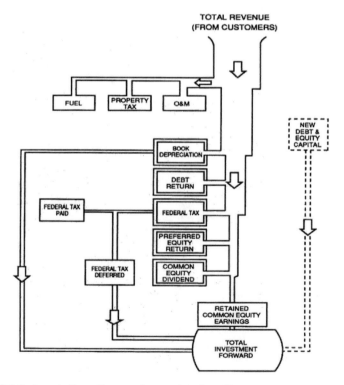

FIGURE 8.1 A cash flow diagram for an electric utility.

property tax, and operating and maintenance (O&M) expenses are deducted first. Then depreciation and debt return (interest paid to bondholders) are subtracted, before calculation of federal taxes. A common practice for utilities is to pay only a fraction of the tax and defer the rest for later. If tax deferral is permitted and practiced, the total tax paid over time is still the same, but the rate of payment is slower at earlier times. Tax deferral allows the utility to use the funds not paid out as taxes for construction instead of having to borrow new money. Thus, in view of the time value of money, tax deferral is advantageous to the utility and to its customers because it tends to reduce the cost of generating electricity. Tax deferral is like depreciation in reverse, from the point of view of the rate of payments over time. (State taxes are not shown explicitly in Fig. 8.1. Certainly, companies pay state taxes, usually, calculated after the federal tax.)

Another practice encountered in business accounting is the selling of preferred and common stock. The essential difference between preferred and common stock is the rate of return. Preferred shares earn a lower rate of return than common shares, but dividends to preferred stockholders are paid before dividends to common stockholders. Owners of preferred stock earn less than those of common stock, but the risk to their investment is less than that of the common stock.

In this chapter, no differentiation is made between common and preferred stock. The equations of the cost of electricity are essentially the same with or without this distinction between the two types of stocks. Deferred taxes will not be shown explicitly either because (1) the treatment of deferred taxes is not the same for all utilities, (2) the cost of electricity calculated with or without them is essentially the same, and (3) the important characteristics of the final equation (Section 8.5.2) and the main conclusions drawn from it do not change if tax deferral is included.

8.2.3 The Electric Utility Regulatory System

From 1935 to 1978, investor-owned electric utilities in the United States operated under the Public Utility Holding Company Act of 1935, which provided for federal regulation, by the Federal Energy Regulatory Commission (FERC), of wholesale power and interstate transmission services. FERC does not regulate government-owned utilities and cooperatives. The purpose of the federal regulations was to ensure that utilities do not discriminate among customers as to service and price. The states regulate local distribution and retail sales to the end-use customer. During these 43 years, the utilities enjoyed a monopoly in their area of operation, but they were subjected to strict state and federal controls. For a utility to obtain a rate change, it must petition and win approval from the pertinent regulatory agencies. The utility's rate base is determined from all costs, including a fair return, after taxes, on the base value of its investment.

In 1978, Congress passed the Public Utility Regulatory Policy Act (PURPA). PURPA required utilities[4] to buy power from non-utility generating (NUG) facilities that use (1) renewable energy sources or (2) cogeneration, that is, use steam both for generation of electricity and for direct heating or other industrial processes. The noble idea behind PURPA was to stimulate the growth of NUGs that would use renewable energy fuels. FERC required utilities to buy power from NUGs whether they needed it or not and to buy it with long-term contracts at prices higher than market, in most cases. It was expected at that time that prices of "conventional" fuels would skyrocket and these contracts with the NUGs would benefit the utilities' customers in the long run. Instead, the opposite happened and PURPA is costing many utilities and their customers money.

In 1992 an Energy Policy Act (EPA 92) was passed; among other provisions, EPA 92 broadened the exemptions from certain regulations for a larger group of NUGs. As a result, the share of nationwide NUG capacity more than doubled in 10 years, reaching 8.5% in 1997. It is interesting to note that since 1988, NUGs have built more than 45% of all new generating capacity in the United States. In addition, EPA 92 authorized FERC to order utilities to provide "open access" to their transmission lines to NUGs and other utilities. FERC did just that in 1996, stipulating that access should be provided at prices comparable to what they charge themselves. This provision of EPA 92 and the subsequent order by FERC opened the gates to full-scale competition for the sale of electricity. Two additional acts were passed by Congress, the Energy Policy Act of 2005 (EPACT 05) and the Energy Independence and Security Act of 2007 (EISA 07), essentially as amendments to PURPA. EPACT 05 and EISA 07 give instructions and orders to states about how to formulate their electric utility regulatory system.

Why deregulate? The main argument for deregulation is this: In a regulated environment, yes, electric utilities are controlled by the State Public Service Commission, but if the company constructs an inefficient/uneconomical project, it will be allowed to pass the costs to the rate payer; therefore, the customer and not the company is penalized for a poor financial decision. Conversely, a deregulated utility carries completely the risk of any investment; thus, the argument goes, a deregulated utility will be more careful about the costs of new generation, presumably its investments will have reduced cost, and the prices of electricity will be reduced.

Consistent with the energy policy acts mentioned earlier in this section, it is up to the individual states to decide about deregulation of the electric utilities operating within their boundaries and to set up the regulatory mechanism for the electricity price structure under which competition will take place. In states where competition has been introduced, it became apparent that certain problems arise and have to be resolved relative to the fair and equitable recovery of costs burdening the utility that owns the facilities (primarily transmission lines) used by its competitors. These problems arise because utilities recover their capital costs over long periods, 30 years or more; by contrast, manufacturers of consumer goods, for example, toy manufacturers, expect to recover their costs as quickly as possible and there are no regulations to stop them—only the market may cause them to fail. Once these problems are resolved, the expectation is that consumers will be able to choose their electricity supplier from a number of alternatives, the way they do now for telephone, cable, Internet, and similar services, and reap the rewards of lower prices as a result of competition among the suppliers.

In this new and evolving financial environment, two trends have been noted. One is separation of construction of plants and generation of electricity from its distribution. Companies have been formed that buy power plants, particularly operating nuclear power plants, with the purpose of producing and selling the electricity to wholesalers. Second is a diversification of utility financial activities into areas completely unrelated to electricity, for example, cable TV, mutual funds, and insurance.

8.2.4 The Effects of Load Demand Variation

As mentioned earlier, a utility is obligated to provide service as demanded by all of its customers at all times. However, this demand is not constant in time. Concentrating on electricity from now on, the demand over a 24-h period changes as shown in Fig. 8.2. An analogous variation is exhibited over the period of a year (high demand during winter and summer, low demand during spring and fall). Because the utility is obligated to satisfy the needs of all customers at all times, it must be ready to meet peak demands,

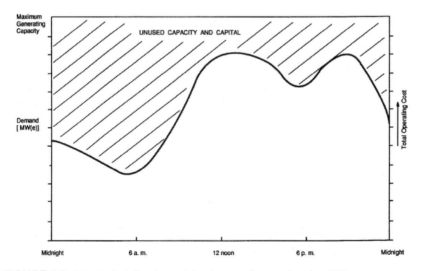

FIGURE 8.2 A typical daily demand load curve for an electric utility.

whenever such demands occur, which, in turn, means that the company must have generating facilities to satisfy peak demands. Under these circumstances, during hours of low demand, a certain fraction of the generating capacity will be idle. However, certain costs associated with a power plant do not disappear if the plant is not operating. Examples are payment of debt, property taxes, insurance, personnel, etc. To reduce the overall cost of generating electricity, a utility employs two general procedures. First, to satisfy the "base load" demand, that is, the minimum demand that is present at all times of a day or during the year, the utility operates continuously the plants that generate electricity with the lowest cost and highest reliability; this condition is satisfied primarily by nuclear plants and secondarily by coal-fired plants and hydro stations. Second, the utility tries to reduce, to the extent possible, the ratio of peak-to-average demand.

Two general methods are used. One is based on changing the cost of a kWh(e), depending on the time of day that the kWh(e) is used. Reduction of the price during night hours should entice customers to use more electricity during that time period. Full implementation of this approach requires the existence of "smart meters," which have not been developed yet. A second method is the "pumped storage" concept. Utilities that operate hydroelectric dams may generate electricity during the day and pump the water back to the reservoir during the night for use during the next day.

8.3 The Special Features of Nuclear Fuel

8.3.1 Nuclear and Fossil Fuels

Fossil fuels are purchased, stored for a relatively short period of time, and then burned. Thus, from the accounting point of view, the "life" of fossil fuels is considered short. However, there is a constant storage stockpile and a constant charge. The picture is quite different for nuclear fuels. Consider the following:

1. Nuclear fuel is purchased as a uranium compound. It goes through conversion, enrichment, and fabrication into assemblies; is burned in the core; is stored (at present on site, in most cases); and will be disposed of many years later. Thus, unlike fossil fuels, many different processes are involved in the purchase, use, and disposal of nuclear fuels.

2. Considerable costs are incurred years before the fuel produces electricity.

3. Nuclear fuel stays on the books of the utility for many years.

4. Nuclear fuel is considered a capital asset.

5. Nuclear fuel does not change, physically, as it is burned. It most certainly does not disappear.

6. There is a storage cost for the used nuclear fuel (before final disposal).

7. The "salvage" value of the nuclear fuel is negative. Remember that the IRS does not allow negative salvage, thus the utility can only take salvage to zero. The federal government is charging the utilities $0.001/kWh for nuclear-generated electricity as a fee for the cost of the eventual disposal of the used fuel (see details in Chapter 9).

8.3.2 The Investment in Nuclear Fuel as a Function of Time

As explained in Chapter 6, investment in a new batch of fuel starts about 2 years before the fuel starts producing power. As funds are committed or spent for the purchase of uranium, its conversion and enrichment, etc., the "worth" of the fuel increases. After the fuel is placed into the core and starts producing power, its worth decreases with burnup (Fig. 8.3). After discharge from the reactor, the used fuel is stored in a pool under water or in air-cooled vaults until the federal government is ready to receive it for final disposal. The storage cost, after discharge, is considered to be a constant cost related to the monitoring and upkeep of the used fuel pool.

8.3.3 Leasing or Buying Nuclear Fuel

It is a common practice of many utilities that own nuclear power plants to *lease* the nuclear fuel instead of buying it outright. It is not easy to discuss the specific economic advantages offered by this operation because leasing of nuclear fuel is a complicated financial procedure that depends on the accounting practices of the utility, its sources of income, and the constraints imposed by the appropriate regulatory agencies. In general, leasing works as follows.

A company is set up, sometimes called a "trust," which may be a subsidiary of the utility or an independent business venture. This entity, called the "lease company," finances 100% of the costs of the nuclear fuel. The

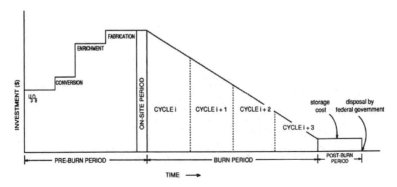

FIGURE 8.3 Investment history of a typical batch of nuclear fuel.

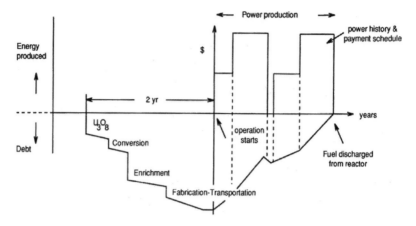

FIGURE 8.4 Debt profile, over time, for leased nuclear fuel.

utility informs the lease company about its requirements for fuel, and the lease company is obligated to meet all financial obligations so that the required fuel is on site at the desired time and ready to go into the core. Up to that time, the utility pays nothing. After the fuel is placed into the reactor and starts producing power, the utility starts making regular payments to the lease company. These payments are proportional to the energy generated by the fuel, and are intended to cover the actual expenses of the lease company plus a return on its investment from the time expenses started accumulating for that batch of fuel.

The cost of leasing the fuel is shown on the books, in some cases, not as a debt but as an operating expense of running the nuclear power plant. Such an arrangement is advantageous not only to the utility but also to the ratepayer, if the leasing cost is less than the allowed rate of return, because in that case the cost of electricity is lower. The "investment" profile, over time, of leased fuel is shown in Fig. 8.4. Notice one detail in Fig. 8.4. During power production, if the plant is shut down for a period of time, the debt increases during that time because the utility does not make payments to the lease company (since zero energy produced), but the interest accumulates.

8.4. Cost Components for Nuclear Electricity Generation

8.4.1 Plant Construction

Construction of a nuclear power plant takes years. The last nuclear construction in the United States, in the late 1970s, took at least 10 years for completion; as of 2011, construction of nuclear plants in Japan and Korea was being completed in 5 years. Even if we consider the 5-year construction period as a minimum, considerable time is involved, as a result of which the total cost should be computed by "present-worthing" all costs at a specific date, and allowance should be made for cost escalation during construction. To illustrate the effect of the time value of money during the construction of a nuclear power plant, an example of actual and present-worth payments is presented in Table 8.3. All costs are time valued to the time when the plant starts operating. The cost of money is assumed to be 8%.

It is practically impossible to provide reliable data on the cost to construct a nuclear plant in the United States; construction started on two plants in 2010, but neither has been completed. The overall cost for a 1000-MWe plant ranges from $5 billion to $10 billion. Obviously, the total cost depends on the number of years it takes to complete construction because of the ever-increasing interest during construction.

Although dollar estimates cannot be provided for construction, it is instructive to list the activities/transactions/areas where the expenses go. This list is provided in Table 8.4. Typical contingency allowances inserted into the cost estimates are shown below.

Item	Allowance (%)
Labor	10
Equipment and materials	5
Proven design	3
Novel design	20
Extrapolated design	5

It is interesting to note that the engineering costs of designing a nuclear power plant may run from 5% to 15% of the total plant capital cost, and the interest during construction may amount to about one-third of the total cost for long construction times (~ 10 years).

8.4.2 Operation and Maintenance

The O&M costs of a nuclear power plant lie at the low end of the spectrum of O&M costs for any type of plant. A nuclear plant of the 1000- to 1100-MWe size employs about 700 people. However, most utilities operate more than one plant per site, in which case personnel are shared and the effective number is less than 700.

8.4.3 Fuel

For operating nuclear power plants, for which the capital cost is zero or very little, the fuel represents $\sim 30\%$ of the total generating costs. Here is a quick estimate of the cost of fuel in cents/kWh(e): Assume burnup of 45,000 MWd/t and the following costs (same as in Example 3.4): uranium: $150/kgU;

TABLE 8.3

Expenditures during Construction of a Nuclear Power Plant,
Present-Worthed to the Beginning of Operations

Years before Operation Begins	Actual Expense per Year (10^6)	Present-Worthed Expense[a] per Year (10^6)
10	80	173
9	90	180
8	40	148
7	220	377
6	220	349
5	220	323
4	220	299
3	240	302
2	240	280
1	130	140
Total	1,740	2,571

[a]Assumed cost of money: 8%.

conversion: $12/kgU (no loss in conversion); SWU: $110/SWU; and fabrication-transportation: $240/kgU. Hence,

$$(150 + 12) * 9.219 + 110 * 6.870 + 240 = \$2,489.18/\text{kgU}$$

TABLE 8.4

Expense Activities during Construction of a Nuclear Plant

Direct costs
Land
Structures
Reactor plant equipment
Turbine plant equipment
Electric plant equipment
Main heat rejection system
Miscellaneous plant equipment

Indirect costs
Construction services
Home office engineering and services
Field office engineering and services

Other
Contingency allowance
Cost escalation allowance
Interest during construction

Electricity produced per kilogram is 45,000 MWd/t $*$ 1000 kW/MW/ 10^3 kg/t $*$ 24 h/day = 1.08 $\times$ 10^6 kWh(th); assuming a 33% thermal efficiency, we obtain

$$1.08 \times 10^6 * 0.33 = 356,400 \text{ kWh(e)}$$

The cost of fuel, then, is ($2489.18/kgU)/[356,400 kWh(e)] = 0.00698 $/ kWh(e) = ~0.7 cent/kWh(e).

8.4.4 Taxes

Taxes for a nuclear plant are no different than for other corporations. Local taxes make such plants very attractive to the community because the size of the tax, as income for the locality, is extremely important; other taxes, such as property taxes, can be lower because of the tax contribution from a nuclear plant.

8.4.5 Regulations

There is no doubt that regulations—federal, state, local—increase the cost of doing business. However, regulations are necessary to ensure the safety of the public and protection of the environment. The nuclear industry is no exception; it is very strictly regulated by the Nuclear Regulatory Commission (NRC). Companies that operate nuclear power plants pay a fee for any interaction with the NRC, for example, to request an amendment to the plant license or to license new fuel. There is no way to pinpoint a number for these regulatory costs; the only thing that can be said is that this cost is known and is incorporated into O&M costs.

8.5 Calculation of the Cost of Electricity

8.5.1 An Approximate Calculation

Before the levelized cost of electricity is computed, it is instructive to calculate an approximate cost, considering expenditures over a single year and disregarding present worth. Let us first break up the costs into three categories: initial and construction cost, annual O&M cost, and annual fuel cost. The cost of producing electricity can now be determined approximately as follows. Let:

e = unit cost of electricity [mill/kWh(e)]

x = annual fixed change rate (yr^{-1})

I = initial cost of plant ($)

$O\&M$ = annual operating and maintenance costs ($/yr)

F = annual fuel cost ($/yr)

E = net electricity generated [kWh(e)/yr].

Then

$$e = 10^3 * \frac{xI + O + F}{E} \text{ mill/kWh(e)} \tag{8.13}$$

The net electricity generated, E, is calculated from the following equation:

$$E[\text{kWh(e)/yr}] = P(\text{MWth}) * CF * 8760\left(\frac{h}{yr}\right) * 1000\left(\frac{kW}{MW}\right) * \eta\left(\frac{kWe}{kWth}\right)$$

$$\tag{8.14}$$

where CF is the capacity factor (see Chapter 6) and η is the thermal efficiency of the plant.

■ **Example 8.4:** What is the approximate cost of electricity produced by a nuclear plant given the following data?: cost of the plant: 6×10^9; cost of money: 8%; annual O&M: $500,000; annual fuel cost: 40×10^6; CF: 90%; design power: 1100 MW(e).

Answer: The electricity produced that year is:

$$E = 1100 \times 10^3 \text{ kWe} * (8760 \text{ h/yr}) * 0.90 = 8.67 \times 10^9 \text{ kWh(e)}$$

$$e = 10^3 \frac{0.08 * 6 \times 10^9 + 5 \times 10^5 + 40 \times 10^6}{8.67 \times 10^9} = \frac{520 \times 10^9}{8.67 \times 10^6}$$

$$= 60 \text{ mill/kWh(e)} = 6 \text{ cents/kWh(e)} \quad ■$$

8.5.2 The Levelized Cost of Electricity

The cost of electricity is not uniquely determined for all utilities or even for different power plants of the same utility. Factors affecting the calculation of the cost are:

1. Federal policies (IRS, FERC, NRC, EPA, et al.)

2. Local policies (state, county, and/or city taxes)

3. Type of power plant (nuclear, fossil, hydro)

4. Method of utility financing (regulated or deregulated).

The general principle of calculating electricity cost is an equation of the form:

Revenue requirements ($) = energy sold [kWh(e)] * price [$/kWh(e)]

Whereas the right side of this equation is straightforward, the same cannot be said about the left side. It is this part that is complicated and, sometimes, controversial because many components of cost are affected in different ways by federal, state, and local regulations and utility accounting practices.

From the discussion presented in the previous sections, it becomes obvious that revenue requirements (interest, return on investment, operation costs, fuel costs, etc.) are not constant in time; they change from year to year. The electricity generated is not constant either from year to year, because the capacity factor is not constant. As a result, the unit cost of electricity would not be the same from year to year. The question arises as to how an average cost can be calculated that is representative of the "average financial conditions" of the company. This is what the concept of the levelized cost of electricity attempts to accomplish.

The levelized cost may be defined for a batch of fuel or for a certain time period (year, one fuel cycle, or life of the plant) and for partial or total generation cost. The levelized cost of electricity per batch (or per period) is defined as that unit cost which, if charged uniformly for each kWh(e) generated by the batch (or during that period), would just enable the utility to:

1. Pay the required return to investors, each investment period, based on the outstanding principal of the batch at the beginning of the investment period.

2. Pay all taxes accrued on the batch (or for the period) on the cash flows pertaining to the batch.

3. Reduce the net investment in the batch by an appropriate amount so as to allow the net investment in the batch to go to zero when the last cash flow pertaining to the batch has occurred.

The equation derived below is based on the concepts first developed by Vondy.[5] It is not unique because, as explained in the beginning of this section, certain factors differ for different utilities. The general principle, however, of the "retirement" of the investment is generally used. We define the following quantities to be used for the levelized cost equation:

E_n = energy [kWh(e)] sold during period n

I_n = investment outstanding at beginning of period n

Z_n = investment during period n

V_n = income (taxable) from other than energy sale during period n

F_n = fuel expense during period n (e.g., storage)

D_n = depreciation during period n

O_n = operating and maintenance during period n

T_n = federal income tax during period n

S_n = state taxes during period n

f = used fuel fee prescribed by the Nuclear Waste Policy Act (NWPA) [1 mill/kWh(e)]

P_n = property (local) taxes during period n

G_n = state gross tax (sales tax) during period n

N = life of investment in years

τ = federal income tax rate

s = state tax rate

g = gross (sales) tax rate

p = property (local) tax rate

e = levelized cost of electricity [$ mill/kWh(e)]

f_b = fraction of investment in the form of bonds

$f_s = 1 - f_b$ = fraction in the form of stocks

r_s = stock rate of return

r_b = bond rate of return.

The equations for the federal, state, sales, and local taxes, respectively, are

$$T_n = \tau(10^{-3}eE_n + V_n - F_n - D_n - O_n - f_b r_b I_n - G_n - P_n - S_n - f \times 10^{-3}E_n)$$

(8.15)

$$S_n = s(10^{-3}eE_n + V_n - F_n - D_n - O_n - f_b r_b I_n - G_n - P_n - f \times 10^{-3}E_n)$$

(8.16)

$$G_n = g(10^{-3}eE_n + V_n)$$
(8.17)

$$P_n = pI_n$$
(8.18)

The total taxes, TT_n, during period n are the sum of Eqs. (8.15) through (8.18). If one defines

$$\tau_s = \tau + s - \tau_s \tag{8.19}$$

the equation for the total taxes becomes:

$$TT_n = \tau[10^{-3}(e - f)E_n + V_n] - \tau_s(D_n + F_n + O_n + f_b r_b I_n)$$
$$+ p (1 - \tau_s)I_n + g(1 - \tau_s)(10^{-3} eE_n + V_n) \tag{8.20}$$

The net income, R_n, during period n is defined as:

$R_n = $ (gross income) $-$ (fuel disposal cost) $-$ (operating and other costs)

$\quad - $ (return on investment) $-$ (debt payment) $-$ (taxes)

Using the previously defined quantities,

$$R_n = 10^{-3}eE_n + V_n - f \times 10^{-3}E_n - O_n - F_n - r_s f_s I_n - r_b f_b I_n - TT_n \tag{8.21}$$

Substituting the value of TT_n from Eq. (8.20) into Eq. (8.21), we obtain

$$R_n = -x'I_n + (1 - \tau_s)([10^{-3}(e - f)E_n + V_n] - g(1 - \tau_s)(10^{-3} eE_n + V_n)$$
$$- (1 - \tau_s)(O_n + F_n) + \tau_s D_n \tag{8.22}$$

where

$$x' = r_s(1 - f_b) + (1 - \tau_s)r_b f_b + p(1 - \tau_s) \tag{8.23}$$

The investment outstanding at the beginning of the $(n + 1)$ period is

$$I_{n+1} = I_n + Z_n - R_n \tag{8.24}$$

or

$$I_{n+1} = (1 + x')I_n + Z_n - (1 - \tau_t)(10^{-3} eE_n + V_n)$$
$$+ (1 - \tau_s)(O_n + F_n) - \tau_s D_n \tag{8.25}$$

where

$$\tau_t = \tau_s + g(1 - \tau_s) \tag{8.26}$$

Let us write this equation for successive years starting with year 1, noting that

$$V_0 = O_0 = D_0 = E_0 = F_0 = 0$$

1. $I_1 = Z_0$

2. $I_2 = (1 + x')Z_0 + Z_1 - (1 - \tau_t)(10^{-3} eE_1 + V_1) + (1 - \tau_s)(O_1 + F_1)$
   $- \tau_s D_1$

3. $I_3 = (1 + x')I_2 + Z_2 + \cdots$
   $= (1 + x')^2 Z_0 + (1 + x')Z_1 - (1 - \tau_t)(1 + x')$
   $\times (10^{-3} eE_1 + V_1) + (1 - \tau_s)(1 + x')(O_1 + F_1)$
   $- \tau_s(1 + x')D_1$

After N years (time periods)

$$IN + 1 = \sum_{n=0}^{N} (1 + x')^{N-n} Z_n - (1 - \tau_t) \sum_{n=1}^{N} (1 + x')^{N-n}(10^{-3} eE_n + V_n)$$

$$+ \sum_{n=1}^{N} (1 + x')^{N-n}(1 - \tau_s)(O_n + F_n) - \tau_s \sum_{n=1}^{N} (1 + x')^{N-n} D_n \tag{8.27}$$

Dividing by $(1 + x')^N$, setting $I_{N+1} = 0$, and solving for the levelized cost, e, we obtain:

$$e = \frac{\displaystyle\sum_{n=0}^{N} (1 + x')^{-n} \left[\frac{Z_n}{1 - \tau_t} - V_n - \frac{\tau_s}{1 - \tau_t} D_n + \frac{1 - \tau_s}{1 - \tau_t}(O_n + F_n + 10^{-3} fE_n) \right]}{10^{-3} \displaystyle\sum_{n=1}^{N} (1 + x')^{-n} E_n}$$

$$\tag{8.28}$$

If the income, V_n, from other than energy sales is partly taxable and partly nontaxable, we can write

$$V_n = V_{n,t} \text{ (taxable)} + V_{n,nt} \text{ (nontaxable)}$$

and Eq. (8.28) takes the form (with property taxes neglected)

$$
e = \frac{\displaystyle\sum_{n=0}^{N}(1+x')^{-n}\left[\frac{Z_n - V_{n,nt}}{1-\tau_t} - V_{n,t} - \frac{\tau_s}{1-\tau_t}D_n + \frac{1-\tau_s}{1-\tau_t}(O_n + F_n + 10^{-3}fE_n)\right]}{10^{-3}\displaystyle\sum_{n=1}^{N}(1+x')^{-n}E_n}
$$

(8.29)

Further, if only federal taxes are considered in the computation, in which case $\tau_t = \tau_s = \tau$, x' becomes

$$
x' = x = r_s f_s + (1-\tau)r_b f_b
$$

(8.30)

and Eq. (8.29) changes to

$$
e = \frac{\displaystyle\sum_{n=0}^{N}(1+x')^{-n}\left[\frac{Z_n - V_{n,nt}}{1-\tau} - V_{n,t} - \frac{\tau}{1-\tau}D_n + O_n + F_n + 10^{-3}fE_n\right]}{10^{-3}\displaystyle\sum_{n=1}^{N}(1+x')^{-n}E_n}
$$

(8.31)

Comparing Eqs. (8.29) and (8.31), it becomes obvious that inclusion of taxes does not change the form of the equation; it simply requires a different definition for x and τ. For the rest of the discussion, Eq. (8.31) is used for simplicity; the arguments to be made and conclusions to be drawn are not different when using either equation.

8.5.3 Comments on the Equation for the Levelized Cost

The quantity x', defined by Eq. (8.23), represents a "composite" effective cost of money that includes all taxes. If only federal taxes are considered, one obtains the quantity x, defined by Eq. (8.30). The quantity x (or x') is called the *discount rate* or *effective cost of money*. It represents the effective cost of money for the utility and it appears, as we might expect, in the present-worth factor $(1 + x)^{-n}$. For a simple loan, the value of x is equal to the interest rate charged by the lending institution. For a utility, the cost of money takes into account the difference between stocks and bonds, as well as the way in which the taxes affect the earnings. The following example presents a calculation of x for a typical set of values for the parameters involved.

■ *Example 8.5:* Calculate the discount rate for a utility that has a debt ratio equal to 52%, a rate of return on stocks equal to 10%, and interest on bonds equal to 8%. Assume a federal income tax rate of 37%.

Answer: Using Eq. (8.30),

$$x = 0.10 * 0.48 + (1 - 0.37) * 0.08 * 0.52 = 0.074, \text{ or } 7.4\% \quad ■$$

The denominator of Eq. (8.31) shows that the energy is "present worthed." That should not be surprising since the electricity produced represents income, and e times the denominator of Eq. (8.31), which is equal to

$$e10^{-3} \sum_{n=1}^{N} \frac{E_n}{(1+x)^n}$$

represents the revenue requirements corresponding to the cost of the fuel over N periods. It equals the amount that, if received as revenue in every period n, would enable the utility to pay bondholders and stockholders their expected return, pay taxes, and retire all investments at the end of the N'th year.

The derivation of Eq. (8.31) is based on the following assumptions:

1. All cash flows occur at the end of the period in which they appear in the equation.

2. Return to investors is paid at the same frequency as taxes.

3. The tax effects of a transaction are felt simultaneously with the transaction itself.

The fact that all cash flows are assumed to occur at the end of the period in which they actually are recorded means that Eq. (8.31) does not include the effects of small changes in the times at which cash flows occur (see assumption 1 above). To correct this, the period-by-period present-worth factor $(1 + x)^{-n}$ is simply replaced by an instantaneous present-worth factor:

$$(1 + x)^{t_R - t_n}$$

where t_R is the reference time in years, and t_n is the year at which cash flow n occurs.

To remove the restriction that the return to investors is paid with the same frequency as taxes, Eq. (8.31) must be rederived without using this assumption. Because the non-coincidence of payment of taxes and investors is a small perturbation, and the algebra involved in obtaining this new equation is relatively complicated, that derivation is not presented here. Thus, in what follows, the assumption is made that investors and taxes are paid at the same time.

Equation (8.31) could involve a second subscript indicating a particular batch. In that case, the levelized cost of a batch of fuel k would have these quantities:

$$e_k, Z_{k,n}, V_{k,n}, F_{k,n}, D_{k,n}, E_{k,n}, \text{etc.}$$

To correct Eq. (8.31) for the fact that the effects of the tax on a transaction are generally felt at some time after the transaction itself occurs, the term representing the transaction itself is simply separated from the term representing the taxes on the transaction. Using different summation indices for the two terms, one can easily show that

$$e_k = \frac{\displaystyle\sum_{n=0}^{N} (1+x)^{t_R - t_{kn}} (Z_{kn} - V_{kn,nt} - V_{kn,t} + O_{kn} + F_{kn} + 10^{-3} f E_{kn})}{10^{-3} \displaystyle\sum_{n=1}^{N} (1+x)^{t_R - t_{kn}} E_{kn} - \tau \displaystyle\sum_{l=1}^{L} (1+x)^{t_R - t_{kl}} E_{kl}}$$

$$+ \tau \frac{\displaystyle\sum_{l=0}^{LN} (1+x)^{t_R - t_{kl}} (-V_{kl,nt} - D_{kl} - O_{kl} - F_{kl})}{10^{-3} \displaystyle\sum_{n=1}^{N} (1+x)^{t_R - t_{kn}} E_{kn} - \tau \displaystyle\sum_{l=1}^{L} (1+x)^{t_R - t_{kl}} E_{kl}} \qquad (8.32)$$

The running index, n, is over all of the fuel payments and credits, other than taxes and return to investors; the running index, l, is over tax periods. Note that any calendar date can be used to represent $n = 0$, with $n < 0$ for prepayments.

One of the methods used to obtain the depreciation D_{kn} is the "unit of production" method based on the thermal energy, Q_{kn}, produced by batch k during period n. According to this method,

$$D_{kn} = \frac{Q_{kn}}{Q_k} DT_k \qquad (8.33)$$

where

Q_k = total thermal energy produced by batch k

DT_k = total depreciation allowance for batch k

If this value of D_{kn} is inserted into the equation and the assumption is made that taxes are paid at the same time revenues are received, Eq. (8.31) takes the form

$$
e_k = \frac{\sum_{n=0}^{N} (1+x)^{t_R-t_{kn}} \left[\dfrac{Z_{kn} - V_{kn,t}}{1-\tau} - V_{kn,nt} - \dfrac{\tau}{1-\tau}\left(\dfrac{DT_k}{Q_k}\right)Q_{kn} + O_{kn} + F_{kn} + 10^{-3}fE_{kn} \right]}{10^{-3} \sum_{n=1}^{N} (1+x)^{t_R-t_{kn}} E_{kn}}
$$

$$(8.34)$$

The equations for the cost of electricity presented in this chapter are based on discrete compounding of interest (cost of money). There is a completely equivalent method, based on continuous compounding,[6] in which the summations are replaced by integrals and the factor $(1 + x)^m$ becomes $\exp(i_c t_n)$ (see Section 8.1.6).

■ **Example 8.6:** Calculate the levelized cost [in mill/kWh(e)] for the batch of nuclear fuel with the following payment schedule and power production: The cost of the batch is $30 million paid in three annual installments of $15 million, $10 million, and $5 million each, with the first installment paid when the batch goes into the core. The batch stays in the core for 3 years. The reactor is an 1100-MW(e) PWR with an average capacity factor of 88%. Only federal taxes, at the rate of 35%, should be considered. The effective cost of money is 8.5%, O&M costs are $500,000 for the whole plant, disposal costs are as per NWPA, and the unit of production method is used for depreciation. The batch produces equal amounts of energy every year, amounting to one-third of the total energy produced by the core.

Answer: Equation (8.34) will be used. Let us identify the values of all the quantities appearing in Eq. (8.34):

$$Z_0 = \$15 \times 10^6$$

$$Z_1 = \$10 \times 10^6$$

$$Z_2 = \$5 \times 10^6$$

$$V_{kn,t} = V_{kn,nt} = F_{kn} = 0$$

$$x = 0.085$$

$$f = 1 \text{ mill/kWh(e)}$$

$$O_{kn} = (0.5 \times 10^6)/3|_{n=1,3}$$

$$\tau = 0.35$$

$$DT_k = \$30 \times 10^6$$

$$Q_{kn}/Q_k = 1/3,$$

$$E_{kn} = 1100 \text{ MWe} * 1000(\text{kWe/MWe}) * 0.88 * 8760 \text{ h/yr} = 8.480 \times 10^9 \text{ kWh(e)}.$$

The numerator is

$$\frac{1}{1 - 0.35}\left[15 \times 10^6(1 + x)^0 + 10 \times 10^6(1 + x)^{-1} + 5 \times 10^6(1 + x)^{-2}\right]$$

$$-\frac{0.35}{1 - 0.35}\frac{1}{3}30 \times 10^6\left[(1 + x)^{-1} + (1 + x)^{-2} + (1 + x)^{-3}\right]$$

$$+\frac{0.3 \times 10^6}{3}\left[(1 + x)^{-1} + (1 + x)^{-2} + (1 + x)^{-3}\right]$$

$$+ 10^{-3}\frac{1100}{3} \times 10^3 * 0.88 * 8760\left[(1 + x)^{-1} + (1 + x)^{-2} + (1 + x)^{-3}\right]$$

$$= 43.78 \times 10^6 - 13.74 \times 10^6 + 0.42 \times 10^6 + 7.21 \times 10^6$$

$$= \$37.67 \times 10^6$$

and the denominator is

$$10^{-3} \text{ (\$/mill)} \times \frac{8.48^9}{3}\left[(1 + x)^{-1} + (1 + x)^{-2} + (1 + x)^{-3}\right][\text{kWh(e)}]$$

$$= 7.21 \times 10^6 \text{ kWh(e)(\$/mill)}$$

$$e = \frac{37.67 \times 10^6}{7.21 \times 10^6} = 5.22 \text{ mill/kWh(e)} \quad \blacksquare$$

8.5.4 The Levelized Cost over a Period of Time

If the levelized cost of electricity during period n is ep_n, one can write the following equation:

$$ep_n * (\text{energy produced during period } n)$$

$$= \left(\begin{array}{c}\text{revenues collected from the sale of} \\ \text{electricity from all batches in the core} \\ \text{during period } n\end{array}\right)$$

Or, using the symbols for the quantities involved, the equation for ep_n becomes for K batches,

$$ep_n = \frac{\sum\limits_{k=1}^{K} e_k E_{k,n}}{\sum\limits_{k=1}^{K} E_{k,n}} \tag{8.35}$$

The equations presented in Sections 8.5.2 through 8.5.4 are not generic and represent only the fuel cost component of the cost of electricity, which amounts to approximately 30% of the total production cost. The specific equation for the cost of electricity for a particular utility may include special terms for costs (or income) that reflect the accounting practices of that company, the constraints imposed by the regional regulatory agencies, and the special conditions of the region served by that utility.

8.6 Comparison of Electricity Generation Costs from Various Plants

For the generation of electricity by nuclear power (fission reactors), this question is always asked: Is the cost of nuclear power competitive with other means of producing electricity? The main concern—a legitimate one—for nuclear power is the cost of construction. Because no new plants have been built in the United States since the late 1970s, no real figure is available. However, studies indicate that the cost of new 1000-MWe plants will be between $5 billion and $10 billion (see also Section 8.4.1). The other major expense, the nuclear fuel, has not escalated very much since 1975. Relevant data are given in Table 8.5.

TABLE 8.5
Nuclear Fuel Costs 1975–2011

Item	1975	1984	1988	1999	2011
Uranium ($/kg)	65.00	130.00	40.00	30.00	150.00
Conversion ($/kg)	2.76	4.30	4.00	6.00	12.00
Enrichment ($/SWU)	53.00	120.00	80.00	90.00	110.00
Fabrication[a]	160.00	176.00	200.00	240.00	240.00
Waste disposal	250.00[b]	NWPA[c]			

[a]Includes transportation costs.
[b]Charge for fuel discharged before April 1983.
[c]One mill/kWh(e), per NWPA, for fuel discharged after April 1983 (see Chapter 9).

Making comparisons of the cost of electricity by different means (nuclear, coal, gas, oil, solar, wind, etc.), especially for the future, is a very problematic task because of all the assumptions that have to be made. Also, how do we include in the calculation "external" costs? External costs are defined as follows by the European Commission's Externalities of Energy research project, ExternE[7]:

> An external cost, also known as an externality, arises when the social or economic activities of one group of persons have an impact on another group and when that impact is not fully accounted, or compensated for, by the first group.

External costs (or externalities), therefore, are costs or benefits to society, as a whole, now and into the future; examples are environmental pollution, deaths to members of the general public, and general degradation of the environment both aesthetic and physical (see also Section 12.11). External costs are not included now in the cost of electricity production. Here is a partial list of the factors that must be considered:

- Price of fuels (uranium, coal, gas, etc.)
- Construction costs
- Federal subsidies
- Possible charge on fossil fuels for greenhouse gas emissions
- Possible charge for environmental degradation (mining, solar panels, wind farms, etc.).

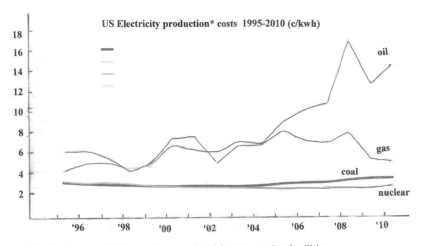

* Production cost=O&M plus fuel; calculated for non regulated utilities

FIGURE 8.5 U.S. electricity production costs, 1995–2010 in cents/kWh(e).

It is interesting to note that the uncertainties concerning these potential "costs" are smaller for nuclear than for any of the other methods of electricity generation. For the four main sources of generating electricity (coal, gas, oil, nuclear), we have real data from past experience, as shown in Fig. 8.5.

Bibliography

Benjamin, James E., Francia, Arthur J., and Strawser, Robert H., *Principles of Accounting*, 3rd ed., Dame Publications (1985).

Eschenbach, T., Lavelle, J.P., and Neaman, D.G., *Engineering Economic Analysis*, Oxford University Press (2009).

"Guide to Nuclear Power Cost Evaluation," TID-7025, National Technical Information Service (Mar. 1962).

Jackson, I., *Nukenomics: The Commercialization of Britain's Nuclear Industry*, Nuclear Engineering International (2008).

Park, C.S., *Fundamentals of Engineering Economics*, Prentice Hall (2003).

Smith, Gerald, *Engineering Economy*, 4th ed., Iowa State University Press (1979).

Suelflow, James E., *Public Utility Accounting: Theory and Application*, Public Utilities Studies Institute, Michigan State University (1973).

Sullivan, W.G., Wicks, E.M., and Koelling, C.P., *Engineering Economy*, Pearson College (2008).

General Websites

Edison Electric Institute, www.eei.org

Nuclear Engineering International, www.nei.org

U.S. Energy Information Administration, www.eia.doe.gov

References

1. "Depreciation," Publication 534, Internal Revenue Service (Rev. Nov. 1988).

2. "Brief Overview of Depreciation," Internal Revenue Service (2011); www.irs.gov/businesses/small/article/0,,id=137026,00.html.

3. Newman, D.G., *Engineering Economic Analysis*, 3rd ed., p. 281, Engineering Press Inc., San Jose, California (1988).

4. Public Utility Regulatory Policy Act (PURPA) of 1978, U.S. Department of Energy; www.doe.gov/search/site/purpa.

5. Vondy, D.R., "Basis and Certain Features of the Discount Technique in a Comparative Evaluation of Advanced Converters," ORNL-3686, Oak Ridge National Laboratory (Jan. 1965).

6. Hughes, J.W., and Hang, D.F., "Program GEM: A General Economic Model to Analyze Nuclear Fuel Cycle Costs," PhD Thesis, Nuclear Engineering Program, University of Illinois, Urbana (1975).

7. "External Costs," Study by Externalities of Energy Research Project, Bro-chure EUR 20198, European Commission (2003).

Problems

8.1. Indicate the depreciation per year for an asset costing $50,000 and hav-ing a salvage value of $2000 and a 5-yr lifetime. Consider all three methods discussed in the text.

8.2. A person purchased an automobile in 2010 for $10,000, paying for it in four equal payments at the beginning of each calendar year, starting on 1-1-11. Assuming an interest rate of 3.5%, what will be the future worth of this money on January 1, 2014?

8.3. At the time of the birth of his child, a father decides to put $7500 in the bank for the child's college education, earning 8% interest. What is the worth of this money when the child graduates from high school?

8.4. Prove Eqs. (8.11) and (8.12).

8.5. Prove that the amounts of money shown in Table 8.2, for plans 1 and 4, are equivalent when they are time-valued to the same date.

8.6. A utility has constructed a nuclear power plant over a period of 12 years, with expenditures per year as shown below. Assuming that the company has a debt ratio of 51%, the rate of return for stocks is 11%, the interest for bonds is 8.5%, and the corporate tax is 40%, what is the total cost of the plant at the time it begins operating? If the utility decides to repay this amount by assigning 30 equal payments over the life of the plant, what should the amount of each payment be?

Year before Operation	Expenditure at End of Year ($)	Year before Operation	Expenditure at End of Year ($)
12, 11, 10	85	4	230
9, 8	110	3	245
7	115	2	280
6	200	1	200
5	220	0	120

8.7. Derive Eq. (8.32).

8.8. Calculate the cost of 1 kg of uranium-fabricated fuel at the time the fuel goes into the core, assuming 12.5% cost of money compounded monthly. Also assume the following:

enrichment: 3.2%; tails: 0.2%; conversion loss: 0.5%; U_3O_8 price: $60/lb$U_3O_8$; conversion: $10/kgU; loss in fabrication: 0.8%; enrichment: $105/SWU; and fabrication-transportation costs: $220/kg.

Assume the start of operation as date zero and that the uranium purchased was paid for 24 months before date zero; conversion cost, paid 15 months before date zero; enrichment cost, paid 10 months before date zero; and fabrication cost, paid 3 months before date zero.

8.9. Is there a financial benefit, in terms of fuel cost alone, if the burnup in LWRs reaches an average of 45 MWd/kgU, from the average of 30 MWd/kgU? For both high and low burnup, assume the uranium fuel prices given in Problem 8.8. For the two different burnups, assume refueling data as given in the table below. For this problem, assume that the total cost for a batch is paid at the time the batch goes into the core. Assume the effective cost of money is equal to 9%.

	30 MWd/kgU	45 MWd/kgU
Enrichment	3%	3.5%
Tails	0.2%	0.2%
Batches in core	3 every 12 months	3 every 18 months
Mass of uranium in core	90 ton	90 ton
Refueling	1/3 (each time)	1/3

8.10. A nuclear power plant loaded with 93 tons of uranium in its core is licensed to operate at the maximum power of 3500 MWth. Its thermal efficiency is 31%. The first core consists of three equal batches with enrichments equal to 2.5%, 2.9%, and 3.1%. For subsequent cycles, the reactor uses 3.2% and 2.6%, in alternate cycles, for the one-third of the core that is replaced during each 18-month refueling, except for the last two batches, which have enrichments of 2.5% and 2.3%, respectively.

The burnup achieved by the fuel is 12 MWd/kgU for the first batch, 26 MWd/kgU for the second batch, 42 MWd/kgU for the third batch, and 45 MWd/kgU for all others except the last two. The next to the last batch has a burnup of 26 MWd/kgU, and the last one 12 MWd/kgU.

Assume that this utility has a debt ratio of 54%, with a 12% equity return and 7.5% bond interest rate. The corporate tax is 38%. The annual operation cost is equal to $600,000 paid at the end of a year of operation.

Depreciation is calculated based on the unit of production method. Disposal charge for the fuel is 1 mill/kWh(e).

Use pertinent uranium data from Problem 8.8. Assuming that the expense for each batch is paid 6 months before the batch is loaded into the core, calculate:

(a) The capacity factor for each cycle of operation

(b) The cost of electricity per batch

(c) The levelized cost of electricity for the life of the plant.

8.11. Repeat Problem 8.10 with the following enrichments and burnups:

Enrichments: 1st core: 3.3%, 3.5%, 4.0%; next batches: 3.5% and 4.0% in alternate cycles, for the one-third of the core that is replaced; the last two batches: 3.3% and 3.0%.

Burnups: 20 MWd/kgU for the first batch; 35 MWd/kgU for the second; and 45 MWd/kgU for the third. For all other batches assume burnup of 45 MWd/kgU except the last two; the next to last batch will have a burnup of 25 MWd/kgU and the last one 17 MWd/kgU.

NINE

HIGH-LEVEL WASTE MANAGEMENT

9.1 General Comments

Every industrial activity produces waste materials, some of which are extremely toxic and may cause illnesses (such as genetic effects or cancer) if inhaled or ingested, or may simply be dangerous (e.g., burnable or explosive). Before the environmental awareness movement started in the 1960s, "normal" methods of disposing of wastes involved discharging them into streams, rivers, lakes, or the sea; discharging them directly into the atmosphere; burning them (in which case the wastes in some form or another again entered the atmosphere); or placing them in landfills, directly on the surface of the ground or in shallow burial sites. Examples of industrial wastes (other than nuclear) are arsenic, mercury, cadmium, and other heavy metals, cyanide and potassium cyanide, and pesticides. Unfortunately, industrial nations were not careful in the past about the disposal of wastes. As a result, many sites exist in many states containing these dangerous substances, most of which remain toxic forever; and in many cases it is not known what the composition of the waste is.

With respect to wastes, the nuclear industry is no exception; it generates radioactive wastes that must be properly treated to protect man and the environment. Radioactive wastes differ from other industrial wastes in two respects. First, the risk that they pose to man decreases with time. Second, the volume of nuclear wastes is much smaller than that of other industries [per unit of the same product, for example, per kWh(e)]. As an example, compare the emissions of a coal-fired plant to those of a nuclear power plant. A 1000-MWe coal plant burns $\sim 11,000$ tons of coal every 24 h, and discharges directly into the atmosphere $\sim 13,700$ t of CO_2, ~ 300 t of SO_2, ~ 30 t of NOx, and ~ 5 t of fly ash containing small quantities of such elements as chlorine, cadmium, arsenic, mercury, lead, and some radioactive elements. A 1000-MWe nuclear plant produces ~ 500 m^3/yr of waste consisting of contaminated clothes, tools, resins (from demineralizers), etc., none of which is released to the atmosphere. The routine radioactive releases from a nuclear power plant that go directly into the atmosphere are well below any limit that could conceivably be of danger to man or the environment. The danger from wastes is not necessarily proportional to their volume, but their management definitely depends on the volume that must be disposed. Electricity generation by nuclear power plants is the only energy-producing industry that incorporates the cost of its waste into the price of its product (see Section 9.4.1).

Radioactive wastes began to accumulate as a result of military and civilian activities that started with the Manhattan Project in the 1940s and continued to accumulate as nuclear power began to be used for the generation of electricity. The wastes were controlled by regulations promulgated by the Atomic Energy Commission (AEC) and its successor the Nuclear Regulatory Commission (NRC),but until about 1980, the federal government had no official detailed plan for the management of nuclear wastes. Today, the management of radioactive wastes is recognized as an integral part of nuclear activities and is treated as such.

Although Congress did not act officially until 1982, the problems of nuclear waste management were studied much earlier. The government, industry, and universities produced a plethora of reports and papers dealing with the subject both here and in other countries.[1-8] The general opinion of the scientific community is that the disposal of radioactive waste is not a technical problem, in the sense that new technology needs to be developed, and it is not a serious task, especially when compared to the problems associated with wastes from other industries. Unfortunately, this opinion is not shared by the public. The perception by the public is that the existence and the disposal of radioactive waste pose a threat to life, a threat much more serious than many other chemical wastes that are handled routinely and to which people are exposed routinely. As a result of the public perception of the problem, the necessary political decisions for the establishment of sites for the disposal of these wastes have not been made.

There is no doubt that radioactive wastes may be dangerous to man and his biological environment. For this reason, a management plan—such as the one provided by two congressional acts that deal with radioactive waste disposal (discussed in Sections 9.4 and 10.2)—is necessary to protect man and his biosphere by isolating the wastes from man's environment for as long as necessary, meaning, until they pose no measurable risk to man. Radioactive waste management consists of all the activities (operational, safety related, administrative) that deal with the confinement, treatment, storage, and disposal of all types of radioactive wastes to satisfy the objectives of protecting human health and the environment now and in the future without imposing undue burdens on future generations.

The damaging potential of radioactive wastes is frequently expressed in terms of their activity, either in curies (Ci) or becquerels (Bq). There is another concept, however, called *toxicity*, that gives a better measure of the degree of potential biological hazard because it takes into account the sensitivity of human beings to radioisotopes after inhalation or ingestion.

To define toxicity, let $DAC(i,k)$ be the derived air concentration (Ci/cm^3) of isotope i, in air or water (index k), as given by the Nuclear Regulatory Commission 10 CFR 20, Appendix B.[9] (Note that DAC has replaced MPC, maximum permissible concentration.) If the activity of isotope i is $A(i)$ Ci, the toxicity is given by

$$\text{Toxicity } (i,k) = A(i)/DAC(i,k) \qquad (9.1)$$

If more than one isotope is involved, a summation is performed over all the isotopes present in the mixture. The toxicity represents the volume of air or water with which the radioactive wastes must be diluted in order for continuous breathing of that air or drinking of that water to result in a dose that is less than that corresponding to the maximum allowed dose to members of the public (100 mrem/yr) from continuous exposure to a concentration equal to the DAC value. Regulations that specify maximum allowed activity for various isotopes are based, in general, on equal toxicity from the isotopes involved.

■ *Example 9.1:* Compare the toxicities of 1 Ci of the isotopes ^{3}H and ^{137}Cs. The DAC values in air are 2.0×10^{-5} μCi/mL and 6.0×10^{-8} μCi/mL, respectively.

Answer: According to Eq. (9.1),

$$\text{Toxicity}(^3\text{H}) = 1.0 \times 10^6 \ \mu\text{Ci}/2.0 \times 10^{-5} \ \mu\text{Ci/mL} = 5.0 \times 10^4 \ \text{m}^3$$

$$\text{Toxicity}(^{137}\text{Cs}) = 1.0 \times 10^6 \ \mu\text{Ci}/6.0 \times 10^{-8} \ \mu\text{Ci/mL} = 1.67 \times 10^7 \ \text{m}^3$$

Therefore,

$$\text{Toxicity}(^{137}\text{Cs})/\text{toxicity}(^3\text{H}) = 1.67 \times 10^7/5 \times 10^4 = 333$$

What this means is that for the same activity, ^{137}Cs is 333 times more hazardous than tritium. ■

As mentioned earlier, radioactive wastes have one advantage over chemical and other industrial wastes in that they decay over time; therefore, the risk that they pose to man decreases over time. In a mixture of radioisotopes in which many different half lives are involved, the importance of isotopes, in terms of hazard, changes over time. Also, the toxicity over time depends on the form of the waste being disposed (nuclear fuel with or without recycling) as Figs. 9.1(a) and (b) show. Notice that with recycling (and transmutation of actinides) the toxicity of the wastes becomes less than that of natural uranium after less than 1000 years.

This chapter and the next one discuss the sources and types of radioactive wastes, the steps to be taken for their disposal in accordance with the congressional acts, and the pertinent rules and regulations promulgated by the federal government agencies, the NRC and the Environmental Protection Agency (EPA). The actions taken by other nations for the disposal of

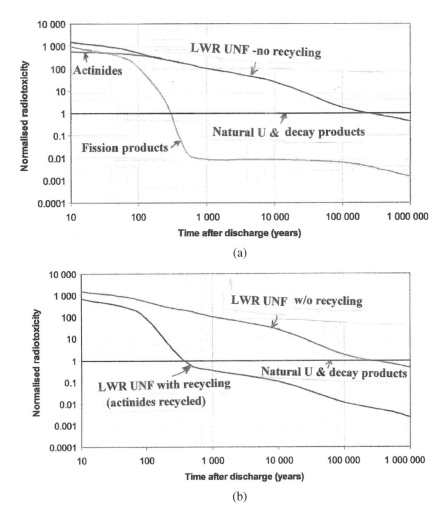

(a)

(b)

FIGURE 9.1 (a) Change of toxicity with time of used nuclear fuel (UNF) without recycling.[10] (b) Change of toxicity with time of UNF with recycling.[10]

radioactive wastes are also presented. Chapter 9 concentrates on high-level wastes and Chapter 10 on low-level wastes.

9.2 Classification of Radioactive Wastes

The five general categories (types) of radioactive wastes are as follows:

1. *High-level waste (HLW):* HLW is defined as follows in the Nuclear Waste Policy Act (NWPA; see Section 9.4): "(A) the highly radioactive material resulting from the reprocessing of spent fuel, including liquid waste produced directly in reprocessing, and any solid material derived from such liquid waste, that contains fission products in sufficient concentrations; and (B) other highly radioactive material that the Commission (NRC), consistent with existing law, determines by rule requires permanent isolation." In a once-through fuel cycle, the used nuclear fuel is considered to be HLW.

2. *Transuranic waste (TRU):* These are defined as wastes containing alpha-emitting isotopes with $Z > 92$, with half lives longer than 5 years, and concentrations greater than 100 nCi per gram of waste. This is the NRC definition. The EPA and the U.S. Department of Energy (DOE) use a slightly different definition, specifying half lives longer than 20 years; the rest of their definition is the same as that of the NRC. TRU is a subset of HLW, which although mentioned, is not formally defined in the NWPA. (In addition to the TRU definition given here, the term TRU is also used to designate all man-made chemical elements with $Z > 92$.)

3. *Low-level waste (LLW):* LLW is defined as follows in the NWPA: "(A) is not HLW, spent nuclear fuel, transuranic waste, or by-product material as defined in Section 11e(2) of the Atomic Energy Act of 1954; and (B) the Commission (NRC), consistent with existing law, classifies as LLW." LLW is generated in all activities involving radioactive materials. Examples of common LLW wastes are contaminated clothing, tools, syringes, cotton swipes, paper, rags, and old calibration sources. Management of LLW is discussed in Chapter 10.[a]

4. *Uranium mill tailings* are also considered radioactive wastes. Because they are not transported from their generation point, they are treated differently, as explained in Chapter 2. Mill tailings are not included in the management of radioactive waste disposal discussed in this chapter.

[a] Some other countries (e.g., European countries) also recognize a type of waste called *intermediate-level waste* (ILW); an examination of the definition of ILW leads to the conclusion that ILW is very close to the U.S. LLW type called GTCC (see Section 10.3.2).

5. *Naturally occurring and accelerator-produced radioactive materials (NORM or NARM)* make up the fifth category of radioactive wastes, which is not regulated by the NRC. Instead, NARM is regulated by the individual states. In terms of disposal, most NARM qualifies as LLW. For this reason, there is no reason to discuss them separately.

9.3 Sources and Examples of Radioactive Wastes

All activities, either civilian or defense related, involving radioactive materials produce radioactive wastes. Examples are nuclear fuel manufacturing, reactor operations, nuclear weapons production, research using radioisotopes, medical operations using radioisotopes for research, diagnosis, and therapy, production of radiopharmaceuticals, and radioisotopic sources used by industry for research or routine measurements.

Civilian wastes consist mainly of used nuclear fuel (UNF), which is considered to be HLW, and LLW. Defense wastes consist of UNF, HLW from reprocessing operations, TRU, and LLW. Research establishments and industry generate primarily LLW; they produce HLW only in exceptional cases when they handle nuclear fuel or fissile material for research.

Table 9.1 gives lifetime waste generation volumes for LWRs. A report by the Secretary of Energy[11] states that as of December 2008, there were in the United States ~58,000 tHM UNF from civilian reactors; government activities had produced 2500 tHM of UNF and 10,300 tHM of HLW.

9.4 HLW Management Policy Acts

9.4.1 The Nuclear Waste Policy Act of 1982 and Its 1987 Amendments

The NWPA was passed by Congress in December 1982 and was signed into law by the president on January 7, 1983 (Ref. 12). The act was amended in 1987 and its amendments became law on December 22, 1987 (Ref. 13). The main provisions of both the original NWPA and its amendments are discussed in this section.

The NWPA is a very comprehensive piece of legislation. It provides detailed step-by-step procedures, with corresponding dates for completion of the various steps, for all the tasks related to the disposal of HLW. Specifically, Title I of the NWPA contains the following four subtitles:

A. *Repositories for Disposal of HLW and Spent Nuclear Fuel:* Details are given of the process to be followed for the site selection for a repository. Consultation and participation of states and Indian tribes

TABLE 9.1
Lifetime Radioactive Waste Generation from a PWR and a BWR*

Waste Type	Reference PWR, 1 GWe		Reference BWR, 1 GWe	
	Volume (m³)	Radioactivity (Undecayed Curies)	Volume (m³)	Radioactivity (Undecayed Curies)
Once-through fuel cycle wastes				
Mill tailings	4.353×10^6	3.710×10^4	4.867×10^6	4.149×10^4
LLW from uranium conversion[a]	3.411×10^2	9.813×10^3	3.814×10^2	1.097×10^4
LLW from uranium enrichment[b]	1.328×10^2	9.716×10^3	1.365×10^2	1.080×10^4
LLW from fuel fabrication	3.063×10^3	7.288×10^0	4.110×10^3	9.781×10^0
LLW from reactor power generation	3.032×10^4	2.866×10^4	5.217×10^4	7.956×10^4
Reactor spent fuel	5.213×10^2	3.270×10^{9c}	6.996×10^2	3.342×10^{9c}
Decommissioning wastes				
LLW	1.510×10^4	1.057×10^5	1.640×10^4	2.532×10^5
Greater than Class C	1.130×10^2	4.070×10^6	4.070×10^1	3.300×10^6
TOTALS	4.403×10^6	3.274×10^9	4.941×10^6	3.348×10^9

Source: "Spent Fuel and Radioactive Waste Inventories, Projections and Characteristics," DOE/RW-0006, Rev. 1, U.S. Department of Energy (Dec. 1985).
*Waste generated from 40 yr of reactor operation and 26 GWe-yr of electric energy production.
[a] Applies to the fluorination/fractionation process.
[b] Applies to the gaseous diffusion process.
[c] Based on activity levels measured 1 yr after reactor discharge. For the PWR, these levels are based on a burnup of 33,000 MWd/MTIHM. Activity levels reported for the BWR are based on a burnup of 27,500 MWd/MTIHM.

is emphasized. Dates are given for the major milestones to be achieved.

B. *Interim Storage Program:* The need for interim storage for spent fuel will be investigated. Although the generators of the spent fuel (the nuclear utilities) are responsible for the storage, the act recognizes the responsibility of the government to provide interim storage facilities, if needed. A storage capacity of no more than 1900 tons of capacity will be considered.

C. *Monitored Retrievable Storage (MRS):* The possibility will be addressed for the construction of a facility for the storage of HLW and spent fuel, with retrieval possible, as an option to the geological repository.

D. *Low-Level Radioactive Waste:* This subsection deals only with financial arrangements for LLW site closure.

Title II of the act deals with the research and development needed for the successful completion of the goals of the NWPA.

Title III establishes an Office of Civilian Radioactive Waste Management (OCRWM), with a director reporting to the Secretary of Energy, and the Nuclear Waste Fund, the mechanism for collection of money from the nuclear utilities to cover the cost of implementing the NWPA.

Within months after the signing of the act the OCRWM was established and contracts between the DOE and the nuclear utilities were signed for the payment of the fee required by the NWPA. The DOE developed a standard contract that represents the official agreement between the parties involved, guaranteeing that for the fee paid by the utilities, the federal government will take the used fuel from the utilities and dispose of it properly. Except for the fee, the utilities have no other responsibility for the disposal of their used fuel. Utilities are, however, responsible for the storage of the used fuel prior to disposal.

The Nuclear Waste Fund is made up from 1 mill/kWh of nuclear electricity generated after April 7, 1983, paid directly to the DOE by each utility operating a nuclear power plant. For used fuel discharged before April 7, 1983, the DOE has established a one-time fee per kilogram of heavy metal in the used fuel. This fee corresponds to approximately 1 mill/kWh(e) generated by that used fuel. The fee for fuel discharged before April 7, 1983, was set at $250/kgU; the estimated revenue from that fuel is $2.3 billion. All fees undergo annual reviews; as of 2012, no adjustments had been necessary. Based on nuclear electricity generation in 2011, the government collects approximately $750 million per year for the Nuclear Waste Fund; as of May 2010, $34.7 billion had been paid by the nuclear utilities, of which $10.8 billion had been spent on the Yucca Mountain Project; the fund has an unspent balance of ~$25 billion.

The process for the selection of a site for the repository proceeded, in the beginning, along the lines prescribed by the NWPA. In February 1984, the DOE identified nine sites as potentially acceptable: one in Nevada, in a geologic medium called tuff; one in Washington in basalt; two in Texas in salt; two in Utah in salt; one in Louisiana in a salt dome; and two in Mississippi in salt domes. By December 1984, environmental assessments prepared for these locations narrowed the selection to three sites for recommendation to the president: Yucca Mountain, Nevada; Deaf County, Texas; and Hanford, Washington. The DOE began organizing programs for characterization of all three sites. The final selection of the first site became a political argument in Congress, since none of the three states desired to be the host for the first repository.

Activities related to MRS also progressed. In April 1985, the DOE identified three candidate sites, in accordance with the NWPA, all located in the state of Tennessee. The congressional delegation of Tennessee opposed the location of the MRS in that state. To avoid a threatened moratorium on NWPA activities, Congress passed amendments to the NWPA in December 1987 that dictated the following:

1. The DOE was instructed to proceed with characterization of the Yucca Mountain site in Nevada as the site for the first repository and stop, within 90 days from the enactment of the act, all activities at the other two sites.

2. If the Secretary of Energy determines the Yucca Mountain site to be unsuitable for development, he should (a) terminate all activities in that site, (b) notify the Congress and the state of Nevada and indicate the reasons for such termination, (c) remove all HLW from the site, (d) take reasonable and necessary steps to return the site to its original condition, (e) suspend all future benefits payments, with respect to that site (see discussion below on benefits), and (f) report to Congress no later than 6 months after such termination about further action to ensure the safe disposal of HLW.

3. The DOE cannot proceed with activities for a second repository. The secretary was scheduled to report to the president and to Congress after January 1, 2007, but no later than January 1, 2010, on whether or not a second repository is needed. *(No such report was submitted because activities for a geologic repository ceased in 2009; see text below.)*

4. The proposed sites for MRS in Tennessee were nullified. An MRS Review Commission was established, consisting of three members, appointed by the president pro tempore of the Senate and the speaker of the House of Representatives, to evaluate the need for MRS.

5. The secretary may enter into a benefits agreement with the state of Nevada concerning the repository, or with another state or Indian tribe concerning an MRS site. *(No such agreement was initiated.)*

6. An office for a nuclear waste negotiator was established within the executive office of the president. The negotiator shall be appointed by the president, by and with the advice and consent of the Senate. The negotiator shall attempt to find a state or Indian tribe willing to host an MRS facility at a technically qualified site. The office shall cease to exist no later than 30 days after December 22, 1992 (five years and 30 days after the enactment of the amendments). *(The office was abolished in 1995.)*

7. A Nuclear Waste Technical Review Board is established, an independent body within the executive branch. The board will consist of 11 members, appointed by the president for a term of four years. The president shall designate one member as chairman. The president will select the members from nominees recommended to him by the National Academy of Sciences. The board shall evaluate the activities of the DOE pertaining to the NWPA and its amendments and report its findings, not less than two times per year, to the Congress and to the secretary of DOE (information about the Nuclear Waste Review Board is given in www.nwtrb.gov).

8. An Office of Sub-seabed Disposal Research is established within the Office of Energy Research of the DOE. The secretary shall establish a university-based sub-seabed consortium to investigate the feasibility of this method of disposal, and he shall report to Congress on the feasibility of this method for disposal of HLW.

9. The secretary shall conduct a study of the use of dry casks for the storage of spent fuel at the sites of nuclear power plants. The secretary shall report to Congress on this matter. (This report[14] was submitted to Congress in February 1989.)

The MRS commission submitted its report to Congress in November 1989; it recommended that Congress authorize construction of emergency storage facilities for UNF and reconsider the subject of interim storage by the year 2000.

In accordance with the 1987 Amendments to the NWPA, DOE started work at the Yucca Mountain site in 1994; the original schedule called for first acceptance of UNF in 1998 (more on repositories in Section 9.6.5). The DOE submitted an application to the NRC for a repository license in June 2008. In Spring 2009, the new U.S. administration declared that Yucca Mountain was not suitable as a geologic repository site; the DOE stopped all work and withdrew the licensing application.

9.4.2 The Blue Ribbon Commission (BRC) of 2010

In January 2010, President Obama issued an executive order to the Secretary of Energy to establish a 15-member commission, designated as the Blue Ribbon Commission (BRC), with the task of examining

> America's Nuclear Future.... The Commission should conduct a comprehensive review of policies for managing the back end of the nuclear fuel cycle, including all alternatives for the storage, processing, and disposal of civilian and defense used nuclear fuel and nuclear waste. This review should include an evaluation of advanced fuel cycle technologies that would optimize energy recovery, resource utilization, and the minimization of materials derived from nuclear activities in a manner consistent with U.S. nonproliferation goals. In performing its functions, the Commission should consider a broad range of technological and policy alternatives, and should analyze the scientific, environmental, budgetary, economic, financial, and management issues, among others, surrounding each alternative it considers. Where appropriate, the Commission may also identify potential statutory changes.

The BRC was directed to provide an interim report within 18 months (which was completed in July 2011) and a final report in 2 years (January 2012). The following recommendations were made by the BRC to the Secretary of Energy (January 2012; http://brc.gov):

1. A new, consent-based approach to siting future nuclear waste management facilities

2. A new organization dedicated solely to implementing the waste management program and empowered with the authority and resources to succeed

3. Access to the funds nuclear utility ratepayers are providing for the purpose of nuclear waste management

4. Prompt efforts to develop one or more geologic disposal facilities

5. Prompt efforts to develop one or more consolidated storage facilities

6. Prompt efforts to prepare for the eventual large-scale transport of used nuclear fuel and high-level waste to consolidated storage and disposal facilities when such facilities become available

7. Support for continued U.S. innovation in nuclear energy technology and for workforce development

8. Active U.S. leadership in international efforts to address safety, waste management, nonproliferation, and security concerns

Implementation of the commission's recommendations requires new legislation in six areas:

1. *Establishing a new facility siting process.* The NWPA, as amended in 1987, now provides only for the evaluation and licensing of a single repository site at Yucca Mountain, Nevada. The act should be amended to authorize a new consent-based process to be used for selecting and evaluating sites and licensing consolidated storage and disposal facilities in the future.

2. *Authorizing consolidated interim storage facilities.* The NWPA allows the government to construct one consolidated storage facility with limited capacity, but only after construction of a nuclear waste repository has been licensed. One or more consolidated storage facilities should be established, independent of the schedule for opening a repository. The act should be modified to allow for a consent-based process to site, license, and construct multiple storage facilities with adequate capacity when needed and to clarify that nuclear waste fee payments can be used for this purpose.

3. *Broadening support to jurisdictions affected by transportation.* The NWPA provides funding and technical assistance for training public safety officials from states and tribes whose jurisdictions would be traversed by shipments of used fuel to a storage or disposal facility. The act should be amended to give the waste management organization (see below) the broader authorities given to DOE in the Waste Isolation Pilot Plant (WIPP) Land Withdrawal Act that supported the successful large-scale transport of TRU to WIPP (including a public information program, support for the acquisition of equipment to respond to transportation incidents, and broad assistance for other waste-related transportation safety programs).

4. *Establishing a new waste management organization.* Responsibility for implementing the nation's program for managing used nuclear fuel and high-level radioactive wastes is currently assigned to the U.S. Department of Energy. Legislation will be needed to (a) move this responsibility to a new, independent, government-chartered corporation focused solely on carrying out that program and (b) establish the appropriate oversight mechanisms.

5. *Ensuring access to dedicated funding.* Current federal budget rules and laws make it impossible for the nuclear waste program to have assured access to the fees being collected from nuclear utilities and ratepayers to finance the commercial share of the waste program's expenses. Legislation is required to provide access to the Nuclear

Waste Fund and fees independent of the annual appropriations process but subject to rigorous independent financial and managerial oversight.

6. *Promoting international engagement to support safe and secure waste management.* Congress may need to provide policy direction and new legislation to implement some measures aimed at helping other countries manage radioactive wastes in a safe, secure, and proliferation-resistant manner, similar to the expired NWPA provisions for technical assistance to non-nuclear weapons states in the area of used nuclear fuel storage and disposal.

Once the new waste management organization of recommendation 2 above has been established, it should:

1. *Develop a set of basic initial siting criteria.* These criteria will ensure that time is not wasted investigating sites that are clearly unsuitable or inappropriate.

2. *Encourage expressions of interest from a large variety of communities that have potentially suitable sites.* As these communities become engaged in the process, the implementing organization must be flexible enough not to force the issue of consent while also being fully prepared to take advantage of promising opportunities when they arise.

3. *Establish initial program milestones.* Milestones should be laid out in a mission plan to allow for review by Congress, the administration, and stakeholders, and to provide verifiable indicators for oversight of the organization's performance.

Finally, the commission recommends that the EPA and NRC develop a generic disposal standard and supporting regulatory requirements early in the siting process. Generally applicable regulations are more likely to earn public confidence than site-specific standards. In addition, having a generic standard will support the efficient consideration and examination of multiple sites.

9.4.3 European Policy

In 2011, the European Council (heads of states) adopted a directive that requires all 27 member states of the European Union (EU) to have, by 2015, a plan for the safe disposal of radioactive waste, employing properly trained and regulated personnel. With this directive, the EU recognized that radioactive waste management (especially HLW) represents a safety issue that crosses national boundaries. The national plans to be developed must (1) cover transport of wastes and (2) include a well-defined timetable for the construction of disposal facilities. The decision for the location of disposal facilities must be based on the voluntary involvement of the host communities.

Two options are acknowledged: The first is disposal of the UNF intact as waste; the second is reprocessing of the UNF, recycling of the U and Pu, and disposal of the remainder as HLW. Exports of wastes among the EU countries will be possible as well as sharing of disposal facilities. Exports outside the EU will be allowed only to countries that have an operational disposal facility meeting the International Atomic Energy Agency (IAEA) safety standards. In the case of reprocessing of EU UNF outside Europe, the ultimate wastes must be returned to the originating EU state.

The directive made the use of IAEA safety standards in waste management and disposal legally binding for EU states; finally, the directive requires that the EU members submit their plans for review by 2015.

9.4.4 Russian Policy

Russia adopted radioactive waste legislation in 2011. The legislation establishes a legal framework for radioactive waste management and a national management system meeting the requirements of the Joint Convention on the Safe Management of Spent Nuclear Fuel and of the Safe Management of Radioactive Waste ratified by Russia in 2006.

The law sets time limits for interim storage and for volume of waste produced by generators. It also defines the conditions considered suitable for disposal and transfer to a national operator, and payment of disposal charges is also prescribed. Import and export of radioactive waste is prohibited, and the law forbids building new facilities for disposal of liquid radioactive waste in geological formations. Russia has used deep-well injection for LLW and ILW for many years, with Seversk being the main site for this activity. Additional legislation regarding UNF and other HLW wastes is expected to follow.

9.4.5 Other Countries' Policies

In the United Kingdom, the Committee on Radioactive Waste Management (CoRWM) made its final recommendations on managing U.K. radioactive waste in July 2006. They recommended that geological disposal coupled with safe and secure interim storage is the way forward for the long-term management of the country's radioactive wastes. In October 2006, the government announced that it had accepted CoRWM's recommendations. The foundation for all activities regarding these wastes is two policy acts: (1) the Health and Safety at Work Act of 1974 (HSWA74) and (2) the Nuclear Installations Act of 1965 (as amended).

In 2002 Canada passed the Nuclear Fuel Waste Act (NFWA). The NFWA requires the nuclear electricity generating companies to set up an organization to make recommendations to the government for the long-term management of their UNF. The legislation also requires the generators of UNF to establish a separate trust fund to finance long-term UNF disposal needs; these funds were established in 2002 and annual contributions are made. Under the NFWA, a Nuclear Waste Management Organization (NWMO) was established in 2002 to carry out the provisions of the act.

In Korea, its Atomic Energy Commission developed the country's National Radioactive Waste Management Policy in 1998. The policy stipulates that the site selection process for a radioactive waste repository be transparent and that the government explain its objectives to ensure the safety of the project to the public. This national policy includes the following:

1. The government will have direct control of the radioactive wastes and will be responsible for their long-term safe management.

2. Radioactive wastes will be safely managed, taking into consideration their biological and environmental impact so as to protect people, society, and the environment from the harmful effects of radiation and to observe international norms on the safety of radioactive waste management.

3. Radioactive waste generation will be minimized.

4. The expenses related to radioactive waste management will be levied on the radioactive waste generator at the point of radioactive waste generation, without imposing undue burden on future generations.

5. Radioactive waste will be managed transparently and openly, and the radioactive waste management project shall be promoted with regard to harmony with the local community, and to community development.

9.5 Used Nuclear Fuel Management

9.5.1 UNF Storage

Until 1977, at which time the U.S. government deferred reprocessing indefinitely, the utilities that owned nuclear power plants operated on the assumption that the used (irradiated) fuel would be shipped to a federal facility a few years after its discharge from the core. Specifically, the nuclear power plants had provisions to store the used fuel on site, in water pools, for about 5 years. Since a nuclear power plant should always have full-core discharge capability (i.e., it should be possible to empty the core of all fuel and store it on site temporarily if a problem developed inside the pressure vessel), the minimum amount of on-site capacity should be equal to 4/3 cores (one full core plus one-third of a fresh fuel reload).

Because the government is not yet in a position to take the UNF away from the power plant sites, the utilities running the nuclear plants had to find ways to expand the storage capacity for UNF. The available choices are as follows:

1. Expand the existing pool physically or build a second pool.

2. Rerack the existing pool; that is, place the assemblies in a tighter grid.

3. Store UNF in air-cooled vaults on site or off site.

4. Consolidate UNF to decrease its volume, thus save space.

5. Stop operation of the plant.

Option 5 is not realistic; it was not considered by any utility. Option 1 was not exercised either because of cost and also because of space constraints, especially for physical expansion of the existing pool. Option 4, consolidation, also was not used.

The fuel may be stored as "unconsolidated" or "consolidated." Unconsolidated fuel is fuel that is stored as intact assemblies; consolidated fuel results when the fuel rods are removed from the fuel assembly and placed in a grid with spacing closer than that of an intact assembly, or placed in a closed-packed array inside a canister.[14,15] Volume savings of 2:1 by consolidation have been demonstrated. The advantages of fuel rod consolidation are (1) maximum fuel rod packing density; (2) greatly enhanced heat transfer characteristics because heat is removed primarily by conduction, rather than convection or radiation; and (3) ability to cut the number of UNF shipping casks required in half.

UNF consolidation is not employed because it carries serious disadvantages. When the assembly is taken apart, there is a risk for individual rods to be damaged and leak fission products. Disassembly of irradiated fuel produces scrap metal parts that are radioactive. The disassembly must be done in a special building using remote control devices. After the operation ends, the building will have to be decommissioned. All this means additional "regulatory" and real financial burdens that make consolidation a very unattractive option, at present.

Going back to the preceding list, options 2 and 3 are the only ones left and they are the ones used by the nuclear utilities. Both the "wet" (option 2) and the "dry" (option 3) storage methods are being used.

Because used reactor fuel had been successfully stored in water pools at many reactor sites, in some cases for more than 30 years,[16–20] this "wet storage method" represented—and still does today—a sound demonstrated technology for the safe storage of irradiated fuel for decades with negligible environmental impact. For this reason, the utilities that needed additional storage increased the on-site used fuel pool capacity by reracking.

The original fuel storage racks in reactor used fuel pools were constructed of stainless steel and permitted 6 in. or more of water between fuel assemblies. To be able to store more fuel safely, the racks were replaced with "high-density racks" constructed of Boral™, a neutron-absorbing composite material consisting of boron carbide evenly dispersed within an aluminum matrix. The use of Boral permitted closer spacing of fuel assemblies without criticality problems. Boron is unique in its ability to absorb thermal neutrons without producing any significant secondary radiation: Only alpha particles, which are easily absorbed by the water of the pool, and a (relatively) soft 0.480-MeV gamma are emitted.

Keep in mind that a basic requirement of any UNF storage facility is to have a value of $k < 1.0$. This subcriticality should be achieved by an appropriate distance between assemblies and the use of solid poisons (e.g., Boral). Obtaining $k < 1.0$ with dissolved boron in the water of the pool is not allowed.[21] Another requirement is for the temperature of the water in the pool to stay below a certain limit. Finally, the pool should be constructed with earthquake-proof walls, for obvious reasons.

Dry cask storage is a method of storing the fuel in a canister that is cooled by a gas and properly shielded.[22,23] The location of storage may or may not be on site. In general, on-site storage is designated as AR (at reactor); off-site storage is called AFR (away from reactor). The NRC allows transfer of UNF from the water pool to dry storage 3 years after discharge; the industry uses 5 to 10 years. The NRC has granted licenses to many dry storage cask designs. Examples are the NAC-128 and MC-10 (February 1990), TN-24 (November 1993), the VSC, a concrete cask (May 1993), and the NACSTC, a combination storage-transport cask (October 1994). A complete list of licensed casks is given in Ref. 24. In licensing the cask, the NRC considered the stored irradiated fuel to have the composition of fresh fuel, that is, no credit is given for burnup. Obviously, with credit for burnup, the spacing between assemblies could be further reduced, thus increasing the storage capacity of a given cask. The NRC is now considering giving burnup credit in certain cases (see Section 9.5.2). Reference 24 provides an excellent survey of UNF storage that covers the whole world.

Figure 9.2 shows a typical metal cask for dry storage of used fuel. It is a cylindrical unit, 8 ft in diameter and 16 ft long, capable of storing 21 to 33 PWR assemblies (9 to 14 tons of heavy metal), or 45 to 70 BWR assemblies (8 to 12 tons of heavy metal). Fully loaded it will weigh 100 to 120 tons. The walls of the cask, made of iron or iron plus lead, are thick enough to provide adequate shielding against gamma rays. In addition, a neutron-absorbing material (e.g., polyethylene or resin) surrounds the circular surface of the cask. The interior of the cask contains fuel "baskets" where the fuel assemblies are placed. The baskets are made of various combinations of steel, aluminum, copper, and boron. Finally, the external surface of the cask may have fins to enhance cooling. The estimated cost of a metal cask is $55 to

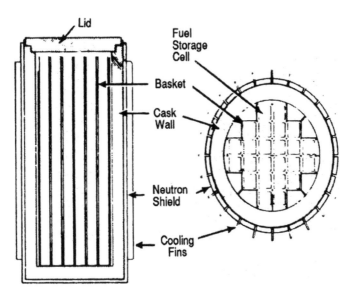

FIGURE 9.2 The design of a typical metal cask for dry storage of used nuclear fuel.[22]

$115/kgHM (kilograms of heavy metal, in 1988 dollars). The storage pad area will be about 25 ft^2 per ton of heavy metal for casks positioned vertically; for horizontal placement, the pad space required will be larger. Figure 9.3 shows a dry cask from a different perspective; finally, Fig. 9.4 shows cask size relative to a human.

A variation of the metal cask is a dual-purpose cask, which can be used for storage as well as for transportation of the fuel. Because the cask will be used for two tasks, it must satisfy the criteria of 10 CFR 72 (Ref. 21) as well as those for transportation of used fuel, 10 CFR 71 (Ref. 25). The dual-purpose casks are very similar in shape and construction to the metal casks. The estimated cost of this cask is $7/kgHM more than that of the metal cask

Figures 9.5 and 9.6 show the conceptual design of concrete storage casks. A concrete storage cask is very similar to a metal one, except that the body of the cask is made of heavily reinforced concrete. Two designs, a ventilated and an unventilated cask, have been proposed. In either case, the concrete wall is thick enough to provide adequate gamma-ray shielding. The baskets holding the fuel are very similar to those of the metal casks. A steel liner covers the inner surface of the concrete body of the cask. An unventilated concrete cask is 8.5 ft in diameter and 18 ft long. A loaded cask will weigh 90 tons. A ventilated concrete cask is 12 ft in diameter and 20 ft long, and when loaded it will weigh 125 tons. More details are given in Ref. 22. The estimated cost of a concrete cask is $45 to $110/kgHM for AR storage (in 1988 dollars).

Dry Storage of Spent Fuel

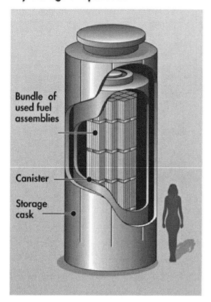
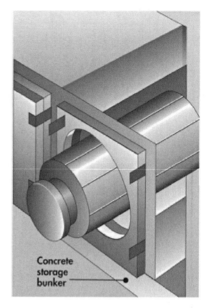

FIGURE 9.3 An outline of a dry storage cask. (Courtesy of U.S. NRC website.)

Several storage systems have been developed. One of them is known as NUHOMS, a horizontal modular concrete storage system. It consists of a canister carrying 24 PWR irradiated assemblies in a helium atmosphere. Each canister is protected and shielded by a massive concrete module with walls 3 ft thick. The decay heat is removed by thermal radiation, conduction, and convection from an air plenum inside the concrete module. Another proposed storage method uses a modular concrete vault. In this design, the used fuel is kept in tubes made of carbon steel that are vertically stored in a concrete vault. Each tube contains a single assembly and one module has a capacity of up to 200 used fuel assemblies.

The fuel will be transported to the location of the vault using a standard transportation cask. There, a fuel-handling machine will remove the assemblies from the cask, one by one, transport them into the vault, and place them into tubes. Once the assembly has been inserted into the tube, a shield plug is placed on the top of the tube. The estimated cost of this method of storage is $75 to $165/kgHM (in 1988 dollars).

Another design is one known as REA-2023, designed for DOE by Ridihalgh, Eggers and Associates. The REA-2023 is cylindrical in shape, like the NUHOMS design, and can be used for transportation as well as storage of fuel. It measures 5 ft in diameter and 16 ft long and can store 52 BWR fuel assemblies or 24 PWR assemblies. Fully loaded, it weighs 100 tons.

FIGURE 9.4 Dry storage casks in a plant site; the intent is to show size relative to a person.

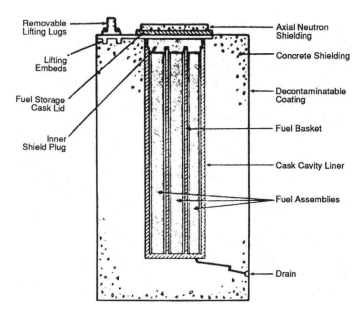

FIGURE 9.5 The design of an unventilated concrete cask for dry storage of used nuclear fuel.[22]

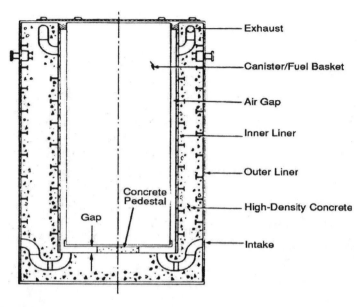

FIGURE 9.6 The design of a ventilated concrete cask for dry storage of used nuclear fuel.[22]

The dose rate at the boundary of a site used to store used fuel must not exceed 0.25 mSv/h (25 mrem/h) (Ref. 18).

The DOE initiated a program for the design and development of a multi-purpose canister (MPC) system. The main idea for the MPC is to have a system that eliminates the need for repeated transfers of the UNF assemblies from container to container during storage, transportation, and disposal, thus avoiding the possibility of damaging assemblies and contaminating containers. The UNF is placed in the MPC, which is then sealed and never opened again. Each MPC is placed inside different "overpack" containers for storage, transportation, or final disposal in a repository.

The NRC rules regarding storage of UNF are found in:

- 10 CFR 20: standards for protection against radiation

- 10 CFR 50: domestic licensing of production and utilization facilities

- 10 CFR 51: environmental protection regulations for domestic licensing and related regulatory functions

- 10 CFR 72: licensing requirements for the independent storage of used nuclear fuel, HLW, and reactor-related GTCC waste (see Section 10.3.2).

9.5.2 Burnup Credit

The term *burnup (BU) credit* with respect to UNF management refers to the following issue. When the NRC calculates criticality of a UNF storage facility (water pool, dry storage, or UNF while being transported), it assumes fresh fuel in the estimation of the multiplication factor k. Clearly such an assumption leads to an overestimation of k for any configuration, because fresh fuel is UO_2 enriched to ~4% in ^{235}U; UNF, on the other hand, contains ~0.6% to 0.7% ^{235}U, lots of fission products (many of them neutron absorbers), and TRU (some of them also neutron absorbers); of course, it also contains some Pu that adds positive reactivity.

In any UNF assembly, the potential reactivity per assembly is clearly less than that of the fresh fuel; so, the industry asked the NRC to take this into account (i.e., give credit for the BU). If the NRC agrees, the storage requirements will be somewhat relaxed and more UNF may be placed in a particular space (pool, storage cask, transportation cask, etc.). The NRC issued a guidance document for BU credit for PWR assemblies in dry storage[26]; the final rule is yet to come.

What worries the NRC and makes it reluctant to allow BU credit are the following issues, which introduce uncertainties:

1. Lack of assay data beyond BU of 40 GWd/t.

2. Uncertainties in BU measurement.

3. Uncertainties in isotopic composition of UNF.

4. BU is not uniform axially along a rod.

5. BU is not the same, at a particular axial location, for different radial locations.

6. The BU credit will depend on the age of the fuel.

9.5.3 Radioactivity from UNF

When the fuel is irradiated in the reactor, three general groups of radioisotopes are formed: fission products, actinides (elements with $Z > 92$), and activation products. More than 350 nuclides have been identified as fission products, many of them with very short half lives. Tables 9.2 and 9.3 show the amounts of fission products and actinides in typical PWR used fuel. Obviously, exact quantities depend on the irradiation history of the fuel and the time after discharge. The concentration of any isotope can be computed by solving a differential equation, as discussed in Section 5.4.3 [see Eq. (5.89)].

In Table 9.2, the activity is given in curies per year. To obtain activity in curies per ton of uranium, multiply by 3 (because it was assumed that the

TABLE 9.2

Radioactivity from Principal Fission Products
in Irradiated Fuel*

Nuclide	Half Life	Activity at Discharge $(1.0 \times 10^6$ Ci/yr)
^{3}H	12.3 yr	1.92×10^{-2}
^{85}Kr	10.8 yr	0.308
^{90}Sr	27.7 yr	2.11
^{95}Zr	65.5 days	37.3
^{106}Ru	368 days	14.8
^{125}Sb	2.7 yr	0.237
^{129}I	1.7×10^7 yr	1.01×10^{-6}
^{131}I	8.05 days	23.5
^{133}Xe	5.27 days	43.9
^{134}Cs	2.05 yr	6.7
^{137}Cs	30.0 yr	2.94
^{144}Ce	284 days	30.2
^{147}Pm	4.4 yr	2.78
^{151}Sm	87 yr	3.41×10^{-2}
^{154}Eu	16 yr	0.191
^{155}Eu	1.81 yr	0.204

Source: Reprinted with permission from M. Benedict, T. Pigford, and H. Levi, *Nuclear Chemical Engineering*, 2nd ed., p. 354, McGraw-Hill Book Co., New York (1981).
*Fuel burnup is 33,000 MWd/tU in a 1000-MWe PWR.

TABLE 9.3

Radioactivity from Principal Actinides in Irradiated Fuel*

Nuclide	Half Life	Ci/yr	kg/tU
^{234}U	2.47×10^5 yr	19.4	0.12
^{236}U	2.39×10^7 yr	7.22	4.18
^{237}Np	2.14×10^6 yr	14.4	0.75
^{236}Pu	2.85 yr	134	9.2×10^{-6}
^{238}Pu	86 yr	1.01×10^5	0.22
^{239}Pu	24,400 yr	8.82×10^3	5.28
^{240}Pu	6,580 yr	1.30×10^4	2.17
^{241}Pu	13.2 yr	2.81×10^6	1.02
^{242}Pu	3.79×10^5 yr	37.6	0.35
^{241}Am	458 yr	4.53×10^3	0.05
^{243}Am	7,950 yr	477	0.09
^{242}Cm	163 days	4.40×10^5	4.9×10^{-3}
^{244}Cm	17.6 yr	7.38×10^4	3.3×10^{-2}

Source: Reprinted with permission from M. Benedict, T. Pigford, and H. Levi, *Nuclear Chemical Engineering*, 2nd ed., p. 354, McGraw-Hill Book Co., New York (1981).
*Fuel burnup is 33,000 MWd/tU in a 1000-MWe PWR, 150 days after discharge.

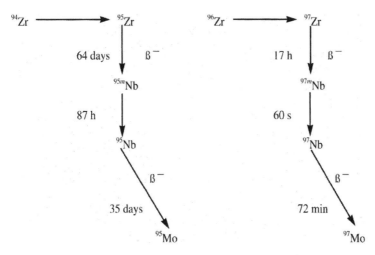

FIGURE 9.7 Activation products of the zirconium in the cladding.

fuel stayed in the core for 3 years) and divide by 82, the assumed mass of fuel in the core, in tons.

To the activity of fission products and actinides one should add the activity of the nuclides produced by the activation of the zirconium in the cladding (see Fig. 9.7).

The concentration and activity of fission products (FPs) has to be known for the following reasons:

For Fuel in the Core:

1. The fuel design must accommodate the buildup of solid and gaseous FPs.

2. Neutron absorption by FPs must be taken into account in reactivity requirements.

3. Knowledge of the activity will help calculate the amount of FPs released in the coolant if a fuel rod fails.

For Used Fuel:

1. Knowledge of the activity is necessary for the proper rad-waste handling and shielding of used fuel.

2. Storage and transportation shielding requirements depend on activity.

To calculate the total activity in used fuel as a function of time, Eq. (5.89) must be solved for all isotopes of interest and the results summed. Two well-known codes that perform that task are ORIGEN, developed at Oak Ridge National Laboratory,[27,28] and CINDER, developed at Los Alamos National Laboratory.[29]

Based on ORIGEN results, analytic fits have been developed to give the activity as a function of time after discharge. One such fit has the following form[30] for PWR irradiated fuel:

$$R(t) = A_1 \exp\left(\frac{1}{A_2 + A_3 t}\right) [\text{Ci/tHM}]| t < 30 \text{ years} \qquad (9.2)$$

$$R(t) = B_1 t^{-a} \left[1 + \frac{B_2}{1 + \left(\dfrac{t}{B_3}\right)^4}\right] \text{Ci/tHM}|30 < t < 1 \times 10^5 \text{ years} \qquad (9.3)$$

where t is the time after discharge (in years) and the constants have the following values:

$$A_1 = 1.42 \times 10^5 \ , \quad A_2 = 0.296 \ , \quad A_3 = 7.22 \times 10^{-2}$$

$$a = 0.680 \ , \quad B_1 = 1.98 \times 10^5 \ , \quad B_2 = 10 \ , \quad B_3 = 88$$

The values of the constants are based on a 1250-MWe PWR operating with an average thermal efficiency of 33%, average specific power of 37.5 MWth/tHM, and a burnup of 33,000 MWd/tU. Similar equations have been developed for a BWR and LMFBR fuel as well as for mixed-oxide (MOX) fuel.

9.5.4 Decay Heat Generated by UNF

The knowledge of the decay heat from used fuel and its decrease with time is extremely important in order to (1) cool the core adequately after a normal or abnormal shutdown (loss-of-coolant accident requirements are based on this quantity), (2) know cooling requirements for the fuel during storage and transportation, and (3) calculate temperatures in a geologic repository. Because of its importance, the federal government and other organizations have supported both theoretical and experimental work in order to not only obtain the value of the decay heat, but also to reduce the uncertainty of the result as much as possible. The results of these efforts have been reported in the literature.[31-41]

The decay heat is measured using either radiometric or calorimetric techniques. Radiometric techniques are based on the measurement of the energy spectrum of the betas and gammas emitted by the fission products.[33] Calorimetric techniques[37,40] use a large calorimeter where all the energy released by the fission products is absorbed and measured. Both techniques encounter difficulties in capturing all the gammas in the finite volume of the detector or the calorimeter and making sure that the gaseous fission products do not escape.

In practice, the energy released by fission products at a certain time after reactor shutdown and for a certain reactor operating history must be known on many occasions. To fulfill this demand, many semiempirical formulas have been developed over the years based on theoretical and experimental results. The first formula was based on the observation that the energy released by fission products follows the simple expression

$$At_f^{-1.2} \ (\text{MeV/s} \cdot \text{fission}) \tag{9.4}$$

where the constant A depends on the units and t_f is the time after the fission occurred. If a reactor operates for time T at constant power, that is, at a constant fission rate, an integration of Eq. (9.4) is necessary to obtain the total decay power from all of the fission products generated during the period T. The result of the integration, expressed in terms of the constant thermal reactor power P_0 (during the period T), is[42]

$$P(t,T)/P_0 = 5.92 \times 10^{-2}[t^{-0.2} - (t+T)^{-0.2}] \tag{9.5}$$

where t is the time in seconds after reactor shutdown, and T is the reactor operation period, also in seconds. The powers P and P_0 could be in any units, provided they are in the same units.

Equation (9.5) is useful for quick calculations, but it is approximate. Better equations have been developed based on more accurate data.[43,44] The American Nuclear Society has developed a Standard (ANS-5.1-2005)[45] based on the best available data. The decay heat is expressed as a summation of 23 exponentials, in terms of two functions, $f(t)$ and $F(t,T)$. The function $f(t)$ is given by

$$f(t_f) = \sum_{i=1}^{23} \alpha_i \exp(-\lambda_i t_f) \ (\text{MeV/s} \cdot \text{fission}) \tag{9.6}$$

where the time t_f is again the time in seconds after the fission occurred. Note that $f(t)$ concerns heat as a result of a single fission. The constants α_i and λ_i, where $i = 1, 23$, are given in Tables 9.4 and 9.5. (If more detail is required, LaBauve et al.[44] give these constants in terms of six energy groups.)

ANS Standard 5.1 lists in detail assumptions and limitations of the document.[45] The most important ones are as follows:

1. The standard is applicable to LWRs operating in the United States.

2. Decay power from ^{239}U and ^{239}Np are prescribed separately.

TABLE 9.4

Constants for the Decay Heat Functions $f(t)$
and $F(t, T)$ for ^{235}U and ^{239}Pu

i	^{235}U Thermal		^{239}Pu Thermal	
	α_i	λ_i	α_i	λ_i
1	5.2800E$-$04[a]	2.7216E$-$00	1.6540E$-$01	8.9246E$-$00
2	6.8588E$-$01	1.0256E$-$00	3.6928E$-$01	6.9005E$-$01
3	4.0752E$-$01	3.1419E$-$01	2.4006E$-$01	2.3618E$-$01
4	2.1937E$-$01	1.1788E$-$01	1.0269E$-$01	1.0118E$-$01
5	5.7701E$-$02	3.4365E$-$02	3.4916E$-$02	3.7193E$-$02
6	2.2530E$-$02	1.1762E$-$02	2.2961E$-$02	1.4319E$-$02
7	3.3392E$-$03	3.6065E$-$03	3.9070E$-$03	4.5094E$-$03
8	9.3667E$-$04	1.3963E$-$03	1.3080E$-$03	1.3211E$-$03
9	8.0899E$-$04	6.2608E$-$04	7.0265E$-$04	5.3481E$-$04
10	1.9572E$-$04	1.8924E$-$04	1.4297E$-$04	1.7297E$-$04
11	3.2609E$-$05	5.5074E$-$05	1.7642E$-$05	4.8918E$-$05
12	7.5827E$-$06	2.0971E$-$05	7.3646E$-$06	2.0155E$-$05
13	2.5189E$-$06	9.9940E$-$06	1.7720E$-$06	8.3687E$-$06
14	4.9836E$-$07	2.5401E$-$06	5.4945E$-$07	2.3620E$-$06
15	1.8523E$-$07	6.6332E$-$07	1.6736E$-$07	6.4594E$-$07
16	2.6592E$-$08	1.2281E$-$07	2.1160E$-$08	1.2822E$-$07
17	2.2356E$-$09	2.7163E$-$08	2.9388E$-$09	2.5166E$-$08
18	8.9582E$-$12	3.2955E$-$09	1.3659E$-$10	1.3176E$-$08
19	8.5968E$-$11	7.4225E$-$10	5.7450E$-$11	7.3568E$-$10
20	2.1072E$-$14	2.4681E$-$10	3.8422E$-$14	2.4663E$-$10
21	7.1219E$-$16	1.5596E$-$13	1.8030E$-$16	3.3490E$-$13
22	8.1126E$-$17	2.2573E$-$14	1.8342E$-$15	1.8761E$-$13
23	9.4678E$-$17	2.0503E$-$14	1.9884E$-$16	3.1544E$-$14

[a] Read as 5.2800×10^{-4}.

3. Decay heat is related to operating power via fission rate and recoverable energy per fission (Q).

4. Decay heat power from activation products in reactor materials is not specified in the standard.

5. The effect of neutron capture in fission products during reactor operation is accounted for.

6. The validity of equations and constants given is good up to 10^{10} s after shutdown.

A reactor usually operates at constant power (i.e., constant fission rate), for a period of time T. To obtain decay heat at time t seconds after shutdown, from the fissions that occurred over period T, Eq. (9.6) is integrated from $t_f = t$ to $t_f = t + T$, giving the result

TABLE 9.5
Constants for the Decay Heat Functions $f(t)$
and $F(t, T)$ for ^{238}U and ^{241}Pu

i	^{238}U Fast		^{241}Pu Thermal	
	α_i	λ_i	α_i	λ_i
1	3.9368E−01[a]	4.3427E−00	3.0934E−01	2.9049E−00
2	7.4588E−01	1.7114E−00	5.4434E−01	6.4911E−01
3	1.2169E−00	6.0572E−01	4.0782E−01	2.5569E−01
4	5.2820E−01	1.9429E−01	1.5828E−01	8.7123E−02
5	1.4805E−01	6.9788E−02	4.1577E−02	2.5068E−02
6	4.5980E−02	1.8809E−02	1.4818E−02	1.3323E−02
7	1.0406E−02	6.1265E−03	5.8176E−03	6.3772E−03
8	1.6991E−03	1.3799E−03	1.9482E−03	2.0221E−03
9	6.9102E−04	5.2799E−04	9.5196E−04	6.2933E−04
10	1.4736E−04	1.6145E−04	1.8208E−04	1.7462E−04
11	2.4049E−05	4.8419E−05	1.5310E−05	4.0172E−05
12	6.9288E−06	1.5644E−05	4.5039E−06	1.5289E−05
13	6.4927E−07	5.3610E−06	9.8277E−07	7.6113E−06
14	4.3556E−07	2.1689E−06	5.1832E−07	2.5083E−06
15	1.6020E−07	6.3343E−07	2.3018E−08	1.1312E−06
16	2.3089E−08	1.2879E−07	1.5817E−07	6.2987E−07
17	2.5481E−09	2.5604E−08	1.8074E−08	1.3149E−07
18	3.5071E−11	9.1544E−09	3.6922E−09	2.4237E−08
19	6.3399E−11	7.3940E−10	5.3843E−11	9.6433E−09
20	4.1599E−14	2.4731E−10	5.3003E−11	7.3467E−10
21	5.3295E−16	1.9594E−13	4.8358E−14	2.4827E−10
22	1.6695E−18	6.4303E−14	9.8516E−16	1.6873E−13
23	4.1058E−16	6.4229E−14	1.3076E−16	8.3639E−15

[a] Read as 3.9368×10^{-1}.

$$F(t,T) = \sum_{i=1}^{23} \frac{\alpha_i}{\lambda_i} \exp(-\lambda_i t) * [1 - \exp(-\lambda_i T)] \frac{\text{MeV/s}}{\text{fission/s}} \qquad (9.7)$$

Table 9.6 gives the values of $F(t,\infty)$ for ^{235}U, ^{238}U, ^{239}Pu, and ^{241}Pu. Figure 9.8 presents a plot of the $F(t,\infty)$ for ^{235}U and ^{239}Pu UNF.

In terms of reactor power, the decay power $P(t,\infty)$ is given by

$$P(t,\infty) = \frac{P_0}{Q} F(t,\infty) \qquad (9.8)$$

where P_0 is, of course, the constant thermal reactor power during operation, and Q is the recoverable fission energy (in MeV). Values of Q for many common isotopes are given in Table 9.7.

TABLE 9.6

The Function $F(t,\infty)$ [(MeV/s)/(fission/s)] for ^{235}U, ^{238}U, ^{239}Pu, and ^{241}Pu

Time after Shutdown (s)	^{235}U	^{238}U	^{239}Pu	^{241}Pu
1	12.38	14.82	10.27	12.14
10	9.497	10.39	8.250	9.150
10^2	6.202	6.392	5.691	5.798
10^3	3.799	3.719	3.522	3.446
10^4	1.912	1.809	1.733	1.657
10^5	0.973	0.938	0.948	0.917
10^6	0.555	0.507	0.516	0.510
10^7	0.249	0.221	0.234	0.240
4×10^7	0.149	0.128	0.136	0.139
10^8	0.120	0.094	0.095	0.089
10^9	0.060	0.046	0.048	0.041
10^{10}	0.0053	0.0054	0.011	0.0061

The decay heat in the core, as a percentage of the operating power, after infinite operational time is shown here for a few representative times after shutdown:

Time after Shutdown	% of Power
1 s	~6
2 h	~1
72 h	~0.5
1 month	~0.3
1 year	~0.2

Equation (9.8) gives the decay heat t seconds after shutdown following operation of the reactor for an infinite time at power P_0. In reality, a reactor always operates for a finite time T (Fig. 9.9). To compute the decay heat for that case, Eq. (9.8) takes the form:

$$P(t,T) = \frac{P_0}{Q}[F(t,\infty) - F(t + T,\infty)] \qquad (9.9)$$

Notice, in the brackets of Eq. (9.9), that the contribution to the decay heat from fission products (as a result of an infinite time operation) at $t + T$ seconds after shutdown is subtracted from the corresponding contribution at t seconds after shutdown; the subtraction is necessary because no fissions occurred for $t < t + T$.

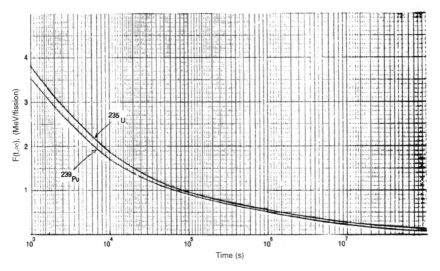

FIGURE 9.8 The function $F(t,\infty)$ for the decay heat from ^{235}U and ^{239}Pu UNF.

TABLE 9.7
Recoverable Energy per Fission for
Many Common Isotopes*

Nuclide	Q (MeV)	Nuclide	Q (MeV)
^{232}Th		^{233}U	
Fast	197	Thermal	200
14 MeV	217	Fast	201
^{234}U		14 MeV	225
Fast	202	^{235}U	
^{236}U		Thermal	203
Fast	205	Fast	203
^{238}U		14 MeV	228
Fast	209	^{237}Np	
14 MeV	230	Fast	204
^{239}Pu		^{240}Pu	
Thermal	211	Fast	211
Fast	212	^{242}Pu	
14 MeV	238	Fast	216
^{241}Pu			
Thermal	213		
Fast	214		

*From Ref. 44.

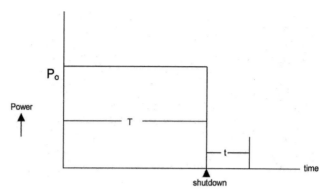

FIGURE 9.9 Power history for a reactor that operated at constant power for time T.

■ *Example 9.2:* A reactor operated for 4 months at a constant power of 1100 MWe with an efficiency of 32%. What is the decay power in the core 2 months after shutdown? Assume all power is produced by ^{235}U.

Answer: From Table 9.7 the recoverable energy per fission is 203 MeV. The thermal power $P_0 = 1100/0.32 = 3437.5$ MWth. The pertinent times and $F(t,\infty)$ values are

$$t = 2 \text{ months} = 5.18 \times 10^6 \text{ s},$$

$$T = 4 \text{ months} = 1.04 \times 10^7 \text{ s}$$

$$F(5.18 \times 10^6,\infty) = 0.326 \text{ MeV/fission},$$

$$F(1.04 \times 10^7 + 5.18 \times 10^6,\infty) = 0.211 \text{ MeV/fission}$$

Using (Eq. 9.9),

$$P(2 \text{ months}, 4 \text{ months}) = (3437.5 \text{ MWth}/203 \text{ MeV/fission})$$

$$\times [0.326 - 0.211](\text{MeV/fission}) = 1.95 \text{ MWth} \quad ■$$

A practical problem that is frequently encountered requires calculation of the decay heat after (1) the reactor operated for several periods at different power levels and (2) more than one isotope was fissioned (which is the correct case). Then, Eq. (9.9) becomes a double summation over reactor operating periods and isotopes:

$$P(t) = \sum_n \sum_i \frac{P_{in}}{Q_i} [F_i(t_n,\infty) - F_i(t_n + T_n,\infty)] \tag{9.10}$$

where P_{in} is the power produced by fissile isotope i, during the n'th time period.

■ **Example 9.3:** A reactor operated for 18 months with the power history shown in Fig. 9.10. The design power is 1150 MWe; thermal efficiency is 32%. Assume that 15% of the power is generated by ^{239}Pu and the rest by ^{235}U. What is the decay heat 10 s after shutdown?

Answer: Equation (9.10) will be used. The following table shows the times and $F(t,\infty)$ values.

Period	t_n	T_n	$F_U(t_n,\infty)$	$F_U(t_n + T_n,\infty)$	$F_{Pu}(t_n,\infty)$	$F_{Pu}(t_n + T_n,\infty)$
1	16 months + 10 s $= 4.1 \times 10^7$ s	2 months $= 5.2 \times 10^6$ s	0.149	0.145	0.136	0.131
2	10 s	16 months + 10 s $= 4.1 \times 10^7$ s	9.497	0.149	8.250	0.136

The $F(t,\infty)$ values are taken from Ref. 45. Notice that the most important numbers are for $t_n = 10$ s and these can be read directly from Table 9.6; for quick calculations, $F(t,\infty)$ values may be read from Fig. 9.8; of course, for exact calculations, Eq. (9.7) must be used.

The thermal power of the plant is $P_0 = 1150/0.32 = 3594$ MWth. The Q values for ^{235}U and ^{239}Pu are given in Table 9.7.

$$P/P_0 = (0.85/203)[0.8(0.149 - 0.145) + 1.0(9.497 - 0.149)]$$

$$+ (0.15/211)[0.8(0.136 - 0.131) + 1.0(8.250 - 0.136)]$$

$$= 0.039 + 0.006$$

$$P = 3594(0.039 + 0.006) = 161.7 \text{ MWth} \quad ■$$

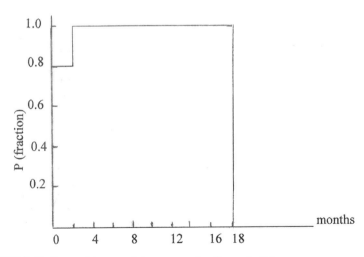

FIGURE 9.10 Power history of the reactor for Example 9.3.

9.5.5 UNF Management Outside the United States

Outside the United States, some countries with nuclear power plants plan for direct disposal of UNF (Canada, Finland, Germany, South Korea, Spain, Sweden); others plan to reprocess or are already doing it (Belgium, China, France, India, Russia, Switzerland, United Kingdom). All of the nations with nuclear power plants are storing the UNF until a geologic repository is ready to accept it for final direct disposal or to accept HLW after reprocessing the UNF (see Sections 9.6.4 and 9.6.5). The following nations have an operational underground laboratory performing research to obtain information about the eventual geologic repository: Belgium, Finland, France, Japan, Russia, Sweden, Switzerland; China will have one ready in 2020. No country has settled yet on the location of an underground geologic repository.

Sweden probably has the most advanced program[46]; it has operated a UNF storage facility called CLAB since 1985. The Swedish program follows these steps:

1. Used fuel is stored on site for at least 6 months after discharge from the reactor.

2. The fuel is transported to a central intermediate storage facility (CLAB) and placed in a specially designed cask.

3. The fuel is stored in the intermediate facility for 40 years.

4. The fuel is transported from the intermediate facility to an encapsulation station located aboveground.

5. The fuel is enclosed in canisters made of 10-cm-thick copper. Copper was chosen because it is not attacked by pure water but only by corrosive substances dissolved in water. Studies of corrosion in copper give the estimate that a 6-cm wall thickness will not be penetrated by corrosion for at least 1 million years. The fuel encapsulation facility will be colocated with the repository.

6. The canisters are transferred to the final repository and are placed in holes at a depth of 500 m (Fig. 9.11).

7. The canisters in the holes are surrounded by a buffer material consisting of highly compacted bentonite clay.

The present plan calls for a repository that consists of parallel horizontal tunnels with vertical deposition holes. The distance between two neighboring holes will be 6 m to ensure that the temperature anywhere in the repository will not exceed 100°C. This temperature limit guarantees that the buffer material surrounding the canisters (bentonite clay) will not become chemically active, which could affect its performance in the long term.

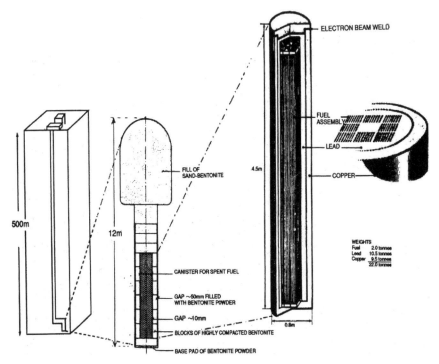

FIGURE 9.11 The Swedish concept for the geological disposal of used fuel assemblies. The same principle can be used for vitrified or other LLW wastes. Only the canister will be different in the two cases.

9.6 Disposal of HLW and TRU Wastes

9.6.1 Characteristics of HLW

As defined in Section 9.2, HLWs are (1) by-products and remnants of the reprocessing operation, (2) UNF, and (3) other materials that may be defined as HLW by the NRC.

The HLW generated after used fuel reprocessing contains more than 99% of the fission products (nonvolatile) and 0.5% of the uranium and plutonium. The main isotopes in this HLW are ^{90}Sr, ^{137}Cs, ^{155}Eu, and Pu, Am, and Cm isotopes.

As an example, the composition of HLW in an average canister from the West Valley, New York, reprocessing plant is given in Table 9.8, in terms of activity. In the United States, only a tiny fraction of HLW, in liquid form, has come from commercial civilian operations (mostly from the West Valley plant, which operated from 1967 to 1972; see Section 7.4.6), since no commercial reprocessing is taking place. The bulk of liquid HLW represents the

TABLE 9.8

Radioactive Inventory in an Average HLW Canister from
the West Valley Reprocessing Plant (1990)

Isotope	Activity (Ci)	Isotope	Activity (Ci)
^{3}H	0.0	^{147}Pm	2.45×10^1
^{14}C	0.0	^{151}Sm	3.07×10^2
^{55}Fe	0.192	^{152}Eu	8.62×10^{-1}
^{59}Ni	0.416	^{154}Eu	1.68×10^2
^{63}Ni	28.0	^{155}Eu	2.32×10^1
^{60}Co	0.814	^{232}Th	6.45×10^{-3}
^{79}Se	1.38×10^{-2}	^{233}U	3.55×10^{-2}
^{90}Sr	2.07×10^4	^{234}U	1.74×10^{-2}
^{90}Y	2.08×10^4	^{235}U	3.72×10^{-4}
^{93}Zr	1.07	^{236}U	1.09×10^{-3}
^{93m}Nb	8.37×10^1	^{237}Np	9.25×10^{-2}
^{99}Tc	0.428	^{238}U	3.13×10^{-3}
^{106}Ru	5.79×10^{-5}	^{238}Pu	3.02×10^1
^{106}Rh	5.81×10^{-5}	^{239}Np	1.36
^{107}Pd	4.33×10^{-2}	^{239}Pu	6.39
^{125}Sb	2.34	^{240}Pu	4.2
^{125m}Te	0.573	^{241}Pu	1.96×10^2
^{126}Sn	0.409	^{241}Am	2.11×10^2
^{126m}Sb	5.73×10^{-2}	^{242}Pu	6.38×10^{-3}
^{126}Sb	5.73×10^{-2}	^{242}Am	1.11
^{129}I	0.0	^{242m}Am	1.11
^{134}Cs	7.03×10^{-1}	^{242}Cm	0.92
^{135}Cs	6.34×10^{-1}	^{243}Am	1.36
^{137}Cs	2.25×10^4	^{243}Cm	0.413
^{137m}Ba	2.13×10^4	^{244}Cm	20.5
^{144}Ce	3.48×10^{-7}	^{245}Cm	3.46×10^{-3}
^{144}Pr	3.49×10^{-7}	^{246}Cm	3.96×10^{-4}

Source: Courtesy of J. C. Pope.

remnants of government weapons activities. Table 9.9 gives the composition of liquid HLW resulting from the reprocessing of LWR fuel in France.[47]

Irradiated used fuel still contains most of its original ^{238}U, about one-third of its original ^{235}U, almost all the fission products, all the transuranic isotopes, and many activation products. Figure 9.12 shows the changes in 1000 kg of nuclear fuel that produced power for 3 years in a commercial LWR. Tables 9.2 and 9.3 summarize the most important isotopic features of typical LWR UNF. The radioactivity and the thermal power of the used fuel decay with time, as shown in Figs. 9.13 and 9.14. The intent of Figs. 9.13 and 9.14 is just to show the trend.

The predominant thinking at this time for the treatment of HLW is to solidify the liquids before disposal, and to place the solidified form in a geological repository (see Section 9.6.3).

TABLE 9.9

Composition of Reprocessing Solution Obtained from French LWR Fuel with a Burnup of 33 MWd/kg

Fission Products (g/L)		Actinides (g/L)		Corrosion Products and Additives (g/L)		Process Additives (g/L)	
Se	0.08	U	2.06	Na	14.71	Al	3.78
Rb	0.53	Np	0.66	Fe	9.08		
Sr	1.26	Pu	0.05	Ni	1.45		
Y	0.70	Am	0.56	Cr	1.54		
Zr	6.95	Cm	0.04	P	0.55		
Mo	5.04	Total	3.37	Total	27.33		
Tc	0.85						
Ru	1.58						
Rh	0.44						
Pd	1.29						
Ag	0.12						
Cd	0.12						
Sn	0.06						
Sb	0.01						
Te	0.71						
Cs	5.43						
Ba	2.42						
La	1.82						
Ce	3.56						
Pr	1.68						
Nd	6.07						
Pm	0.10						
Sm	1.21						
Eu	0.20						
Gd	0.12						
Total	42.35						

9.6.2 Characteristics of TRU

As defined in Section 9.2, TRUs are man-made isotopes with an atomic number Z of 92, a half-life longer than 5 years, and a concentration greater than 100 nCi/g of waste. The United States is the only country that has defined this category of waste. In the radioactive waste programs of other nations, TRU waste is considered HLW and is treated as such.

The bulk of U.S. TRU is generated by DOE activities having to do with the defense programs using the Pu separation processes. Examples of TRU waste are contaminated glove boxes, filters, tools, and chemical sludges produced by Pu recovery streams. Other activities that may generate TRU are the manufacturing of Pu heat sources, UNF processing, nuclear fuel research activities, and decontamination and/or decommissioning operations. Since the

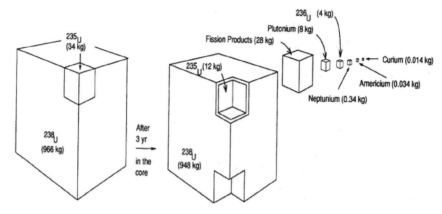

FIGURE 9.12 The change of nuclear fuel as a result of fissions. The fresh fuel is UO_2. The irradiated fuel contains most of the original ^{238}U, about one-third of the original ^{235}U, and almost all the fission products and transuranic elements.

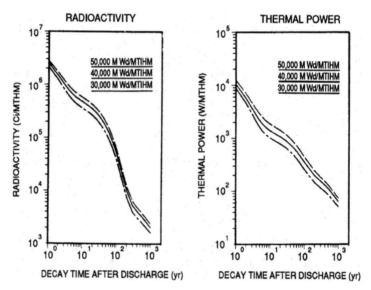

FIGURE 9.13 The decrease with time of the radioactivity and thermal power from PWR used fuel.

composition of TRU depends on the source, it is difficult to give a truly representative composition. In general, in TRU one finds isotopes of Np, Pu, Am, Cm, and Cf.

Before 1970, all TRU was buried in shallow burial grounds (pits and trenches) covered with soil at government-owned as well as commercial sites.

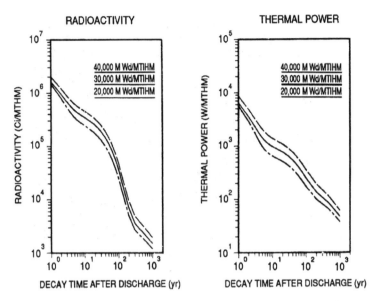

RADIOACTIVITY

THERMAL POWER

DECAY TIME AFTER DISCHARGE (yr)

DECAY TIME AFTER DISCHARGE (yr)

FIGURE 9.14 The decrease with time of the radioactivity and thermal power from BWR used fuel.

In 1970, the U.S. government decided that TRU required better confinement methods and started storing the TRU instead of burying it.

TRU wastes emit alphas and some soft X-rays (low keV range); because of that, most TRU can be handled with the shielding provided by the waste package. It is then called "contact-handled" (CH) TRU. CH TRU does not require remote handling because most of its radioactivity comes from alpha particles, which do not penetrate the walls of the package. Some isotopes found in TRU emit energetic gamma rays and neutrons (from spontaneous fission), but only 1% of TRU emits enough gamma rays, neutrons, and betas to require special precautions, in which case it is called "remotely handled" (RH) TRU.

The toxicity of TRU wastes is due to the fact that they contain heavy elements that are alpha emitters. Alpha emitters located outside the body are not dangerous to man because these alpha particles, with kinetic energy <10 MeV, have a range shorter than the thickness of human skin. By contrast, alpha-emitting substances that are ingested and, in particular, inhaled are very harmful because they will deliver, as a consequence of their short range, large amounts of energy in a small volume, resulting in high radiation dose rates.

■ *Example 9.4:* What is the dose equivalent rate in tissue, per picocurie, of an isotope emitting one 6-MeV alpha particle per decay?

Answer: The range of an alpha particle[48] in tissue is 48 μm. Assuming that the alpha kinetic energy is deposited uniformly in the lungs with mass

1 kg, the absorbed dose D per alpha is (taking the density of tissue equal to 1000 kg/m^3)

$$D = \text{(energy deposited)/mass}$$

$$= (6 \text{ MeV} * 1.602 \times 10^{-13} \text{ J/MeV})/1 \text{ kg} = 9.61 \times 10^{-13} \text{ J/kg}$$

or

$$D = 9.61 \times 10^{-13} \text{ Gy/alpha particle}$$

Using a quality factor of $Q = 20$ for alpha particles, the dose equivalent,[48] $H = Q * D$, becomes,

$$H = 9.61 \times 10^{-13} * 20 = 1.92 \times 10^{-11} \text{ Sv/alpha}$$

If the total activity is 1 pCi, the dose equivalent rate, H, is

$$1.92 \times 10^{-11} * 3.7 \times 10^{-2} = 7.11 \times 10^{-13} \text{ Sv/s} = 2.56 \times 10^{-7} \text{ rem/h} \quad \blacksquare$$

From the point of view of chemical properties, elements found in TRU are heavy metals and, as such, if digested they go through the digestive system tract with a relatively small fraction being absorbed. Because of this property, TRU is much less hazardous when ingested than when inhaled.

The handling and processing of TRU, before disposal, and the disposal options are discussed in Sections 9.6.3 and 9.6.4. A special repository, the Waste Isolation Pilot Project, was constructed and is operating in the United States specifically to handle TRU (see Section 9.6.7).

9.6.3 Solidification of Liquid HLW

A very comprehensive review of advances in the solidification of HLW and disposal methods appears in Refs. 49 through 51. Since the present thinking is to dispose of HLW in solid form, a method and a medium must be found for its solidification. Three general methods of solidification are under consideration:

1. *Calcination:* The waste is heated up to the point where it becomes completely dry. What remains after calcination is a powder-like substance.

2. *Cementation:* The liquid waste is mixed with cement and is poured into a container where it is allowed to dry into a concrete block.

3. *Vitrification:* The waste is mixed with glass frit to form a solid glass containing the waste in solid solution. Vitrification is the preferred method because of the several advantages offered by glass.

In the United States, the Slurry-Fed Ceramic Melter (SFCM), developed at Battelle Pacific Northwest Laboratories, is the vitrification method used.[52,53] In the SFCM process, the waste slurry and the glass frit are continuously fed into the melter (Fig. 9.15) where the waste is mixed with the molten glass and then discharged into canisters where it solidifies. In France, the AVM (Atelier de Vitrification de Marcoule) process is used. In the AVM process, shown schematically in Fig. 9.16, vitrification is accomplished in two steps. First, the liquid waste is passed through an electrically heated rotating calciner where it is completely dried up. The dried waste leaves the calciner tube by gravity through the lower end at a temperature of 300°C to 400°C. Second, it enters the melting furnace where it is mixed with glass frit of the required composition to form the desired glass. In the furnace, the mixture is heated up to the glass melting point (1100°C) and the molten glass mixture is poured into a canister where it solidifies after it cools.

The ideal containment material should (1) retain in insoluble form all the fission products and the other chemical elements contained in the liquids from used fuel reprocessing; (2) have suitable mechanical properties;

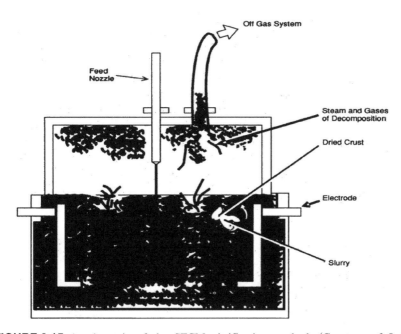

FIGURE 9.15 A schematic of the SFCM vitrification method. (Courtesy of J. C. Pope.)

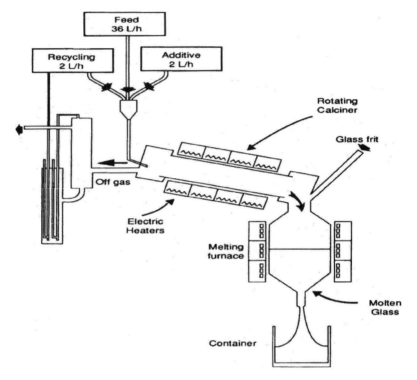

FIGURE 9.16 A schematic of the AVM method used in France. (Courtesy of J. C. Pope).

(3) have stable properties over thousands of years; and (4) be relatively inexpensive and easy to handle.

Glass comes close to fulfilling all of these requirements because glass (1) has a low leach rate and low solubility in water; (2) has high solubility for the nuclides found in HLW and TRU; (3) shows resistance to radiation damage; (4) requires moderate temperatures for preparation; and (5) is a material with which man has considerable experience over thousands of years. Egyptian, Greek, Chinese, and Roman artifacts made of glass or ceramic, 3000 or more years ago in some cases, have been recovered intact after being buried or staying under seawater for all those years. It is reasonable to assume that glass specially designed and placed in an environment more benign than seawater will last at least that long. Research on many possible forms of glass is still being conducted in the United States and in many other countries. It seems certain, at this time, that the first generation of vitrified waste will be based on some form of borosilicate glass, the typical composition of which is presented[54] in Table 9.10. The general physical properties of glass waste forms are given in Table 9.11.

TABLE 9.10
Typical Borosilicate Glass Composition

Material	Weight (%)	Material	Weight (%)
SiO_2	27.3	CaO	1.5
B_2O_3	11.1	MgO	1.5
Na_2O	4.0	SrO	1.5
K_2O	4.0	BaO	1.5
ZnO	21.3	Waste	26.3

The second generation of waste form may be based on the SYNROC process, developed by Ringwood in Australia.[55–62] SYNROC is a titanate-based material that is still under investigation. Borosilicate glass is preferred, at this time, because it is the glass form relatively easily formed and best developed. Formation of SYNROC requires a more complex process, but SYNROC offers the promise of low leachability, excellent long-term stability, and increased waste loading.

Several types of materials have been considered for the canister in which the vitrified waste is placed. Examples are Type 304L stainless steel, plated carbon steel, titanium, and recycled contaminated steel. After all advantages and disadvantages were considered, the most promising candidate currently seems to be the Type 304L stainless steel. A typical canister size considered in the United States is 3 m high with a 0.60-m outer diameter and a wall thickness equal to 9.53 mm (3/8 in.). Each canister will contain 1700 kg of glass, of which 45 kg will be radionuclides. The maximum decay heat from a canister will be 700 W, with a maximum activity of 300 kCi and radiation level of 5500 rem/h on contact (600 rem/h at 1 m). The reduction of the decay heat as a function of time is shown in Fig. 9.17.

TABLE 9.11
Physical Properties of Glass Waste Forms

Property	Value
Thermal conductivity at 100°C	0.55 Btu/(h·ft·°F)
Heat capacity (100°C)	0.22 cal/(g·°C)
Fractional thermal expansion	$1.22 \times 10^{-5}/°C$
Young's modulus	9.0×10^9 psi
Tensile strength	9.0×10^3 psi
Compressive strength	1.0×10^5 psi
Poisson's ratio	0.2
Density (100°C)	2.5 to 3.0 g/cm^3
Softening point	502°C

Source: Courtesy of J. C. Pope.

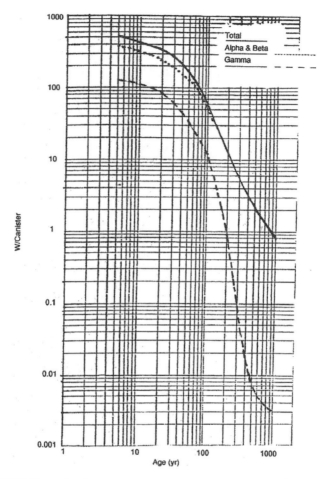

FIGURE 9.17 Example of canister decay heat change with time. (Courtesy of J. C. Pope.)

The canisters used by the French are smaller in size. They have a height of 1.3 m, an outside diameter of 0.43 m, and a 5-mm-thick refractory stainless steel wall. Each canister will contain 400 kg of vitrified glass.

At present, there are many plants operating or under construction—both in the United States and in other countries—that vitrify HLW. In the United States, there are two operating plants. One is the Defense Waste Processing Facility (DWPF) at the Savannah River site in Aiken, South Carolina, and the other is the West Valley Demonstration Project (WVDP) in West Valley, New York. There is one under construction in Hanford, Washington, the Hanford Tank Waste Treatment and Immobilization Plant (WTP), scheduled to be completed by 2016 and start full operation by 2022.

9.6.4 Disposal Methods

Whichever method is chosen for the disposal of the radioactive wastes, it has to satisfy two fundamental objectives: (1) the protection of the environment not only for the benefit of the generations that produce the wastes, but also for future generations, and (2) protection of people, not only those alive today but also future generations. The term *protection* should not be interpreted as meaning that the disposal will carry zero risk. No human activity is without some degree of risk. Instead, protection means that the method of disposal will result in a risk acceptable to society, that is, acceptable in view of the benefits received by the society from the activities that generate the wastes (electricity generation, radioisotopes applications, etc.).

The first choice that has to be made is between the two general approaches of dispersal and containment.[63] Dispersal refers to the deliberate release of radioactive materials to the environment, controlling both the rate and the amount released, and its subsequent dilution by the air and water of the earth to concentrations that are considered safe. Dispersal is practiced by the nuclear industry, but is limited to the release of small amounts of activity and only of a few selected isotopes.

Containment refers to placing the wastes behind one or more barriers— natural or man-made—to ensure their isolation from the biosphere for as long as it is considered necessary. Potential releases to the environment should be of such quantity that the ensuing risk is acceptable. During the period when the site is in use (i.e., still accepting wastes), retrieval of the wastes will be possible; after the site is closed, retrieval will not be possible and monitoring of the site will not be necessary.

Because the disposal of wastes involves projection of events over many thousands of years, inevitably introducing uncertainties in any action plan, the concepts of reversibility and retrievability (R&R) have been discussed (for more details see www.oecd-nea.org/rwm/rr/reims2010/index.html). *Reversibility* refers to the ability to reverse or reconsider decisions during the implementation of a disposal method; *retrievability* refers to the ability to recover (retrieve) and remove the waste after it has been emplaced in the repository. Of course, as long as the location of the waste is known, retrievability is always possible (it will be a mining operation). If retrievability is integrated in the disposal plan, two advantages materialize: (1) The cost of retrieval will be reduced (relative to the cost with disposal not implying retrievability) and (2) it will put the mind of skeptics at ease (if a mistake was made, we can retrieve the waste and find a better method of disposal). Finally, retrievability offers another potential benefit: If future generations discover that the wastes have some useful function, they can retrieve and use them.

Over the years, the following disposal methods have been considered[1–4,64]:

1. *Deep geologic disposal:* The wastes will be placed in a stable geologic formation, deep underground, by means of a passive method.

Geologic disposal is the dominant method at this time, and for this reason it is discussed in detail in Section 9.6.6.

2. *Ice sheet disposal:* Figure 9.18 shows three variations of this method. In Fig. 9.18(a) the canister containing the waste is lowered into a hole dug in the ice. The weight and the heat from the canister will keep propelling the canister downward until it reaches the bottom of the ice and stays there. In Fig. 9.18(b), the canister is placed in a drilled hole at a depth of 50 to 100 m and anchored with the help of cables and plates. The anchor plates will stop the downward movement at a depth of 200 to 500 m. Eventually, snow and ice will cover the anchor plates, but retrievability will be possible for 200 to 400 years. In Fig. 9.18(c), the canisters will be placed in a surface facility and will be air cooled. The housing facility will have expandable legs. When the legs reach their maximum length, the whole structure will act as a heat source and begin to move downward through the melting ice. Retrievability is estimated to be possible for 400 years.

The problems associated with ice sheet disposal are three. First, there is a risk of an accident when the wastes are transported to the cap, probably by ship. Second, there is some uncertainty about the

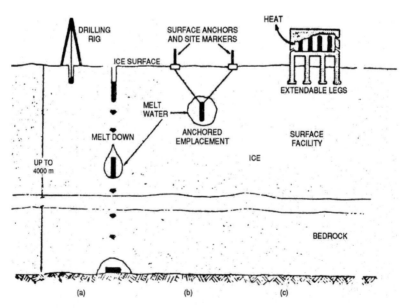

FIGURE 9.18 The three concepts for ice sheet radioactive waste disposal: (a) melt-down or free flow, (b) anchored emplacement, and (c) surface facility with expandable legs.

movement of the ice sheets. Third, international treaties may not allow the placement of any waste on the ice cap.

3. *Outer space:* The idea is to place the wastes in a rocket and shoot them toward the sun. There are two problems with this concept. One is cost and the other is the risk of an aborted mission that may return the wastes to earth in a place and manner not acceptable.

4. *Sub-seabed disposal:* There are places on the ocean floor, at depths of about 5 miles, where tectonic plates meet and form a sort of a deep ditch. Materials placed in such places will tend to drift between the plates and downward, that is, toward the center of the earth. The idea has merit, but more research is needed. One of the amendments of the NWPA addresses this problem and instructs the DOE to study it. No serious consideration was ever given to this method of disposal.

9.6.5 The Form of the Waste for Disposal: Transmutation

The requirements for HLW disposal depend strongly on the form of the waste that will be placed in a geological repository. One big decision is whether or not the waste is placed as intact UNF assemblies or as reprocessed or non-reprocessed vitrified HLW. Obviously, the waste form will depend on the fuel cycle(s) that are eventually adopted. Advantages of the various fuel cycles are presented in Ref. 65.

The HLW (either UNF or vitrified HLW) has to be isolated from the environment for a long period of time because some of the radioisotopes in the waste have long half lives (e.g., ^{237}Np, $T_{1/2} = 2.14 \times 10^6$ years; ^{239}Pu $T_{1/2} = 2.41 \times 10^4$ years). If a process or method can be found to change these long-lived radioisotopes either into stable ones or new ones with shorter half lives, the effort required to isolate the wastes, both in resources and money, will be considerably reduced. Such a process exists and is called *transmutation*. Serious thought has been given to the idea that transmuted waste should be placed in a geologic repository instead of intact UNF assemblies or vitrified waste with the composition shown in Tables 9.8 and 9.9.

In transmutation, nuclear reactions, which produced the radioisotopes to begin with, can be used to alter them, in particular to transmute them into other isotopes that are stable or have shorter half lives. Radiations that can be used for the transmutation are neutrons, produced by fission or fusion reactors or from nuclear explosives, or charged particles, produced by accelerators. Fission reactors, particularly breeders, perform a transmutation of sorts when they burn the plutonium (and other transuranics) generated either in the same or in different reactors. Fusion reactors may offer the possibility of transmutation of materials placed in their blankets; however, fusion reactors are not operational yet. Also, since one of the reasons fusion reactors look more attractive than fission reactors is the expectation that very little radioactivity will have to be handled during and after their operation, transmutation may not be allowed. There is renewed interest recently in accelerator-driven systems (ADS). In an ADS, an accelerator (most likely a proton accelerator) producing protons with kinetic energy of 800 to 1000 MeV will generate neutrons by spallation reactions taking place when the protons hit a metal target (W, Pb, or Hg); the number of neutrons is augmented by surrounding the target with a blanket of fissionable material (U or Th); despite the fissions that occur, the system is subcritical under all conditions. Calculations show that an ADS can generate enough neutrons (a 1.0×10^{15} n/cm^2·s thermal neutron flux is expected) for the transmutation of most of the actinides and fission products. The neutron energy will be in a range that favors fission rather than neutron absorption; thus, fission products with relatively short half lives will be produced rather than TRU with long half lives. A "bonus" of using an ADS will come from the heat produced, which will be enough to generate electricity that will supply all the needs of the ADS plus an extra amount to be sold to external customers. Potential benefits of transmutation are presented in Ref. 66.

9.6.6 Geologic Repository Features

A geologic repository will look, on the surface, like a mine (Fig. 9.19). A region of ~2000 acres (~8×10^6 m^2) will form the exclusion area within which the main on-surface facilities will be built (administration building, waste handling building, etc.). Underneath, at a depth of between 600 and 1200 m, the HLW will be placed in excavated tunnels called *waste emplacement rooms*. Figure 9.20 shows a conceptual placement design for a UNF cask in an emplacement tunnel. The waste, either UNF assemblies or HLW vitrified and contained in a metal canister, will be deposited in these rooms or in holes drilled in the rock. For a period of 50 to 100 years, the wastes will be retrievable. After the operation of the repository has been confirmed to be as designed, the rooms will be backfilled with the excavated rock. The backfilling provides an extra barrier between the wastes and the environment and also reinforces the structural integrity of the mined geologic medium.

The geologic medium of the repository is only one of three barriers that will contain and isolate the wastes from the biosphere. The other two are the double-walled canister and the waste form itself (Fig. 9.21). It is expected that the canister wall will be corroded in 300 years, thus exposing the glassified waste directly to the surrounding rock. Then, the next barrier, the waste form itself (either glass or ceramic) will offer protection. This waste form (vitrified) was chosen because of its low leachability and solubility in water. Thus, the transfer of material from the glass to the surrounding medium will be an extremely slow process. Finally, the material that is leached from the waste form has to penetrate the third barrier, the geologic medium itself before it reaches the biosphere. Let us examine briefly the properties of the geologic media considered for waste disposal, namely, salt, tuff, basalt, and

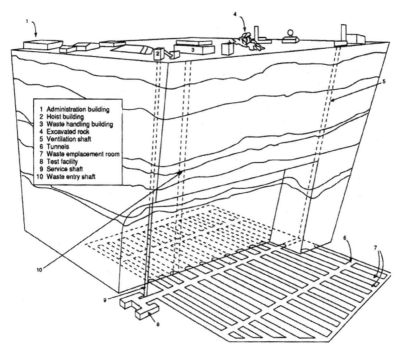

1 Administration building
2 Hoist building
3 Waste handling building
4 Excavated rock
5 Ventilation shaft
6 Tunnels
7 Waste emplacement room
8 Test facility
9 Service shaft
10 Waste entry shaft

FIGURE 9.19 A conceptual diagram of a geological repository. The surface buildings look almost like those of a common underground mine. The wastes will be placed in excavated tunnels at a depth of 600 to 1200 m.

granite. The most important properties of the host medium are summarized in Table 9.12. Although none of these media is perfect, any one of them could become the host for a satisfactory repository.

Salt, either bedded or domed, exhibits high plasticity, which means that any cracks created for any reason will tend to close up on their own. At the same time, salt is highly soluble in water, but in places where one finds large deposits of salt, water is absent (if it were present, it would have dissolved the salt). Finally, salt is plentiful in the continental United States— some 256 million acres are known with the required deposit size.

Tuff is a volcanic material. It is volcanic ash that has been compressed under its own weight. Tuff may range from soft and relatively loose to more tightly compacted. Large deposits of this rock are found in the western states, especially in arid regions.

Basalt is also volcanic material. It has come upward through fissures in the earth's crust and flooded large areas in sheet-like formations. The deposits of basalt are usually extensive. The total deposit is made up of many sheets of lava, each coming from a different volcanic eruption. Basalt is very hard, dense, and strong and contains hardly any moisture.

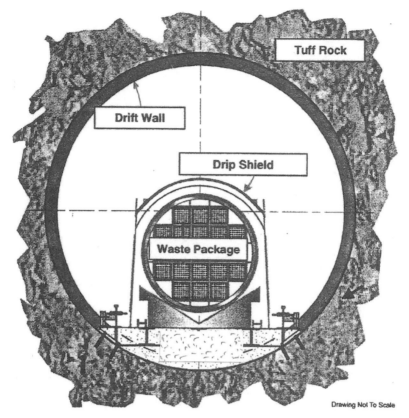

FIGURE 9.20 Conceptual design of a cask placement in a repository tunnel.

Granite and related rocks are very abundant in the upper 5 miles of the earth's crust, formed as the result of molten material that cooled down. The most attractive property of granite is its strength—granite is used to preserve the openings of shafts, tunnels, and chambers during mining operations. Granite contains very little water and its minerals tend to reduce corrosion of metals and to retard the movement of waste. Granitic formations have been stable for as long as 2.5 billion years.

To summarize, the only conceivable way by which the wastes may escape to man's environment is if water reaches the wastes, dissolves them, and carries them to the biosphere as it moves through the ground. For such a scenario to take place, water must penetrate the host rock (which was selected because of the lack of water), then it must move through the crushed rock, the overpack (possibly a metal cylinder made of steel or titanium), and the canister wall (also metal) to finally reach the glass (or ceramic) that contains the wastes. If, despite all these barriers, some radioactive material is dissolved

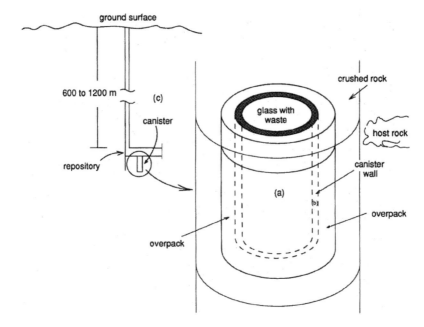

FIGURE 9.21 The isolation of the wastes is based on the multiple barrier approach: (a) the glass form, (b) the canister, and (c) the geologic medium.

TABLE 9.12
Basic Properties of Potential Geologic Media

Property	Salt	Basalt or Granite	Tuff
Plasticity	High	None	Variable
Solubility	High	Very low	Very low
Sorptive capacity	Low	Fair	Variable
Compressive strength	Moderate	High	Moderate
Thermal diffusivity	High	Low	Low
Thermal stability against chemical decomposition	High	High[a]	High
Permeability	Almost nil	Very low	Variable

Source: Office of Nuclear Waste Isolation 1983 briefing.
[a] High potential dewatering of clay in basalt.

in water, that water must still pass back through the same barriers before it reaches the biosphere.

Selection of a site is based on geologic, environmental, and land use criteria and on demographics. Typical geologic criteria are the following: type of rock, geologic stability, seismic activity, depth and lateral extent of the rock, groundwater flow, presence of or proximity to active faults, surface water bodies, and surface terrain characteristics. Environmental criteria are taken into account by preparing an environmental impact statement in accordance with the National Environmental Policy Act of 1969. The land use and demographics criteria answer questions such as these: Is the land already committed to nuclear activities? What are the population patterns in the area? What is the population density? What are other potential uses of the land (agriculture, mining, oil and gas exploration, etc.)?

As discussed in Section 9.4.1, the NWPA amendments of 1987 designated the Yucca Mountain site in Nevada as the site that will be characterized for the first U.S. repository. The geologic medium of this site is tuff. Work started at Yucca Mountain in 1994 and continued until 2009 (information about the project can be found at www.ymp.org). In 2009, the new administration stopped all work at the site and in 2010 announced the formation of a Blue Ribbon Commission, as discussed earlier in Section 9.4.2, to examine possible options for HLW disposal.

Despite all of these careful measures that will be taken for the disposal of HLW, the critics say that there is no experimental evidence to support a process that is supposed to contain the wastes for thousands of years. Such an assertion is not quite true. Nature provided us with some extraordinary evidence. In Gabon, West Africa, in a place called Oklo, a nuclear fission reactor started up on its own about 1.8 billion years ago. It operated over several hundred thousand years and then shut down again on its own. This event became possible because at that time the isotope ^{235}U was 3% of natural uranium (about the same fraction as in today's LWRs). Apparently, the combination of uranium ore and groundwater was such that this particular area had the same composition as that of the fuel and moderator in present-day LWRs. This "natural" reactor produced about 10 tons of HLW before it shut itself down, probably because of fuel "depletion." It has been determined that most solid fission products and all the TRU elements hardly moved; they remained there, locked in the ore, where they decayed. Surely a repository designed with additional barriers should perform at least as well as random disposal in a rock without any extra precautions for the isolation of the wastes.

9.6.7 The Waste Isolation Pilot Plant

The Waste Isolation Pilot Plant (WIPP) is a project undertaken by the DOE (with congressional authorization) for the purpose of providing a research and development facility to demonstrate the safe disposal of radioactive wastes resulting from the defense activities of the United States, primarily TRU waste. Exempted from NRC regulation, WIPP was ready for operation in 1988, as scheduled. After all questions about safety issues were addressed satisfactorily, the first TRU waste arrived at WIPP in March 1999.

The WIPP facility is located 25 miles south of Carlsbad, New Mexico, in a 10,240-acre area, of which 30 acres constitute the primary zone. It looks very much like a geological repository. The wastes are placed at a depth of 660 m (2150 ft) in bedded salt. The WIPP is designed for a maximum capacity of 176,000 m^3 (6,200,000 ft^3) of CH TRU and 7100 m^3 (250,000 ft^3) of RH TRU. Consistent with its mission as a research and development facility, WIPP will be the site of many experiments involving the disposal of both TRU and HLW, although the primary objective is the study of TRU disposal. Some examples of programs that are planned follow.

The durability of the drum carrying the wastes will be studied; the effectiveness of the backfill will be evaluated; data obtained directly from the disposal medium will help validate rock mechanics codes; *in situ* thermal-structural experiments will provide direct experimental data; and simulated HLW packages will provide information regarding unexpected problems encountered with this method of disposal. The objective will be to study the behavior of the wastes in salt and demonstrate that this method of disposal satisfies all the applicable health, safety, environmental, and security safeguards.

Waste packages sent to WIPP have to satisfy many requirements. Among them are the following: A waste container must be noncombustible, weigh no more than 11,300 kg (25,000 lb), must not exceed 3.7 × 2.4 × 2.6 m^3 (12 × 8.5 ft^3) in size, and its thermal power must not exceed 3.5 W/m^3 (0.1 W/ft^3). The surface dose rate should not exceed 2 mSv/h (200 mrem/h) at any point, with a neutron contribution of 0.50 mSv/h (50 mrem/h) reported in the data describing the package. Nuclear criticality conditions should be avoided by keeping concentrations below certain limits (200 g per 55-gal drum; 100 g per 30-gal drum; 5 g per cubic foot in boxes, up to 350 g maximum). To know and control gas generation, each package should provide the total alpha activity, a description of the waste form, and the mass of the organic material contained.

During the pilot phase of the project, all wastes placed in WIPP will be retrievable. As of 2011, after more than 10 years of successful operation, many rooms have been filled with TRU and their openings are closed with concrete blocks/panels, as planned. Drawing on the experience obtained so far, there is discussion and research under way at WIPP for disposal of GTCC waste either at that site or in a new repository in salt specifically dedicated to GTCC disposal (GTCC is defined in Sec. 10.3.2).

9.6.8 HLW Disposal Programs Outside the United States

All countries with nuclear activities have, or are developing, programs for the disposal of LLW and HLW. Before programs of individual countries are presented, an international project sponsored by Canada, Finland, France, Japan, Sweden, Switzerland, the United Kingdom, and the United States, called STRIPA, is discussed. The objective of the STRIPA project,[67] named after the Stripa Mine in central Sweden where the experiments are performed, was to provide practical experience in carrying out *in situ* tests at depths similar to those of an actual repository; the project allowed for the development of common techniques to be used by all of the participating countries for site characterization in their territory.

The Stripa rock is gray to light red, medium-grained granite. The experiments were conducted at a depth of 350 m. To simulate the heat generated by the HLW, electric heaters were placed in storage holes. Temperatures, pressures, and water uptake in the compacted bentonite were recorded and compared with calculated values.

A second phase of the STRIPA project involved the study of the migration of nuclides in the rock for a distance of up to 50 m. Short-lived radioisotopes were used as tracers, in connection with a hydraulic test of fracture flow between adjacent boreholes, to study the migration of nuclides along fracture planes for a distance of up to 10 m. STRIPA activities took place from 1980 to 1992; the results of the experiments are presented in Ref. 68.

The remainder of this section presents information about the most important vitrification programs in the world, as reported in the open literature. Because France has the most comprehensive reprocessing and vitrification program of any country and also because all of the other countries use the French vitrification technology, details are given only for the French program.

In France, LWR fuel is reprocessed and the recovered Pu is made into MOX fuel that is put back into its PWRs for electricity generation. Well-developed procedures and methods for the treatment of HLW have been established. For an interim period that lasts from 1 to 5 years, the liquid HLWs coming from reprocessing are stored in refrigerated double-walled stainless steel tanks with an estimated life of 50 years. After this temporary storage, the HLWs are vitrified. The first pilot facility, named PIVER, was started at Marcoule in 1969. It used a batch process and produced 12 tons of glass until 1973. In view of the excellent results obtained, an industrial-size facility was built, based on the AVM continuous process mentioned earlier, that started operating in 1978 (see Fig. 9.16 earlier in the chapter). The AVM was designed to process 60 L/h of liquid HLW and produce 25 kg/h of waste glass. The glass solidifies in containers made of 5-mm-thick refractory stainless steel with a diameter of 0.43 m and a height equal to 1.3 m, each filled with ~400 kg of glass. The containers are closed, decontaminated, and sent to an intermediate storage facility located at Marcoule. This facility, occupying an area of 400 m^2, consists of reinforced concrete shafts, 10 m deep, cooled by forced air. Each shaft carries 10 containers.

Intermediate storage of the glass is necessary for two reasons: (1) It provides reversibility of the process, and (2) it allows for a considerable decrease of the surface temperatures of the canisters before they are sent to the geologic repository.

More recently, a new vitrification technology was developed called the Cold Crucible Induction Melter (CCIM) technology. Implementation of CCIM technology started in 1980, and the first vitrified waste by this method was produced in 2010 (Ref. 69). In the first stage of CCIM, the liquid HLW solution is calcined at ~440°C; next, the calcinated solution is mixed with glass frit (the vitrification additive) and the mixture is introduced into a metallic vessel where it is melted at ~1100°C using induction heat; finally, the liquid (melted) mixture is poured into a metallic container where it cools off and solidifies. The CCIM technology has the potential to increase the capacity of vitrification plants by making possible increased temperature and faster operations with higher reactivity and higher concentration of fission products in glass.

Studies are in progress in France to determine the best geologic formation for the construction of a repository. The types of media considered are salt, granite, and clay.

The United Kingdom has two vitrification facilities: one at Sellafield and one at Windscale. Germany has a plant at Döttingen and a second one at Karlsruhe (called VEK).[70] Russia has a facility at Mayak, and Japan has two plants: one in Tokai and the second in Rokkasho (where their reprocessing plant is located). Korea has a pilot facility at Taejon. India has one at Tarapur.

9.7 Transportation of Radioactive Materials

9.7.1 Transportation Regulations

The federal regulations pertaining to transportation of radioactive materials are issued by three federal agencies: the U.S. Department of Transportation (DOT), the NRC, and the U.S. Postal Service. The DOT rules are found in Title 49 of the Code of Federal Regulations, Parts 100–177 (49 CFR 100–177) and Parts 178–199 (49 CFR 178–199). The NRC regulations are found in 10 CFR 71. Finally, the Postal Service regulations are found in 39 CFR 124. The transportation regulations do not differentiate between HLW and LLW. The criteria that determine the requirements for shipment depend on the activity and the isotopes contained in a package.

There are also international bodies that deal with the transportation of radioactive materials, the primary one being the International Atomic Energy Agency located in Vienna, Austria. The IAEA has been the primary agency for the establishment of regulations governing the transportation of such materials, regulations that formed the basis of most international agreements on the subject.

Federal rules and regulations change frequently. Persons routinely involved with transportation of radioactive materials must be certain that they have at hand and apply the current regulations. The material in this section is based on the 1983 revisions of the DOT and the 2010 revisions of the NRC regulations.[71,72]

The United States has more than 50 years of experience in the transportation of radioactive materials, both HLW and LLW. As a result of careful selection of the packages used to transport the materials and the special precautions taken by the carrier (both in terms of the vehicle and the route followed), no member of the public has been injured by release of radioactivity in an accident involving radioactive cargo.

9.7.2 Definitions and Classifications

The definitions and classifications that follow are based on the 10 CFR 71 January 2010 revision[72] and apply to HLW as well as LLW. A selection was made of those terms that are the most frequently encountered. For more details the reader is directed to consult 10 CFR 71.

- *Source material:* U or Th or any combination of the two in any physical or chemical form; or ores that contain by weight 1/20th of 1% (0.05%) or more of U, Th, or any combination of the two. Source material does not include special nuclear material (see next entry).

- *Special nuclear material (SNM):* Pu, ^{233}U, U enriched to the isotope 233 or 235, and any other material that the NRC determines to be SNM, but does not include source material; or any material artificially enriched by any of the foregoing, but not including source material.

- *By-product material:* (1) Material that became radioactive after being exposed to radiation generated in the process of utilizing SNM (SNM and source materials are not included). (2) Tailings or wastes produced by the extraction or concentration of U or Th from processed ore (underground ores depleted by solution mining do not constitute by-product material within this definition). (3.i) Any discrete source of ^{226}Ra that is produced, extracted, or converted after extraction, before, on, or after August 8, 2005, for use for a commercial, medical, or research activity; or (3.ii) any material that (A) has been made radioactive by use of a particle accelerator and (B) is produced, extracted, or converted after extraction, before, on, or after August 8, 2005, for use for a commercial, medical, or research activity. (4) Any discrete source of naturally occurring radioactive material, other than source material, that (i) the NRC, in consultation with relevant federal agencies, determines would pose a threat to the public health and safety or the common defense and security, similar to that posed by a discrete ^{226}Ra source, and (ii) before, on, or after August 8, 2005, is extracted or converted after extraction for use in a commercial, medical, or research activity.

- *Special form radioactive material:* Radioactive material that satisfies the following conditions: (1) It is either a single solid piece or is contained in a sealed capsule that can be opened only by destroying the capsule. (2) The piece or capsule has at least one dimension greater than 5 mm. (3) It satisfies the test requirements of paragraph 10 CFR 71.75 (this paragraph specifies certain tests the package must satisfy, e.g., drop, bending, and heat tests). An example of a special form of radioactive material is a solid metal source sealed in a high-integrity container.

- *Normal form radioactive material:* Material that does not qualify as "special form radioactive material." Examples are waste material in a plastic bag, liquid in a bottle within a metal container, powder in a glass or plastic bottle, and gas in a cylinder.

- *Low-specific-activity (LSA) material:* Radioactive material with limited specific activity, which is nonfissile or is excepted under 10 CFR 71.75 and which satisfies the descriptions and limits set below. Shielding materials surrounding LSA material may not be considered in determining the estimated average specific activity of the package contents. LSA material must be in one of the following three groups:

  1. LSA-I:
     (i) U and Th ores, concentrates of U and Th ores, and other ores containing naturally occurring radioactive nuclides that are not intended to be processed for the use of these radionuclides;
     (ii) Solid unirradiated natural U or depleted U or natural Th or their solid or liquid compounds or mixtures;
     (iii) Radioactive material for which the A_2 value (A_1 and A_2 activities are discussed below; also see Table 9.13 for numerical values) is unlimited; or
     (iv) Other radioactive material in which the activity is distributed throughout and the estimated average specific activity does not exceed 30 times the value for exempt material activity concentration determined in accordance with 10 CFR 71, Appendix A.

  2. LSA-II:
     (i) Water with tritium concentration up to 0.8 TBq/L (20.0 Ci/L); or
     (ii) Other material in which the activity is distributed throughout, and the average specific activity does not exceed 10^{-4} A_2/g for solids and gases, and 10^{-5} A_2/g for liquids.

  3. LSA-III solids (e.g., consolidated wastes, activated materials), excluding powders, that satisfy the requirements of 10 CFR 71.77, in which:

TABLE 9.13

Values of A_1 and A_2 Activities for Selected Isotopes

Isotope	A_1 (TBq)	A_1 (Ci)	A_2 (TBq)	A_2 (Ci)
^{14}C	40	1081	3.0	81
^{60}Co	0.4	10.8	0.4	10.8
^{99}Mo	1.0	27	0.6	16.2
^{123}I	6.0	162	3.0	81
^{129}I		Unlimited		
^{137}Cs	2.0	54	0.6	16.2
^{210}Pb	1.0	27	0.05	1.35
^{226}Ra	0.2	5.4	0.003	0.081
^{238}Th	0.5	13.5	0.001	0.027
^{233}U	40	1081	0.09	2.43
^{235}U		Unlimited		
^{238}U		Unlimited		
^{237}Np	20	540	0.002	0.054
^{239}Pu	10	270	0.001	0.027
^{240}Pu	10	270	0.001	0.027
^{241}Pu	40	1081	0.06	1.62
^{241}Am	10	270	0.001	0.027
^{252}Cf	0.05	1.35	0.003	0.081

From 10 CFR 71, Appendix A, 2010.

(i) The radioactive material is distributed throughout a solid or a collection of solid objects, or is essentially uniformly distributed in a solid compact binding agent (such as concrete, bitumen, ceramic, etc.);

(ii) The radioactive material is relatively insoluble or it is intrinsically contained in a relatively insoluble material so that even under loss of packaging, the loss of radioactive material per package by leaching, when placed in water for 7 days, would not exceed $0.1\ A_2$; and

(iii) The estimated average specific activity of the solid does not exceed $2 \times 10^{-3}\ A_2/\text{g}$.

- *Fissile material:* This term refers to the nuclides ^{233}U, ^{235}U, ^{239}Pu, and ^{241}Pu, or any combination of these nuclides. Fissile material means the fissile nuclides themselves, not material containing fissile nuclides. Unirradiated natural U and depleted U, and natural U or depleted uranium that was irradiated in thermal reactors only, are not included in this definition. Certain exclusions are described in 10 CFR 71.15.

- *Surface-contaminated object (SCO):* This refers to a solid object that is not itself classified as radioactive material, but that has radioactive material distributed on any of its surfaces. SCO is further subdivided

TABLE 9.14

General Values for A_1 and A_2

Comments	A_1 (TBq)	A_2 (TBq)	Activity Concentration (Bq/g)	Activity Limits for Exempt Material for Exempt Consignments (Bq)
Only β- or γ-emitting nuclides are known to be present	0.1	0.02	10	1.0×10^4
Only α-emitting nuclides are known to be present	0.2	9×10^{-5}	0.1	1000
No relevant data are available	0.001	9×10^{-5}	0.1	1000

From 10 CFR 71, Appendix A, 2010.

into SCO-I and SCO-II depending on the type and level of surface activity (see 10 CFR 71.4).

- *A_1 and A_2 activities:* A_1 is the maximum activity of special form radioactive material permitted in a type A package; A_2 is the maximum activity of radioactive material, other than special form, LSA, and SCO material, permitted in a type A package. The A_1 and A_2 quantities are given for each isotope in 10 CFR 71, Appendix A, Table A-1 (reproduced in this chapter as Table 9.13).

- *Type A and B quantities:* Type A quantity means a quantity of radioactive material, the aggregate radioactivity of which does not exceed A_1 for special form or A_2 for normal form of radioactive material. Type B quantity means a quantity of radioactive material greater than type A.

- *Transport index (TI):* TI is a dimensionless number (rounded up to the next 10th) placed on the label of a package to designate the degree of control to be exercised by the carrier during transportation. The TI is the number determined by multiplying the maximum radiation level in mSv/h at 1 m from the external surface of the package by 100 (equivalent to the maximum radiation level in mrem/h at 1 m).

The A_1 and A_2 values for individual radionuclides not listed in Table 9.13 are given in Table 9.14. For mixtures of nuclides whose identities and respective activities are known, the following formula should be used to determine the maximum quantity transported in a type A package:

$$\sum_i \frac{Ac(i)}{A_j(i)} \le 1 \; , \quad i = \text{isotope}, j = 1 \text{ or } 2 \tag{9.11}$$

where $Ac(i)$ is the activity of radionuclide i in the mixture, and $A_j(i)$ is the A_1 or A_2 activity of isotope i from Table 9.13. If this ratio is less than 1, use package type A; if it is greater than 1, package type B must be used. Alternatively, an A_1 or A_2 value for a mixture may be determined from the equation

$$A_j \text{ (for a mixture)} = \frac{1}{\displaystyle\sum_i \frac{f(i)}{A_j(i)}} \; , \quad j = 1 \text{ or } 2 \tag{9.12}$$

where $f(i)$ is the fraction of activity of nuclide i in the mixture and $A_j(i)$ is the appropriate A_j value for that nuclide taken from Table 9.13.

A few examples applying the definitions given above follow.

■ **Example 9.5:** A package contains 200 pCi/g of ^{226}Ra. Should it be considered LSA?

Answer: Yes, because according to LSA-II(ii), 100 pCi/g $< 10^{-4} A_2/g = (10^{-4} * 0.541 \times 10^{12}$ pCi/g $= 5.41 \times 10^7$ pCi/g). ■

■ **Example 9.6:** A package contains 10 Ci/g of ^{233}U. Should it be considered LSA?

Answer: No, because from LSA-II(ii), 10 Ci/g $= 10^{13}$ pCi/g $> 10^{-4} A_2/g = (10^{-4} * 0.027 \times 10^{12}$ pCi/g $= 2.7 \times 10^6$ pCi/g). ■

■ **Example 9.7:** A package contains the following three isotopic activities:

^{137}Cs $= 5$ Ci

^{239}Pu $= 1$ mCi

^{60}Co $= 3$ Ci.

Could this activity be transported in a type A package?

Answer: Apply Eq. (9.11):

$$\frac{5}{13.5} + \frac{1}{5.41} + \frac{3}{10.8} = 0.89 < 1$$

Yes, a type A package may be used. ■

■ **Example 9.8:** What is the A_2 activity for the package of Example 9.7?

Answer: Use Eq. (9.12). From the data given (total activity $= 8.001$ Ci), we obtain

$$f(1) = 5/8.001 = 0.625 \; , \quad f(2) = 10^{-3}/8.001 = 1.25 \times 10^4 \; ,$$

$$f(3) = 3/8.001 = 0.375$$

and

$$A_2 = \frac{1}{\dfrac{0.625}{13.5} + \dfrac{1.25 \times 10^{-4}}{5.41 \times 10^{-3}} + \dfrac{0.375}{10.8}} = 9.6 \text{ Ci} \quad \blacksquare$$

There is another class of materials, called mixed waste, that is regulated by the NRC and the EPA. Mixed waste is defined as waste that is considered radioactive (i.e., is subject to regulations applying to radioactive materials) and contains hazardous waste that is either (1) listed as hazardous waste in Subpart D of 40 CFR 261 (Title 40 CFR contains EPA rules and regulations) or (2) exhibits any of the hazardous waste characteristics identified in Subpart C of 40 CFR 261. The hazardous component of mixed waste is regulated under the Resource Conservation and Recovery Act. Handling, packaging, and disposing of mixed waste requires special care and adherence to both NRC and EPA regulations.

9.7.3 Shipper–Recipient Responsibilities

Both the shipper and the recipient of a package containing radioactive material have certain responsibilities; here is a list of the most important ones:

Shipper Responsibilities:

1. Select proper packaging.
2. Check materials license of the recipient. (Does it allow the material being shipped?)
3. Use correct labels.
4. Check package for external (surface) contamination.
5. Check radiation levels on the outside of the package.

Recipient Responsibilities:

1. Check shipping papers. (Is this what was ordered?)
2. Are contents allowed (covered) by your license?
3. Check package for external (surface) contamination.
4. Check radiation levels on the outside of the package.
5. Check contents after package is opened. (Is this what was ordered?)

9.7.4 Testing of Shipping Casks for UNF

More than 10,000 used fuel elements have been shipped in the United States during the past 30 years without any radiation release, despite a few serious

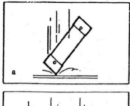

For certification by the NRC, a cask must be able to withstand a series of accident conditions. These conditions were developed in a National Academy of Sciences committee's recommendations on tests that would simulate damage to spent fuel casks in the most severe credible accidents. The mechanical tests (free drop and puncture), the thermal (fire) test, and the water-immersion (3 feet) test are performed in sequence to determine the cumulative effects on one package. A separate cask is subjected to the deep water-immersion (50 feet) test. Paraphrased descriptions of the regulatory tests follow.

Mechanical

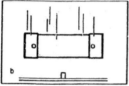

a. Free drop—Thirty-foot drop of the spent fuel cask onto a flat, horizontal, unyielding surface* with the cask positioned so that its weakest point is struck.

b. Puncture—Forty-inch free drop of the cask onto a 6-inch-diameter steel bar at least 8 inches long; the bar is to strike the cask at its most vulnerable spot.

Thermal

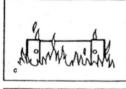

c. Fire—After the mechanical tests are completed, the package is totally engulfed in a fire or furnace at 1475°F for 30 minutes.

Water Immersion

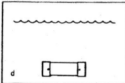

d. Immersion of all packaging surfaces under at least 3 feet of water for 8 hours; immersion of entire packaging under 50 feet of water for 8 hours.

*The "unyielding surface" criteria require that the result of the impact be borne completely by the cask. Drops from heights 2.5 to 3 times greater onto normal hard surfaces would be comparable. Drop tests have been conducted at much greater heights (2000 feet) without breaching the cask containment.

FIGURE 9.22 Integrity standards that must be satisfied by used fuel transportation casks.

road accidents. This excellent safety record is due to the design characteristics of the casks used for the transportation of used fuel. For the transportation of UNF, the safety factors have been placed in the cask and not on the transporter; regular trucks, rail, or barges are used for the transportation of UNF.

Before any cask is allowed to be used for transportation of used fuel, it must be certified by the NRC. Certification[73] is awarded after the cask satisfies the set of standards shown in Fig. 9.22. Proof that the cask is certifiable is obtained by performing a series of tests using the actual casks filled with a material simulating fuel in terms of density and weight.

The Transportation Technology Center at Sandia National Laboratories (SNL) in Albuquerque, New Mexico, has conducted a series of full-scale tests involving new cask designs. These tests, based on the standards shown in Fig. 9.22, were conducted to verify computer models of cask damage in postulated accidents. Examples of tests follow:

1. *Crash tests:* A tractor-trailer truck carrying a cask was crashed into a massive concrete wall at 61 mph and at 84 mph. No damage was

observed on the cask at 61 mph; at 84 mph, however, the cask was deformed as predicted by calculations. No (simulated) radioactivity was released. There was leakage of nonradioactive coolant fluid, but not until the cask was lifted from the wreckage.

2. *Locomotive test:* A locomotive traveling at 80 mph rammed broadside into a cask mounted on a truck. The locomotive was severely damaged but the cask was only slightly dented, almost exactly as predicted by the computer simulation of the test. No radioactivity escaped to the environment.

3. *Crash fire test:* A railroad car carrying a cask was crashed into a massive concrete barrier at 81 mph. Then the cask and the railroad car were subjected to an intense jet fuel fire for 125 min, totally engulfing them. As a result of the fire, the lead shield between the inner and outer walls melted. After 100 min, the pressure from the molten lead eventually caused a small crack (0.004 in. wide), through which some molten lead escaped. No radioactivity escaped. The cask design was corrected after this test to prevent the escape of molten lead.

4. *Drop test:* A cask formerly used for shipping used fuel from a research reactor was dropped from a helicopter and crashed on the desert ground at 235 mph. Although the cask was buried in more than 4 ft of the hard, packed soil, its only damage consisted of paint scratches.

Scientists at SNL also simulated terrorist attacks using explosive devices. The detonation of an explosive on a full-scale used fuel shipping cask indicated that 1% of the contents would be released to the environment. The weight of the cask should discourage would-be hijackers from attempting to steal it by removing it from the carrying vehicle. Removal of the fuel itself from the cask would likewise be difficult, since the closure plug weighs several tons. If the hijackers succeeded in removing the plug, they could receive a lethal radiation dose from the exposed fuel assemblies.

A used fuel cask must satisfy the following radiation limits[25]: (1) a dose rate of not more than 2 mSv/h (200 mrem/h) at any point on the surface of the cask; (2) a dose rate of not more than 0.10 mSv/h (10 mrem/h) at any point 2 m away from the cask boundary; and (3) a dose rate of not more than 0.02 mSv/h (2 mrem/h) at any normally occupied position (e.g., the seat of the truck driver).

A variety of casks have been designed and tested or are being used. Lighter casks, from 25 to 40 tons, are designed to hold one to seven assemblies and be carried by truck. Heavier casks, up to 120 tons, may carry up to 36 or more assemblies and be transported by rail. In general, the casks are cylindrical in shape with multiple walls for structural integrity and protection against gamma and neutron radiation emitted by the used fuel. In one such design, shown in Fig. 9.23, the fuel assemblies are sealed in a water-filled stainless steel cylinder with walls 0.5 in. thick, clad with 4 in. of a heavy metal, usually lead, for radiation shielding. This container is surrounded by 5 in. of water and encircled by a corrugated stainless steel outer package. Another cask, designed by the Babcock & Wilcox Company and designated "BR-100," is shown in Fig. 9.24. This cask is to be carried by rail or barge.

9.8 Emergency Preparedness: Response to Accidents

The Federal Emergency Management Agency (FEMA) has developed procedures and guidelines to be followed in the case of an accident involving radioactive materials. FEMA was established as a federal agency in 1979; in 1996, it was elevated to cabinet rank; in 2003, it became the major agency of the new Department of Homeland Security. FEMA is responsible for the federal response to any kind of disaster, including nuclear-related events. FEMA chairs the Federal Radiological Preparedness Coordinating Committee (FRPCC), composed of representatives from 20 federal departments and agencies. The FRPCC coordinates emergency management assistance from all federal agencies to state and local governments; it develops policies and procedures for radiological preparedness and response; and it coordinates research efforts in this field. FEMA has prepared a document[74] that gives

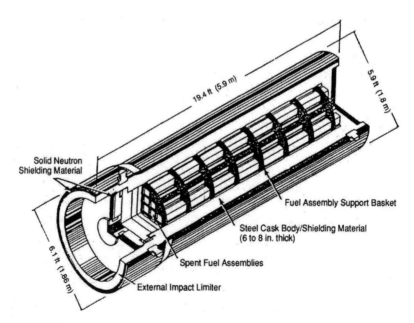

FIGURE 9.23 Conceptual drawing of a 76-ton rail cask.

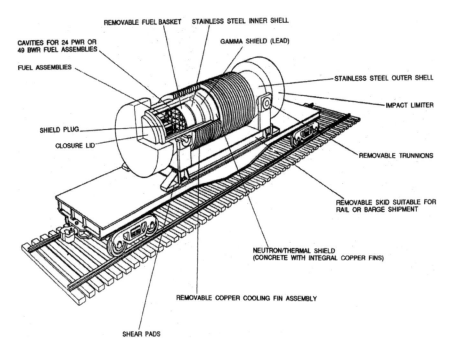

FIGURE 9.24 The BR-100 rail/barge transportation cask.

guidelines for state and local personnel with responsibility for emergency response plans.

In addition to FEMA, DOT has provided materials to states for training of fire, police, and ambulance personnel, and the DOE has eight regional offices for radiological assistance. Also, every state has set up a State Emergency Management Agency (SEMA). Finally, the Institute of Nuclear Power Operations has developed a voluntary assistance agreement among the electric utilities, under which they will assist each other in cases of radioactive materials transportation accidents.

Bibliography

Berlin, R.E., and Stanton, C.C., *Radioactive Waste Management*, Wiley-Interscience (1989).

Blue Ribbon Commission on America's Nuclear Future, "Report to the Secretary of Energy," (Jan. 2012); http://brc.gov.

Code of Federal Regulations, Title 10, "Energy," Part 60, "Disposal of High-Level Radioactive Wastes in Geologic Repositories," U.S. Nuclear Regulatory Commission (10 CFR 60) (Jan. 2010).

Code of Federal Regulations, Title 10, "Energy," Part 61, "Licensing Requirements for Land Disposal of Radioactive Waste," U.S. Nuclear Regulatory Commission (10 CFR 61) (Jan. 2010).

Code of Federal Regulations, Title 10, "Energy," Part 71, "Packaging and Transportation of Radioactive Material," U.S. Nuclear Regulatory Commission (10 CFR 71) (Jan. 2010).

Going the Distance? The Safe Transportation of Spent Nuclear Fuel and High-Level Radioactive Waste in the US, National Research Council, National Academies Press (2006).

High Level Radioactive Waste Management, A. Croff, Ed., American Society of Civil Engineers (1995).

Miller, W., *Geological Disposal of Radioactive Waste and Natural Analogues*, Pergamon Press (2005).

Principles and Standards for the Disposal of Long-Lived Radioactive Waste," Vol. 3, N. Chapman and C. McCombie, Eds., Elsevier Science (2003).

Pusch, R., *Geological Storage of Highly Radioactive Waste: Current Concepts and Plans for Radioactive Waste Disposal*, Springer (2010).

Pusch, R., Yong, R., and Nakano, M., *High Level Radioactive Waste (HLW) Disposal: A Global Challenge*," WIT Press (2011).

Saling, J.H., and Fentiman, A.W., *Radioactive Waste Management*, Taylor and Francis (2001).

Savage, D., *The Scientific and Regulatory Basis for the Geological Disposal of Radioactive Waste*, Wiley (1996).

U.S. Congress, "Joint Convention on the Safety of Spent Fuel and Radioactive Waste Management" (2010).

General Websites

Nuclear Engineering International, www.nei.org

U.S. Department of Energy, www.doe.gov

U.S. Nuclear Regulatory Commission, www.usnrc.gov

References

1. Kubo, A.S., and Rose, D.J., "Disposal of Nuclear Wastes," *Science*, **182**, 1205 (1973).

2. Rochlin, G.I., "Nuclear Waste Disposal: Two Social Criteria," *Science*, **195**, 23 (1977).

3. Angino, E.E., "High-Level and Low-Level Radioactive Waste Disposal," *Science*, **198**, 885 (1977).

4. American Physical Society Study Group on Nuclear Fuel Cycles and Waste Management Report, Part II, *Rev. Mod. Phys.*, **50**, *1* (1978).

5. Deutch, J.M., "Report of Task Force for Review of Nuclear Waste Management," DOE/ER-0004/D, UC-70 Draft, U.S. Department of Energy (Feb. 1978).

6. "DOE Waste: Special Issues," Draft, Interagency Review Group Report of Subgroup #3 (1978).

7. LaPorte, T.R., "Nuclear Waste: Increasing Scale and Sociopolitical Impacts," *Science*, **201**, 22 (1978).

8. Molaro, J.C., "High Level Nuclear Waste Management in the U.S.: A Time of Decisions," *Nucl. Safety*, **19**, 356 (1978).

9. *Code of Federal Regulations*, Title 10, "Energy," Part 20, "Standards for Protection Against Radiation," U.S. Nuclear Regulatory Commission (10 CFR 20) (under revision as of July 1988).

10. "Potential Benefits and Impacts of Advanced Nuclear Fuel Cycles with Actinide Partitioning and Transmutation," No. 6894, Organisation for Economic Co-operation and Development, Nuclear Energy Agency (2011).

11. "Report to the President and Congress by the Secretary of Energy on the Need for a 2nd Repository," DOE/RW-0595, U.S. Department of Energy, (2008).

12. Nuclear Waste Policy Act of 1982, Public Law 97-425 (Jan. 7, 1983).

13. Nuclear Waste Policy Amendments Act of 1987, Public Law 100-203 (Dec. 22, 1987).

14. "Final Version: Dry Cask Storage Study," DOE/RW-0220, U.S. Department of Energy (Feb. 1989).

15. Johnson, E.R., "Centralized Disassembly and Packaging of Spent Fuel in the DOE Spent Fuel Management Scheme," *Trans. Am. Nucl. Soc.*, **52**, 73 (1986); also "Fuel Rod Consolidation," *Nucl. News*, p. 68 (Mar. 1988).

16. Richards, L.M., and Szulinski, M.J., "Subsurface Storage of Commercial Spent Nuclear Fuel," *Nucl. Technol.*, **43**, 155 (1979).

17. Johnson, A.B., Jr., "Spent Fuel Storage Experience," *Nucl. Technol.*, **43**, 165 (1978).

18. Calabro, R.R., Stanford, R.E.L., and McBride, J., "Spent Fuel Storage: The Utility View," *Nucl. News*, p. 58 (Apr. 1983).

19. Thomas, J.A., and Ross, S.R., "Spent Fuel Storage: A Private Sector Option," *Nucl. News*, p. 62 (Apr. 1983).

20. Alvarez, R., Beyea, J., Janberg, K., Kang, J., Lyman, E., Macfarlane, A., Thompson, G., and von Hippel, F.N., "Reducing the Hazards from Stored Spent Power-Reactor Fuel in the United States," *Science and Global Security*, **11**, *1*, 1 (2003).

21. *Code of Federal Regulations*, Title 10, "Energy," Part 72, "Licensing Requirements for the Storage of Spent Fuel in an Independent Spent Fuel Storage Installation," U.S. Nuclear Regulatory Commission (10 CFR 72) (Jan. 2010).

22. *Industry Spent Fuel Storage Handbook*, 2010.102048, Electric Power Research Institute (July 2010).

23. "Survey of Wet and Dry Spent Fuel Storage," TEDDOC-1100, International Atomic Energy Agency (1999).

24. *Code of Federal Regulations*, Title 10, "Energy," Part 72.214 (10 CFR 72.214) (Jan. 2010)

25. *Code of Federal Regulations*, Title 10, "Energy," Part 71, "Packaging and Transportation of Radioactive Materials," U.S. Nuclear Regulatory Commission (10 CFR 71) (Jan. 2010).

26. NUREG/CR-6781, "Recommendations on the Credit for Cooling Time in PWR BU Credit Analyses," U.S. Nuclear Regulatory Commission (Jan. 2003).

27. Croff, A.G., "ORIGEN-2: A Versatile Computer Code for Calculating the Nuclide Compositions and Characteristics of Nuclear Materials," *Nucl. Technol.*, **62**, 335 (1983).

28. Bell, M.J., "ORIGEN, the ORNL Isotope Generation and Depletion Code," ORNL428, Oak Ridge National Laboratory (May 1973).

29. England, T.R., Wilczynski, R., and Whittemore, N.L., "CINDER-7: An Interim Report for Users," LA-5885-MS, Los Alamos National Laboratory (Apr. 1975); see also LA-6472-PR (1976) and LA-6266-PR (1976).

30. Malbrain, C.M., Lester, R.K., and Deutch, J.M., "Analytic Approximation in the Long-Term Behavior of Spent Fuel and High Level Waste," *Nucl. Technol.*, **57**, 292 (1982).

31. Shure, K., "^{235}U Fission Product Decay Energy 1972—Reevaluated," WAPD-TM1119, Bettis Atomic Power Laboratory (Oct. 1972).

32. Tobias, A., "The Energy Released from Fission Products," *J. Nucl. Energy*, **27**, 725 (1973).

33. Perry, A.M., Maienschein, F.C., and Vondy, D.R., "Fission Product Afterheat—A Review of Experiments Pertinent to the Thermal-Neutron Fission of ^{235}U," ORNL-TM4197, Oak Ridge National Laboratory (Oct. 1973).

34. Gunst, S.B., Conway, D.E., and Connor, J.C., "Measured and Calculated Rates of Decay Heat in Irradiated ^{235}U, ^{233}U, ^{239}Pu, and ^{232}Th," *Nucl. Sci. Eng.*, **56**, 241 (1975).

35. Friesenhahn, S.J., et al., "^{235}U Fission Product Decay Heat for 1 to 1E5 Seconds," EPRI-NP-180, Electric Power Research Institute (Feb. 1976).

36. England, T.R., "Recent Comparison of Decay Spectra, Heating and Absorption Effects," LA-UR-766-2140, Los Alamos National Laboratory (Sep. 1976).

37. Yarnell, J.L., and Bendt, P.J., "Decay Heat from Products of ^{235}U Thermal Fission by Fast Response Boil-off Calorimetry," LA-NUREG-6713, Los Alamos National Laboratory (1977).

38. Dickens, J.K., et al., "Fission Product Energy Release for Times Following Thermal Neutron Fission of ^{235}U Between 2 and 14,000 Seconds," ORNL/NUREG-14, Oak Ridge National Laboratory (Oct. 1977).

39. Bjerke, M.J., Holm, J.S., Shay, M.R., and Spinrad, B.I., "A Review of Short Term Fission Product Decay Power," *Nucl. Safety*, **18**, 596 (1977).

40. Friesenhahn, S.J., and Lurie, N.A., "Measurements of ^{235}U and ^{239}Pu Fission Product Decay," EPRI-NP-998, Electric Power Research Institute (1979).

41. Stamatelatos, M.G., and England, T.R., "Decay Spectra of Fission Products from ^{235}U Thermal Fission: Comparison with Experiments," *Nucl. Technol.*, **45**, 219 (1979).

42. Glasstone, S., and Sesonske, A., *Nuclear Reactor Engineering*, Van Nostrand Reinhold (1967).

43. Schrock, V.E., "A Revised ANS Standard for Decay Heat from Fission Products," *Nucl. Technol.*, **46**, 323 (1979).

44. LaBauve, R.J., England, T.R., and George, D.C., "Fission Product Analytic Impulse Source Functions," *Nucl. Technol.*, **56**, 322 (1982).

45. ANS Standard 5.1, "Decay Heat Power in LWRs," American Nuclear Society (2005).

46. "Final Storage of Spent Nuclear Fuel-KBS-3," SKBF/KBS, Swedish Nuclear Fuel Supply Co. (May 1983).

47. Jouan, A., Ladirat, C., and Moncouyoux, J.P., "Present Status of the French Continuous Fission Product Vitrification Process," *Advances in Ceramics*, Vol. 20, *Nuclear Waste Management II*, p. 105, American Ceramic Society (1986).

48. Tsoulfanidis, N., *Measurement and Detection of Radiation*, McGraw-Hill (1983).

49. *The Treatment and Handling of Radioactive Wastes*, A.G. Blasewitz, J.M. Davis, and M.R. Smith, Eds., Battelle Press (1982)

50. *Treatment, Recovery, and Disposal Processes for Radioactive Wastes— Recent Advances*, J.D. Duffy, Ed., Noyes Data Corp. (1983).

51. *Advances in Ceramics*, Vol. 20, *Nuclear Waste Management II*, D.E. Clark, J.B. White, and A.J. Machiels, Eds., American Ceramic Society (1986).

52. Schreider, R.F., Davis, J.C., and Mellon, J.B., "Immobilizing Defense Waste: The Savannah River Project," presented at AIF Fuel Cycle Conf., Kansas City, Missouri, March 1983.

53. Mairson, R.C., "Nuclear Waste Management: The West Valley Project," presented at AIF Fuel Cycle Conf., Kansas City, Missouri, March 1983.

54. "Annual Report on the Characterization of HLW Glasses," PNL-2625, Battelle Pacific Northwest Laboratory (June 1978).

55. Ringwood, A.E., Kesson, S.E., Ware, N.G., Hibberson, W.O., and Major, A., "Immobilization of High Level Nuclear Reactor Wastes in SYN-ROC," *Nature*, **278**, 219 (1979).

56. Ringwood, A.E., Kesson, S.E., Ware, N.G., Hibberson, W.O., and Major, A., "The SYNROC Process: A Geochemical Approach to Nuclear Waste Immobilization," *Geochem. J.*, **13**, 141 (1979).

57. Reeve, K.D., Tewhey, J.D., and Ringwood, A.E., "Recent Progress on SYNROC Development," *The Scientific Basis for Nuclear Waste Management*, Vol. 3, G. McCarthy, Ed., pp. 147–154, Plenum Press (1981).

58. Newkirk, H.W., Hoenig, C.L., Ryerson, F.J., Tewhey, J.D., Smith, G.S., Rossington, C.S., Brackmann, A.J., and Ringwood, A.E., "SYNROC Technology for Immobilizing U.S. Defense Wastes," *Am. Ceram. Soc. Bull.*, **61**, 559 (1982).

59. Oversby, V.M., and Ringwood, A.E., "Immobilization of High-Level Nuclear Reactor Wastes in SYNROC: A Current Appraisal," *Scientific Basis for Nuclear Waste Management*, Vol. 6, S.V. Topp, Ed., pp. 75–82 (1982).

60. Ringwood, A.E., "Immobilization of Radioactive Wastes in SYNROC," *American Scientist*, **70**, 201 (1982).

61. Reeve, K.D., and Ringwood, A.E., "The SYNROC Process for Immobilizing High Level Nuclear Wastes," *Radioactive Waste Management*, Vol. 2, pp. 307–324, Proc. Ser. IAEA-43/127, International Atomic Energy Agency (1984).

62. Sobolev, I.A., Dmitriev, S.A., Stefanovsky, S.V., Vlasov, V.I., and Babaev, N.S., "Development of SYNROC Melting Process for Conditioning of Partitioned HLW," 5th International Nuclear Conference on Recycling, Conditioning and Disposal, Nice, France, 1998.

63. "Disposal of Radioactive Wastes: An Overview of the Principles Involved," Nuclear Energy Agency, Organisation for Economic Co-operation and Development (1982).

64. Hollister, L.D., Anderson, D.R., and Heath, C.R., "Subseabed Disposal of Nuclear Wastes," *Science*, **213**, 1321 (1981).

65. "Advanced Nuclear Fuel Cycles and Radioactive Waste Management," No. 5990, Organisation for Economic Co-operation and Development, Nuclear Energy Agency (2006).

66. "Potential Benefits and Impacts of Advanced Nuclear Fuel Cycles with Actinide Partitioning and Transmutation," No. 6894, Organisation for Economic Co-operation and Development, Nuclear Energy Agency (2011).

67. "The International STRIPA Project: Background and Research Results," Nuclear Energy Agency, Organisation for Economic Co-operation and Development (1983).

68. Olson, O., and Gale, J.E., "Site Assessment and Characterization for High-Level Waste Disposal: Results from the STRIPA Project, Sweden," *Quart. J. Eng. Geol. Hydrogeol.*, **28**, 517 (1995).

69. Naline, S., Giouyaud, F., Robineau, V., Girold, C., and Carpentier, B., "Vitrification 2010—A Challenging French Vitrification Project to Retrofit a Cold Crucible Inductive Melter at the La Hague Plant," Waste Management Conference, Phoenix, Arizona, 2010.

70. Fleisch, J., Gruenewald, W., Roth, G., Schwaab, E., Tobie, W., and Weishaupt, M., "Cold Test Operation of the German VEK Vitrification Plant," Waste Management Conference, Phoenix, Arizona, 2008.

71. *Code of Federal Regulations*, Title 49, "Transportation," Parts 100-177 and 178-199, "A Review of the Department of Transportation Regulations for Transportation of Radioactive Materials," U.S. Nuclear Regulatory Commission (Rev. 2011).

72. *Code of Federal Regulations*, Title 10, "Energy," Part 71, "Packaging and Transportation of Radioactive Materials," U.S. Nuclear Regulatory Commission (10 CFR 71) (Jan. 2010).

73. "Transporting Spent Fuel—An Overview," USDOE-OCRWM, DOE/RW-0065-Dist. Category UC-71, U.S. Department of Energy (Mar. 1986).

74. Civil Preparedness Guidelines (CPG) 1-8, "A Guide for Development of State and Local Emergency Operations Plans," Federal Emergency Management Agency (Oct. 1985); see also CPG 1-8A, "A Guide for the Review of State and Local Emergency Operations Plans," FEMA (Oct. 1985).

PROBLEMS

9.1. Which is more dangerous, 1.0 Ci of ^{90}Sr or 50 mCi of ^{239}Pu? The derived air concentrations (DACs) for these two isotopes are 8×10^{-9} μCi/cm^3 and 3×10^{-12} μCi/cm^3, respectively.

9.2. In a nuclear power plant, 5 kg of wastes with a total activity of 2 μCi was accumulated, of which 1 μCi was from ^{241}Am. The rest of the activity is due to isotopes with $Z < 92$. How would you characterize this waste?

9.3. Characterize the materials listed below as LLW, TRU, or HLW:

(a) Gloves contaminated with ^{60}Co and 10 Ci of fission products

(b) A fuel rod from a BWR after 100 MWd/t burnup

(c) Shoe covers sprayed with tritiated (^{3}H$_2$O) water

(d) Uranium mill tailings

(e) 5 g of irradiated LWR fuel containing 550 nCi of ^{252}Cf.

9.4. Obtain an expression for the activity of a fission product (in Ci/W) under the following assumptions: (a) the fission rate over the power run is held constant, (b) neutron absorption by this isotope is negligible, (c) the fission product is produced in fission with a yield of y atoms/fission, and (d) the fission product decays with a half life $T_{1/2}$. Assume both a short and long half life compared to the power run T.

9.5. Calculate the decay heat, as a fraction of operating power, at 1 s, 2 h, 72 h, 1 month, and 1 year after shutdown.

9.6. A power reactor operated for 300 effective full-power days (EFPD) at 1050 MWe with an efficiency of 33%. What is the decay power generated in the core 20 min after shutdown? Assume only ^{235}U fissions.

9.7. For the reactor power history shown below, calculate (a) the availability factor, (b) the capacity factor, (c) the EFPD during that period, (d) the burnup during that period, and (e) the decay power in the core at 1 s and at 1 month after shutdown. Assume all power was generated by fissions in ^{235}U. The core contains 87 tons of uranium and generates 1100 MWe with an efficiency of 31%.

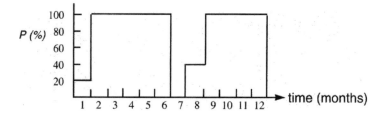

9.8. Repeat part (e) of Problem 9.7 assuming that 20% of the power is produced by fissions in ^{239}Pu.

9.9. Calculate the decay power 1 s after shutdown of an 1150-MWe LWR that operated for a year with the power history shown below and a thermal efficiency of 32%. Use first Eq. (9.5) and then the ANS Standard 5.1[45] equations [Eqs. (9.7) and (9.8)]. Compare the results.

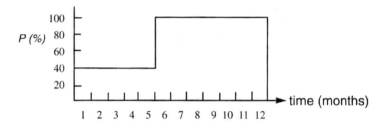

9.10. A package contains 1 mCi/g of ^{137}Cs. Is this considered an LSA package?

9.11. Can a type A package be used to transport the following mixture?: 10 Ci of ^{14}C, 3 mCi of ^{237}Np, and 0.5 Ci of ^{210}Pb

9.12. Define the materials given below as source material, SNM, or by-product material.

   (a) 100 t of Th ore

   (b) 1 kg of ^{241}Pu

   (c) 10 mg of ^{3}H

   (d) 20 g of U enriched to 5% in ^{235}U

TEN

LLW MANAGEMENT AND DECOMMISSIONING OF NUCLEAR FACILITIES

10.1 Sources of Low-Level Wastes

As explained in Sections 9.2 and 9.3, all activities involving radioactive materials produce low-level radioactive wastes (LLW). In addition to nuclear fuel-related activities and reactor operations, other major sources of LLW are industrial establishments, research laboratories, medical establishments, and radiopharmaceutical laboratories.

Examples of LLW are contaminated items like clothing, tools, swipes and other trash, liquids containing radioisotopes, and disposable medical items. Nuclear power plants generate filters, resins, protective clothing, tools, contaminated oils, and other items fulfilling the definition given in Section 9.2. Used nuclear fuel is not LLW; it is HLW. Figure 10.1 shows actual and projected LLW generated in the United States for the period 1960–2020.

10.2 The LLW Policy Act of 1980 and Its 1985 Amendments

Before the Low Level Radioactive Waste Policy Act (LLRWPA) and its amendments are discussed,[1] it will be useful to review the status of LLW disposal before the passage of the act. First of all, keep in mind that all 50 states generate LLW regardless of whether or not they have operating nuclear reactors on their soil. A large fraction of LLW is generated by research establishments, industry, and hospitals that use radioisotopes. When the LLRWPA was passed in 1980, only three sites were open to accept LLW; one in Barnwell, South Carolina; a second in Richland, Washington; and the third in Beatty, Nevada. The governors of those three states pressed Congress to do something about additional LLW disposal sites by threatening to reject LLW coming to them from other states. Congress responded in 1980 by passing the LLRWPA, which dictates that each state is responsible for the disposal

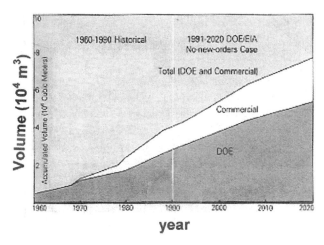

FIGURE 10.1 LLW generated in the United States. Historical data until 1990; projected to 2020. (Data from U.S. Environmental Protection Agency website.)

of all LLW generated within its borders. The act assumes that LLW can be safely and efficiently managed and stored on a regional basis. To carry out the disposal of LLW, a state may enter into "compacts" with other states to establish and operate regional disposal facilities, subject to congressional approval. These compacts will be legal entities created on the basis of a contract signed by all of the member states and will be administered through a "compact commission" created by the state hosting the facility. The extent of the authority of the compact commission will depend on whether or not the host state (in which the site is located) is an agreement state.[a] If the host state is an agreement state, then it can license and regulate its LLW site. If not, the NRC will do it. The licensing requirements for LLW sites are described in 10 CFR 61 (Ref. 2).

No compact can take effect without congressional consent. Congress may, by law, review its consent every 5 years after the compact goes into effect and withdraw consent if necessary. After January 1, 1986, any such compact would have been allowed to restrict acceptance of LLW to that from within its region only and reject any request for disposal of LLW generated outside its region.

Immediately after the passage of the LLRWPA, the states began the process prescribed by the act in an attempt to comply, but it became clear well

---

[a] An agreement state is one that entered into an agreement with the U.S. Nuclear Regulatory Commission (NRC), pursuant to Section 274 of the Atomic Energy Act of 1954, as amended, under which the NRC has given to such state the authority to regulate the radioactive materials within its borders, with the exception of nuclear materials in quantities large enough to form a critical mass. As of 2012 there were 37 agreement states.

before the January 1, 1986, deadline that no compacts would be ready for approval by that date. For this reason, Congress initiated and passed amendments to the act in December 1985 and the president signed them into law on January 15, 1986.

The 1985 amendments modified two important aspects of the LLRWPA. First, a transitional period was established from January 1, 1986, to December 31, 1992, during which time-limited access to the existing disposal sites was provided until compacts had been approved and new sites started operating. Second, and more important, the Act set up penalties, in the form of surcharges, for states that did not meet the specified milestones. The surcharges ranged from $10 to $120 per cubic foot of LLW. The U.S. Department of Energy (DOE) would hold 25% of the surcharge payments in an interest-bearing account. The various state compacts would have received rebates from that account, depending on the progress made toward having a site selected, prepared, and licensed.

A national limit of 2.8 million cubic feet of LLW per year was established for disposal at the existing facilities. So as not to exceed the limit, the act imposed an annual limit on LLW generated by the electric utility industry and encouraged LLW generators to reduce the volume of their wastes.

The main milestones specified by the LLRWPA and its amendments are as follows:

1. By July 1, 1986, a compact was to have been ratified or intent to develop a site certified. Failure to meet this deadline resulted in doubling of the surcharge—from $10 to $20 per cubic foot, for 6 months. All surcharge rebates were lost. The option existed to deny access after January 1, 1987.

2. By January 1, 1988, the host state was to have been identified, a developer selected, and a siting plan prepared. Failure to meet this deadline resulted in doubling of the surcharge for 6 months, and then quadrupling of it for the next 6 months. All surcharge rebates from July 1, 1986, to January 1, 1988, were lost. The option existed to deny access to LLW sites after January 1, 1989.

3. By January 1, 1990, an application for an operating license for a disposal site had to have been submitted, by an individual state or through a compact, or the governor had to certify in writing to the NRC that the state would be able to provide for proper management and disposal of its LLW. If this milestone were not met, all surcharge rebates between January 1, 1988, and January 1, 1990, would be lost, and the option existed to deny access to disposal facilities after January 1, 1990.

4. By January 1, 1992, the governor's certification was not deemed sufficient—to be in compliance, a license application must have been

submitted for a state or a compact. The consequences of noncompliance were a tripling of the surcharge rate to $120 per cubic foot until a license application had been submitted, and denial to a LLW site after January 1, 1993, by licensed compacts.

5. By January 1, 1996, all states were required to have a LLW disposal site. No surcharge rebate payments were made after this date. Each state was fully responsible for all LLW generated within its borders (i.e., they took title possession and liability).

10.2.1 The LLW Compacts

The compact groupings as of 2010 appear as follows (also shown in Fig. 10.2):

- **Northwest**: WA (host state), OR, ID, MT, WY, UT, AK, HI
- **Rocky Mountain**: NV (host state), CO, NM
- **Southwestern**: CA (host state), AZ, ND, SD
- **Midwest**: OH (host state), IN, MN, WI, IA, MO
- **Central**: KS, OK, AR, LA
- **Central Midwest**: IL (host state), KY
- **Texas**: TX (host state), VT
- **Appalachian**: PA (host state), DE, MD, WV
- **Southeast**: GA, TN, VA, MS, AL, FL
- **Atlantic**: SC (host state), NJ, CT
- **Unaffiliated**: NE, MI, NY, NH, MA, RI, ME, NC, DC, Puerto Rico

It is quite possible that many of these compacts may be modified; present alliances may break up, and new ones may emerge. After the LLRWPA was passed, compacts started to emerge without any unaffiliated states. The breakup of the original compacts and the birth of unaffiliated states are primarily the result of the tacit agreement that the state that generates most of the LLW will be the compact host state. For example, in the beginning Illinois was a member of the Midwest compact; had it stayed, Illinois would have to have agreed to be the host state. Politics dictated otherwise, so Illinois split and picked up Kentucky to form a new compact. With Illinois out, Michigan would have been the host state of the Midwest compact—but the story repeated itself: Michigan did not want to do it and was expelled from the compact. A similar story developed on the Southeast compact with North Carolina. Presumably, unaffiliated states will develop their own disposal sites. Based on the map of compacts shown in Fig. 10.2, it appears that many more LLW sites will be developed than are actually needed. As a result, the economy of scale will be lost and disposal costs will be higher than they could have been with a smaller number of bigger sites.

FIGURE 10.2 A map of the U.S. LLW compacts as of 2010. * = Active disposal sites (3). Alaska and Hawaii belong to the NW compact; shaded states are unaffiliated (10). The reader should consult the NRC website for the most current information. (Data from U.S. Nuclear Regulatory Commission website.)

The status of LLW disposal sites as of 2011 was as follows. There are four licensed disposal facilities. One is at Barnwell, South Carolina, accepting wastes from all LLW generators except North Carolina; the second is at Hanford, Washington, with access restricted to only the Northwest and Rocky Mountain compacts (facilities at both South Carolina and Washington accept Class A, B, and C wastes; see Section 10.3.2); the third is at Clive, Utah, and is restricted to only Class A waste and slightly contaminated soils. Clive does, however, accept wastes from anywhere. The fourth, the Texas compact facility, located in Andrews County, opened for business in December 2011; it will accept LLW from Texas, Vermont, 36 other states, and the federal government.

10.3 Disposal of LLW

10.3.1 Characteristics of LLW

LLWs are subdivided into three physical forms: liquids, wet solids, and dry solids.

Liquid LLWs are fluids that have been contaminated with radioactive materials. Examples are chemical regenerative solutions, decontamination solutions, liquid scintillators, contaminated oils, and other miscellaneous organic and inorganic fluids. The liquids are produced as a result of several different operations at a nuclear power plant. Examples are ion-exchange media (used in demineralizers for water cleanup); contaminated oils from oil/water separators, reactor coolant pumps, or hydraulic scrubbers; liquid scintillators used for radiation monitoring; laundry waste streams; and discharges from equipment and floor drains.

Wet solids are relatively thick slurries containing a certain fraction of solids. Examples include evaporator bottoms, spent ion-exchange resins, and expended loaded filter cartridges. Research programs and medical establishments produce LLW in the form of animal carcasses, tissues, excreta, biological cultures, etc.

Dry solids are contaminated trash, swipes, clothes, tools and equipment, and irradiated hardware.

Radionuclides present in LLW differ depending on the source of the wastes. Nuclear reactor operations generate LLW containing activation products and, perhaps, a small quantity of fission products and transuranic isotopes. Industrial and institutional (hospitals and research labs) LLWs contain ^{3}H, ^{14}C, ^{60}Co, ^{137}Cs, ^{99}Tc, ^{22}Na, and others.

10.3.2 Classification of LLW into A, B, C, and GTCC Classes

Radioactive wastes that may be buried in near-surface disposal sites are divided into three classes (see 10 CFR 61.55) according to the long- and short-lived isotopes they contain:

- *Class A:* This is waste that has the least amount of radioactivity; it is usually segregated from other waste classes at the disposal site. The physical form and characteristics of Class A waste must meet the minimum requirements set forth in 10 CFR 61.56a (see Section 10.3.3).

- *Class B:* This class of waste is more radioactive than Class A; it must satisfy the minimum and stability requirements stated in 10 CFR 61.56b.

TABLE 10.1

Activity Concentrations Used for the Classification of LLW

(a)

Nuclide	Concentration (Ci/m³)
^{14}C	8
^{14}C in activated metal	80
^{59}Ni in activated metal	220
^{94}Nb in activated metal	0.2
^{99}Tc	3
^{129}I	0.08
Alpha-emitting TRU with $t_{1/2} > 5$ yr	100 (nCi/g)
^{241}Pu	3,500 (nCi/g)
^{242}Cm	20,000 (nCi/g)

(b)

Nuclide	Concentration (Ci/m³)		
	Column 1	Column 2	Column 3
Total of all nuclides with $t_{1/2} > 5$ yr	700	a	a
^{3}H	40	a	a
^{60}Co	700	a	a
^{63}Ni	3.5	70	700
^{63}Ni in activated metal	35	700	7,000
^{90}Sr	0.04	150	7,000
^{137}Cs	1	44	4,600

From Ref. 2.

[a] No limits established for these nuclides in columns 2 or 3. Other considerations (external radiation or internal heat generation) may limit their concentrations. These wastes will be Class B, unless other considerations determine them to be Class C.

- *Class C:* This is the most radioactive of the three types of LLW that are allowed to be stored in near-surface burial sites. Class C waste must satisfy the requirements of Classes A and B and in addition requires additional measures to be taken at the disposal facility against inadvertent intrusion.

Another class of waste is the *greater-than-Class C (GTCC)* wastes. These are wastes that are more radioactive than Class C and are not considered appropriate for shallow burial. Disposal of GTCC waste is considered the responsibility of the federal government; it must be placed in a geologic repository, unless the NRC approves GTCC waste disposal in a licensed site.

A waste package is classified as being Class A, B, C, or GTCC based on the type, volume concentration, and the half lives of the nuclides included in the package. The classification procedure can be understood with the help of Table 10.1, reproduced from 10 CFR 61.55. Classification of packages into A, B, C, or GTCC is done as follows:

Class A: A package is Class A if any of the following three conditions apply:
1. It does not contain any nuclides listed in Table 10.1(a) or (b).
2. It contains nuclides listed in Table 10.1(a) with concentrations equal to or less than 10% of the values given in Table 10.1(a).
3. It contains nuclides listed in Table 10.1(b) with concentrations equal to or less than the values given in column 1 of Table 10.1(b).

Class B: A package is Class B if it contains nuclides listed in Table 10.1(b) with concentrations greater than the values given in column 1 but less than or equal to the values given in column 2.

Class C: A package is Class C if any of the following two conditions apply:
1. It contains nuclides listed in Table 10.1(a) with concentrations greater than 10% of the values given in the table but less than or equal to those values.
2. It contains nuclides listed in Table 10.1(b) with concentrations greater than the values given in column 2 but less than or equal to the values given in column 3.

Class GTCC: A package is Class GTCC if any of the following two conditions apply:
1. It contains nuclides listed in Table 10.1(a) with concentrations greater than the values given in the table.
2. It contains nuclides listed in Table 10.1(b) with concentrations greater than the values given in column 3.

GTCC waste consists of metals activated in a reactor (hence, found in decommissioning), sealed sources (used to sterilize medical products, to detect flaws in welds, as gauges in various measurements, as radiotherapy units), contaminated equipment, glove boxes, filters, etc. Radionuclides found in GTCC waste[3] include ^{137}CsCl, ^{238}Pu, ^{239}Pu, ^{240}Pu, ^{241}Am, ^{243}Am, and ^{244}Cm.

If a package contains more than one isotope from the *same column of either Table 10.1(a) or (b),* the fraction rule must be used to determine the class. If

$$\sum_i \frac{C_i(package)}{C_i(table)} < 1$$

where C_i = concentration of i'th nuclide in the package and table, respectively, the waste belongs to the class determined by the values of C_i used for the fraction rule (see Examples 10.2 and 10.3 below). If the summation is greater than one, the package belongs to the next higher class. If the package contains nuclides from both tables, the most restrictive classification applies as determined from the concentration of nuclides from part (a) or (b) of the table.

Packages containing the isotopes indicated by an asterisk in columns 2 and 3 of Table 10.1(b) will be Class B no matter what their concentrations are, unless other isotopes dictate a different classification. The concentrations of these isotopes are limited by effects such as external radiation and internal heat generation limits dictated by transportation, handling, and disposal requirements.

■ *Example 10.1:* A LLW package contains ^{63}Ni in a concentration of 65 Ci/m^3. Determine the class of this waste.

Answer: Using Table 10.1(b), the waste is Class B because the concentration of the isotope exceeds that of column 1, but not column 2. ■

■ *Example 10.2:* A LLW package contains ^{63}Ni in a concentration of 15 Ci/m^3 and ^{90}Sr in a concentration of 50 Ci/m^3. Determine the class of this waste.

Answer: Because both concentrations exceed those of column 1 of Table 10.1(b), they must be compared to values in column 2. For ^{63}Ni, the fraction is $15/70 = 0.21$; for ^{90}Sr, the fraction is $50/150 = 0.33$. The sum of the fractions is $0.54 < 1.0$; therefore, this waste is Class B. ■

■ *Example 10.3:* A LLW package contains ^{63}Ni in a concentration of 60 Ci/m^3 and ^{90}Sr in a concentration of 90 Ci/m^3. Determine the class of this waste.

Answer: Because both concentrations exceed those of column 1 of Table 10.1(b), they must be compared to values in column 2. For ^{63}Ni, the fraction is $60/70 = 0.86$; for ^{90}Sr, the fraction is $90/150 = 0.60$. The sum of the fractions is $1.46 > 1.0$; therefore, this waste is Class C. ■

■ *Example 10.4:* A LLW package contains 0.075 Ci/m^3 of ^{129}I and 750 Ci/m^3 of ^{32}P. Determine the class of this waste.

Answer: The half life of ^{32}P is 14.3 days. The presence of ^{32}P makes it Class B waste [concentration greater than column 1, Table 10.1(b)]. The presence of ^{129}I at a concentration of 0.075 Ci/m^3 $> 0.1 * 0.08$ Ci/m^3 makes it Class C waste. Since the most restrictive classification applies, the waste is Class C. ■

■ *Example 10.5:* A LLW package contains 230 Ci/m^3 of ^{59}Ni. What is the class of this waste?

Answer: This is GTCC waste because the ^{59}Ni concentration exceeds that listed in Table 10.1(a). ■

The LLRWPA Amendments Act directed[1] the NRC to establish criteria, standards, and procedures for exemption from regulation of certain radioactive wastes with low concentrations of radioactivity and/or quantities of radioactivity. Such wastes would be "below regulatory concern" (BRC). In 1989, the term BRC was replaced by "exemption from regulatory control" (ERC). The nuclear industry performed many studies,[4] supported by the Electric Power Research Institute, having to do with evaluation, assessment, risk, and cost–benefit analysis of ERC waste. The NRC was sympathetic to the establishment of the class ERC waste but Congress did not support the idea.

10.3.3 Disposal Requirements for Class A, B, C, and GTCC Wastes

The disposal requirements are described in 10 CFR 61.56; they are stated as minimum and stability requirements.

Minimum requirements: The following minimum requirements must be met:

1. The waste must not be packaged for disposal in cardboard or fiberboard boxes.

2. Liquid waste must be solidified or packaged in sufficient absorbent material to absorb twice the volume of the liquid.

3. Liquids contained in solid waste shall not exceed 1% of the waste volume.

4. Waste must not be explosive or reactive at normal temperatures and pressures and must not lead to an explosive reaction with water.

5. The waste must not contain or be capable of generating toxic gases, vapors, or fumes harmful to people handling it. (This does not apply to gaseous waste; see item 7 below.)

6. Waste must not be pyrophoric. Pyrophoric materials contained in the waste shall be made nonflammable before disposal.

7. Gaseous waste must be packaged at a pressure of <1.5 atm at 20°C and total activity must be less than 100 Ci per container.

8. Wastes containing hazardous, biological, pathogenic, or infectious material need special treatment.

Stability requirements: The purpose of stability is to ensure that the waste does not structurally degrade and affect the overall stability of the site; stability also aims at reducing exposure to an inadvertent intruder.

1. *Structural stability:* The waste package must maintain its form and physical dimensions under the expected disposal conditions, such as weight of overburden and compaction equipment, moisture, microbial activity, chemical changes, and radiation effects.

2. Liquid waste or waste containing liquid, in addition to satisfying minimum requirements 2 and 3 above, must be converted into a form that contains less than 1% of the volume of the waste free as standing and noncorrosive liquid when the waste is in a container designed to ensure stability, or 0.5% for waste processed to a stable form.

3. Void spaces within the waste and between the waste and its package must be minimized.

Every package must be clearly labeled identifying its class as A, B, or C. For GTCC packages, additional requirements may be imposed after the decision is made where to place them. There is discussion about placing them in a salt geological repository (see Section 9.6.7).

10.3.4 Volume Reduction Methods

Volume reduction of LLW is attractive because when the storage space is reduced, the disposal charge (and surcharge), calculated in dollars per cubic foot, is also reduced.[5,6] For this reason, all generators of LLW use volume reduction methods when applicable. Care must be exercised, however, because volume reduction may shift the waste from a lower class to a higher one since volume reduction increases the activity concentration.

Volume reduction is achieved in one of three ways: compaction, incineration, or evaporation. Studies have been done[5,6] on the best ways to reduce the volume, and many commercial firms offer their services or sell the machines that achieve this goal. Companies that offer commercially available compactors advertise compaction ratios of more than 10. The bulk density of solid LLW is about 160 to 240 kg/m^3 (10 to 15 lb/ft^3). Compacted waste may have a density of more than 1000 kg/m^3.

Incineration is used if the equipment is available and the method is allowed for the wastes at hand. Incineration offers volume reductions that are even greater than that of compaction. The radioactivity is, essentially, immobilized in the ashes; the ashes are solidified before disposal. Gaseous effluents during incineration must be dealt with in accordance with federal air quality standards.

Evaporation is another method offered commercially for the concentration of radioactive liquid effluents. As with incineration, evaporated materials must comply with air quality standards.

Some commercial radioactive waste volume reduction systems combine evaporation, incineration, and compaction.

10.3.5 Solidification of LLW

Certain LLW can be solidified. Examples are filter sludge, chemical concentrates (boric acid, sodium sulfate), decontamination solutions, contaminated oil, and fuel fabrication sludges. Solidification media are cement, bitumen (an asphalt-type material), urea formaldehyde (no longer permitted in the United States), and Dow media (a polyester-styrene-type material provided only by the Dow Chemical Company).

Bitumen is an inexpensive material that offers high volume reduction because the water is evaporated first; it produces blocks of waste with excellent leachability and aging qualities. Cement (silicated Portland) produces a solid with leaching characteristics similar to or better than those of plain

Portland cement. By introducing ion-exchange additives, the leaching properties can be further improved.

The market offers several different systems for purchase. The specific system to be installed depends on the type and volume of wastes and the type of generator (nuclear reactor, hospital, or research establishment).

10.3.6 LLW Disposal Sites

After treatment, the LLW is packaged for shipment to the disposal site. The requirements and a description of the containers that must be used for LLW burial are given in Section 10.5, which deals with the transportation of LLW. Here, only a brief description of LLW disposal sites is given.

In the United States, and in most other countries that have such disposal programs, LLW is placed for disposal in shallow trenches. The wastes are placed in open slit trenches (Fig. 10.3) about 1000 ft long, 100 ft wide, 20 to 50 ft deep, and sloped toward the open end. A few feet of sand or gravel are placed at the bottom of the trench before the wastes are stored. Then, when filled with waste, the trenches are backfilled with sand, capped with clay, and finally covered with topsoil on which vegetation is planted. The trenches are marked with permanent monuments that describe the contents, the site boundaries, the dates during which the trench was open, and other pertinent information. Variations of this method of disposal may appear in the sites to be

FIGURE 10.3 A LLW open-trench-type site in Richland, Washington.

developed by the state compacts; the variations will, primarily, manifest themselves in new methods of packing that will make better use of space.

10.3.7 LLW Disposal Programs Outside the United States

All countries with nuclear activities of any sort have a program for the disposal of LLW (one option is shipment to another country, by agreement). In general, the big LLW producers have instituted programs similar to those followed in the United States, namely, burial of the wastes in shallow ground. Brief descriptions of the most important foreign programs follow.

In France LLWs are disposed of on the surface, in tumuli covered with clay and earth (Fig. 10.4) or in trenches in concrete monoliths (Fig. 10.5). The choice of method depends on the type and the activity level. LLWs are placed in tumuli if the type and contents of the package can guarantee safe disposal by this method. Most reactor-produced LLW belong to this category. These wastes are delivered in metal drums or concrete containers. If the packaging does not provide adequate protection against the radioactivity before storage, the waste is placed in a concrete monolith that provides the extra protection needed. Using concrete monoliths in addition to radiological protection results in more efficient use of space.

Sweden's LLW is stored in a repository, called the SFR, located 60 m below the seabed of the Baltic Sea. The SFR will provide storage space for 60,000 m^3 of waste, enough to serve all 12 Swedish reactors. It has minimal

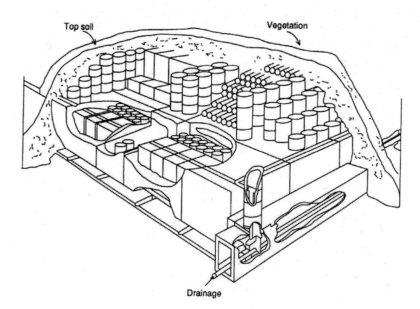

FIGURE 10.4 The French tumulus concept, used for the disposal of LLW.

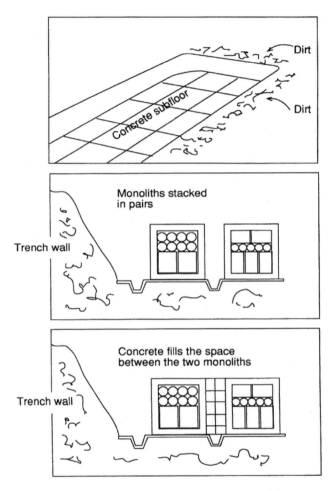

FIGURE 10.5 Disposal of French LLW using concrete monoliths.

surface facilities. A tunnel leads to the repository, which is composed of two main areas: One consists of four horizontal rock caverns 160 m long and 14 to 18 m wide, and the second is a huge concrete silo, 50 m deep and 25 m in diameter, constructed inside a rock chamber 30 m in diameter and 70 m high. The silo will be used for the disposal of intermediate-level waste (ILW).[b] Remote handling facilities are available. The first wastes were accepted[7] in April 1988.

[b]Some other countries, for example, European countries, recognize a type of waste called intermediate-level waste (ILW). Examining the definition of ILW leads to the conclusion that ILW is very close to the U.S. LLW type called GTCC, which is discussed in Section 10.3.2.

In Finland, LLW and ILW are placed in bedrock (tonalite) in a repository that consists of two rock silos each 20 m in diameter and 30 m high, built at a depth of 60 to 90 m.

Near-surface operating sites, in addition to those in the United States and France, exist in the United Kingdom, Japan, and Spain.

10.4 Decommissioning of Nuclear Facilities

10.4.1 What Is Decommissioning?

Decommissioning is the term used to encompass all of the activities that must take place at the end of a plant's life to ensure that the site where the plant is located does not pose any hazard to the public and can, therefore, be considered property suitable for unrestricted use [see 10 CFR 50 (Ref. 8)]. Decommissioning is required not only for nuclear power plants, but for every industrial facility that reaches the end of its life. The "end of life" may arrive because the facility may be too expensive to maintain, remodel, operate, or clean up after an accident, or simply is not needed anymore. Decommissioning of a nuclear facility is different from that of other industrial plants because of the radioactivity involved. Decommissioning is defined as follows in 10 CFR 50:

> To remove a facility or site safely from service and to reduce residual radioactivity to a level that permits (1) release of the property for unrestricted use and termination of the license or (2) release of the property under restricted conditions and termination of the license.

The nuclear facilities mentioned by 10 CFR 50 include nuclear power plants, chemical plants handling radioactive materials (conversion, enrichment, fuel fabrication, and reprocessing plants), medical and industrial establishments, and radiopharmaceutical labs. Of these types of facilities, nuclear reactor decommissioning is the most difficult to handle. Decommissioning of chemical facilities amounts, essentially, to decontamination. The rest of this section deals with nuclear power plant decommissioning.

Nuclear plants have a finite lifetime and every utility that owns a commercial nuclear plant is obligated by law to make plans for decommissioning. Regulation 10 CFR 50.82.4 states:

> Prior to or within 2 years following cessation of operations, the licensee shall submit a Post-shutdown Decommissioning Activities Report (PSDAR) to the NRC and a copy to the affected state(s). The report must include a description of the planned decommissioning activities along with a schedule for their accomplishment, an estimate of expected costs, and a discussion that provides the reasons for concluding that the environmental impacts associated with site-specific decommissioning activities will

be bounded by appropriate previously issued environmental impact statements.

A nuclear utility is, therefore, required to show that when the reactor is shut down for the last time, a well-planned, organized effort will commence that will remove hazardous materials from the site and, eventually, unless there are other reactors on the same site, return the site to unrestricted use. The decommissioning plans must contain sufficient detail to show that the operation can be accomplished safely. In particular, the plans should address the disposal of the radioactive wastes (i.e., existence of a disposal site) and the existence of adequate funds (see Section 10.4.5). The licensee will be required to maintain detailed records on all aspects of decommissioning (e.g., as-built drawings) and will be given a time period within which the task should be accomplished. All activities should obey the "as low as reasonably achievable" (ALARA)[c] exposure principle.

To help the utilities achieve this goal, the NRC addressed decommissioning in many parts of the 10 CFR; in addition to 10 CFR 50, some aspects of decommissioning are addressed in 10 CFR parts 20, 30, 40, 51, 70, and 72. The NRC also supported various studies[9,10] and special reports[11–17]; in addition, the DOE issued a "Decommissioning Resource Manual."[18]

Decommissioning activities of nuclear power plants in the United States do not include the removal and disposal of used nuclear fuel (UNF), which is considered to be an operational activity, or the removal and disposal of nonradioactive structures and materials beyond those necessary to terminate the NRC license. However, the cost for both of these activities may be included in the decommissioning cost (see Section 10.4.5).

Decommissioning is considered completed when all the radioactive components have been moved from the site, the site has been decontaminated (if needed), and the total effective dose equivalent (TEDE) to an average member of the critical group (see 10 CFR 20.1003 for these definitions) is less than 0.25 mSv/yr (25 mrem/yr). When these conditions are met the site is returned to unrestricted use. If the site is planned for restricted use, the NRC criteria are more complex. The annual TEDE must be less than 0.25 mSv (25 mrem) with institutional controls in place and 1 mSv (100 mrem) or 5 mSv (500 mrem) with no institutional controls. Examples of institutional controls are engineered barriers (fences) and/or restrictions for the use of the site (e.g., no farming or parks allowed). Institutional control may also include ownership by the federal or a state government, in which case public access may be restricted. Whether or not the 1 mSv or 5 mSv applies depends on what additional effort is required to reduce the dose both in terms of financial resources and overall risk to workers, the public, and harm to the

---

[c]The ALARA principle means that it is not enough to keep exposure below the maximum allowed limit; every (reasonable) effort should be made to reduce exposure as much as possible.

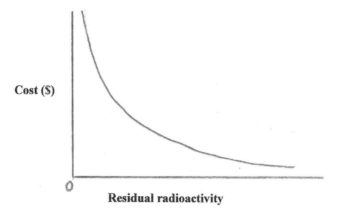

Cost ($)

Residual radioactivity

FIGURE 10.6 Financial cost versus residual radioactivity in a site.

environment. In general, the cost of removing residual radioactivity from a site changes as shown in Fig. 10.6.

For successful decommissioning, the following steps should be followed:

1. Form advisory boards with local people participating.

2. Determine, as accurately as possible, the natural radiation background level at the site.

3. Model and compute expected radiation exposure to workers and the public.

4. Apply the ALARA policy to all activities.

5. Secure groundwater protection per EPA standards.

10.4.2 Decommissioning Methods

When a nuclear plant is shut down for good, the first task is the removal of the fuel from the pressure vessel and its shipment to a federal facility (either a MRS or a geologic repository) to be disposed of in accordance with the NWPA (see Sections 9.4 and 9.5). Since the disposal of UNF is not considered part of the decommissioning process, most of the radioactive materials involved in decommissioning are LLW, with possibly a small amount of TRU in cases where fuel assemblies leaked and some transuranic elements escaped from the fuel rods.

Three decommissioning methods are being seriously considered and, in the United States, are known by these acronyms: DECON, SAFSTOR, and ENTOMB. They are also known as prompt dismantling, mothballing, and entombment, respectively. A brief description of each method follows.

- *DECON:* All radioactive materials are removed (components, structure, etc.) relatively soon after final shutdown. On completion of the operation, the nuclear license is terminated and the site is released for unrestricted use.

- *SAFSTOR:* All liquid radioactive materials and all portable solid radioactive materials are removed. The remaining structures and equipment are secured and continuously monitored to ensure protection of the public. Use of the facility is controlled by an amended nuclear license. Eventually, the rest of the plant is dismantled and the license terminated as with DECON.

- *ENTOMB:* This is the same as SAFSTOR except that the facility is sealed completely, for example, by covering everything with concrete, thus creating one monolithic structure. No accessible area is contaminated and the entombed radioactive materials are monitored for as long as necessary to permit the activity to decay to such a level that the site can be returned to unrestricted use.

The method that will be chosen depends on many factors, but the two most important ones are cost and the total exposure to workers and the public. Of the three methods, the third one seems to be the least attractive because, according to proposed NRC rules, the licensee must demonstrate that the site could be released for unrestricted use 100 years after shutdown. If the site has only one reactor and the utility has no plans to build others, DECON should be the best method. If, on the other hand, the site has more than one reactor or the utility plans to build additional power plants, SAFSTOR may be attractive since the site will not be released for unrestricted use anyway, so monitoring by the personnel who work on the site would not incur too much additional expense. SAFSTOR will also reduce both occupational doses and amounts of radioactive wastes, relative to DECON. For example, if the plant is in SAFSTOR condition for 30 years, the radioactivity from ^{60}Co will be reduced to 1/50th of the amount present immediately after shutdown.

Whatever method is chosen, note that 85% of the volume of a nuclear power plant never becomes radioactive. Immediately after shutdown, about 99% of the radioactivity—in the form of fuel and LLW—is shipped away for disposal before decommissioning begins.

10.4.3 Radioactive Materials Involved in Decommissioning

Two general types of radioactive materials are involved in decommissioning: contamination carried by the water coolant circulating through the core, and activation products produced by neutron absorption, both inside and outside the pressure vessel. If decontamination is necessary, it will be carried out by one of the methods discussed in Section 10.4.4.

TABLE 10.2

Most Important Radioisotopes to Consider in Decommissioning

Isotope	Half Life	Radiations Emitted
^{60}Co	5.2 yr	1.17 and 1.33 MeV γ; 0.314 and 1.48 β
^{59}Ni	80,000 yr	Internal bremsstrahlung up to 1.06 MeV
^{94}Nb	20,000 yr	0.702 and 0.871 MeV γ; 0.490 MeV β

The major activation products are in the pressure vessel and the reactor internals, and the most important radioisotopes are ^{60}Co, ^{59}Ni, and ^{94}Nb. Table 10.2 gives the half lives and the radiations emitted. Cobalt-60 emits the most penetrating radiation. The other two isotopes cause concern because of their very long half lives.

The major radioactive components that can be treated as LLW are heat exchangers, the inside surfaces of which are contaminated and will probably be shipped intact to the LLW disposal site; instrumentation cables, which will be coiled and shipped in containers to the LLW site; steam generators, which will probably be shipped intact after their openings have been welded shut; reactor coolant pumps, the inside surfaces of which are contaminated, will be shipped intact; the pressurizer, which, after the interior has been cleaned, will be shipped to the LLW site, serving as its own container; the biological shield, which will be taken apart before shipping; and the reactor pressure vessel, which is the biggest component and contains the largest amount of radioactivity. In terms of total volume of materials involved (activated matter, contaminated equipment, and decontaminating materials), the estimate, depending on the method, is 13,500 to 16,000 m^3 (475,000 to 560,000 ft^3).

10.4.4 Decontamination Methods

Decontamination is the process of removing radioactive material that has been deposited on the surface of structures, components, or on the ground. Although decontamination does not eliminate the radioactive material—it simply transfers it to another medium—it is helpful in two respects. First, it lowers the radiation level in the work area, thus reducing the exposure to workers. Second, the volume of LLW is reduced, thus decreasing the cost of disposal. A review of decontamination methods is the subject of Ref. 19.

Four methods or processes are used for decontamination: chemical, physical, electropolishing, and ultrasonic. Before any of these methods is applied on contaminated surfaces, common janitorial practices (like vacuuming, sweeping, mopping, scrubbing with ordinary detergents, etc.) are used to remove as much of the radioactive material as possible.

Chemical decontamination methods use chemical solutions to remove the material that has been deposited on the surface. The type of solution depends on the material to be removed and the type of surface on which it is lodged. Acid solutions are commonly used. Common decontamination chemicals are potassium permanganate ($KMnO_4$), sodium hydroxide (NaOH), ammonium citrate [$(NH_4)_2HC_6H_5O_7$], sulfamic acid (NH_2SO_3H), sulfuric acid (H_2SO_4), nitric acid (HNO_3), phosphoric acid (H_3PO_4), and hydrochloric acid (HCl). Recently, a polymer-based decontamination product called Decon-Gel (www.decongel.com) came to the market; it is described as a "safe, water soluble, peelable hydrogel with unique capacity to bind, encapsulate, and remove surface radioactive and chemical contaminants."

Physical methods include the use of high-pressure water jets, pneumatic pistons, jackhammers, and rotating abrasive disks. The rubble so removed is compacted, packaged, and shipped as LLW.

Electropolishing is a quick, effective method for cleaning metal surfaces. When placed in a bath of phosphoric acid, the object to be cleaned forms the negative terminal. Electrical current passing through the metal removes a few surface atomic layers along with the radioactive material stuck on the surface.

Ultrasonic methods can be used with relatively small items, like valves and pumps. The item to be cleaned is placed in a bath of liquid and ultrasonic waves are directed through it. Resulting pressures of up to 10,000 psi help dislodge the material from the surface. Chemicals or abrasives added to the liquid bath enhance the effectiveness of contaminant removal.

Another decontamination method, known as *nondestructive cleaning* (NDC), uses solid CO_2 particles. The NDC process decontaminates by thrusting the small solid CO_2 particles, using dry compressed air, against the contaminated surface. Upon impact, the CO_2 particles shatter and flash into dry CO_2 gas, causing a rapid volume expansion of about 10 to 1. Cleaning is accomplished by the CO_2 gas entering the microscopic pores of the surface and flushing out the foreign matter lodged there. Larger foreign matter is lifted off the surface by the CO_2 steam, falls on the floor, and is vacuumed away. No secondary waste is generated by the NDC process. The NDC equipment is a mobile, self-contained, stand-alone decontamination facility.

10.4.5 Financing and Cost of Decommissioning

The main objective of the government regulations regarding decommissioning is to make sure that whatever plan a utility adopts, that plan will be workable and, most important of all, there will be sufficient money available to complete the decommissioning operation, regardless of when the plant is shut down. That is, the financing of decommissioning should be such that it can be carried out even if the plant is shut down unexpectedly, well before its planned end of life.

Assurance that the funds needed for decommissioning will be available is provided by one of the following three methods[20]:

1. *Prepayment:* At the start of operations, the licensee deposits enough funds into an account to pay the decommissioning costs. The account is separate from the licensee's other assets and remains outside the licensee's control of cash or liquid assets. Prepayment may be in the form of a trust, escrow account, government fund, certificate of deposit, or deposit of government securities.

2. *External sinking fund:* An external sinking fund is established and maintained by setting funds aside periodically into an account separate from the licensee's assets and outside the licensee's control. The total amount of these funds will be sufficient to pay decommissioning costs when it is anticipated that the licensee will cease operations. An external sinking fund may be in the form of a trust, escrow account, government fund, certificate of deposit, or deposit of government securities.

3. *Surety method, insurance, or other guarantee method:* A surety method may be in the form of a surety bond, letter of credit, or line of credit. Any surety method or insurance used to provide financial assurance must be open ended or, if written for a specific term, such as 5 years, must be renewed automatically. An exception is allowed when the issuer notifies the commission, the beneficiary, and the licensee of its intent not to renew within 90 days or more preceding the renewal date. The surety or insurance must also provide that the full face amount be paid to the beneficiary automatically preceding the expiration date without proof of forfeiture if the licensee fails to provide a replacement acceptable to the commission within 30 days after receipt of notification of cancellation. In addition, the surety or insurance must be payable to a trust established for decommissioning costs, and the trustee and trust must be acceptable to the commission. The surety method or insurance must remain in effect until the commission has terminated the license.

From the point of view of the NRC, the preferred funding is the first method because it provides the total amount needed for decommissioning at the beginning of the life of the plant and is not under the control of the licensee. Then, no matter what happens to the licensee's assets (e.g., bankruptcy) and regardless of when the plant will be shut down (at the end of its license or any time earlier), decommissioning is certain to be completed.

The reported cost of decommissioning a nuclear power plant carries a substantial degree of uncertainty because decommissioning depends on many factors, such as:

• Plant design

• Plant size

• Local labor market

TABLE 10.3
Decommissioning Costs

Plant Name	Power (MWe)	Cost (10^6\$)	Method	Remarks
Fort St. Vrain	330	189	DECON	Completed in 1996
Trojan	1130	210	DECON	1993 dollars
Haddam Neck	619	344		1996 dollars, estimate
Maine Yankee	830	275		1997 dollars, estimate
Big Rock Point	67	290		1997 dollars, estimate
Ranch Seco	913	441		1995 dollars, estimate
Yankee Rowe	175	306		1995 dollars, estimate

From Ref. 20.

- Method (DECON, SAFSTOR, ENTOMB)

- Sequence and timing of the various tasks

- Cost of LLW disposal

- Plans for UNF storage.

Table 10.3 shows typical costs from some decommissioned reactors and estimates for others. The costs shown as estimates do not include the cost of nonradioactive site remediation and cost of UNF storage; these two cost components add another \$100 million to \$150 million. In 2011 dollars, the range for the estimated cost of decommissioning was \$400 million to \$500 million, excluding the cost of UNF storage or nonradioactive site remediation.

10.4.6 Decommissioning Experience

Many research and power reactors, here and abroad, have been decommissioned during the past 40 years. Table 10.4 lists the decommissioned U.S. reactors. One should add to this list reactors decommissioned or being decommissioned in the United Kingdom, France, Germany, Belgium, Canada, China, North Korea, and Japan.

The first commercial nuclear power plant to be decommissioned in the United States was Shippingport in Pennsylvania. The DOE was in charge of the project and the chosen decommissioning method was DECON. The work started in January 1985 and was completed in 1989. Decommissioning of Shippingport was completed in 1990 at a cost of about \$100 million.

Is technology available for the safe decommissioning of nuclear power plants? The answer to this question certainly has to be yes, considering the research and power reactors that have been successfully decommissioned in the United States and the rest of the world. The technological expertise exists and has been tested. If any new technology is introduced in this endeavor, it

TABLE 10.4
Decommissioned U.S. Reactors as of April 2011

Reactor	Type	Thermal Power (MW)	Location	Shutdown Date	Status	Fuel Onsite?
Big Rock Point	BWR	67	Charlevoix, MI	08/29/97	ISFSI only[a]	Yes
Dresden 1	BWR	700	Morris, IL	10/31/78	SAFSTOR	Yes
Fermi 1	Fast breeder	200	Monroe Co., MI	09/22/72	DECON	No
Fort St. Vrain	HTGR	842	Platteville, CO	08/18/89	ISFSI only	Yes
GE VBWR	BWR	50	Alameda Co., CA	12/09/63	SAFSTOR	No
Haddam Neck	PWR	1825	Haddam Neck, CT	12/09/96	ISFSI only	Yes
Humboldt Bay 3	BWR	200	Eureka, CA	07/02/76	DECON	Yes
Indian Point 1	PWR	615	Buchanan, NY	10/31/74	SAFSTOR	Yes
LaCrosse	BWR	165	LaCrosse, WI	04/30/87	DECON	Yes
Main Yankee	PWR	2772	Bath, ME	12/06/96	ISFSI only	Yes
Millstone 1	BWR	2011	Waterford, CT	07/21/88	SAFSTOR	Yes
N.S. Savannah	PWR	80	Norfolk, VA	11/70	SAFSTOR	No
Pathfinder	Superheat BWR	190	Sioux Falls, SD	09/16/67	License terminated	No
Peach Bottom 1	HTGR	115	York Co., PA	10/31/74	SAFSTOR	No
Rancho Seco[b]	PWR	2772	Sacramento, CA	06/07/89	ISFSI only	Yes
San Onofre 1	PWR	1347	San Clemente, CA	11/30/92	DECON	Yes
Saxton	PWR	28	Saxton, PA	05/01/72	License terminated	No
Shoreham	BWR	2436	Suffolk Co., NY	06/28/89	License terminated	No
Three Mile Island 2	PWR	2772	Middletown, PA	03/28/79	SAFSTOR	No
Trojan	PWR	3411	Portland, OR	11/09/92	ISFSI only	Yes
Yankee Rowe	PWR	600	Franklin Co., MA	10/01/91	ISFSI only	Yes
Zion 1 and 2	PWR	3250	Zion, IL	02/21/97 09/19/96	DECON	Yes

From Ref. 20.

[a] An independent spent fuel storage installation (ISFSI) is a stand-alone facility within the plant boundary constructed for the interim storage of used nuclear fuel. "ISFSI only" means the plant license has been reduced to include only the used fuel storage facility.

[b] Rancho Seco has a low-level waste storage facility in addition to its ISFSI.

will be in the area of robotics, which will allow remote handling of most activities, thus reducing accumulated radiation doses to personnel.

10.5 Transportation of LLW

Transportation regulations and the classifications of packages were discussed in Section 9.7. Those rules and definitions apply to HLW as well as to LLW. The only item left to be discussed is the containers specifically used for LLW transportation.

Information about containers used for the transportation of radioactive materials is given 10 CFR 71 and in 49 CFR 173 (Refs. 21 and 22), particularly details about tests the packages must satisfy to qualify for shipping radioactive materials. In general, three types of containers are allowed: Type A, Type B, and "other." The requirement for a Type A or B container is based on the A_1 and A_2 activity values (see Table 9.13).

A radionuclide or a mixture of radionuclides may be transported in a Type A container if its activity is Class A quantity, as defined in Section 10.3.2. A Class B quantity must be transported in a Type B container. Examples of such containers are shown in Fig. 10.7

Typical Type A Packaging

Package Must Withstand Normal Conditions (173.465) of Transport Only Without Loss or Dispersal of the Radioactive Contents.

Fiberboard Box

Wooden Box

Steel Drum

Typical Type B Packaging

Package Must Stand Both Normal (173.465) and Accident (10 CFR Part 71) Test Conditions Without Loss of Contents.

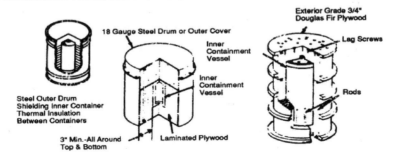

FIGURE 10.7 Sketches of typical Type A and Type B packages.

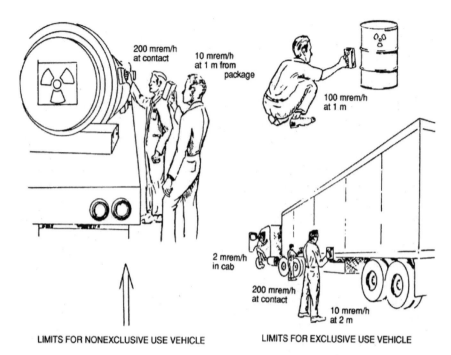

FIGURE 10.8 The radiation dose rate limits for packages transported by exclusive and nonexclusive vehicles.

Radioactive materials that qualify as *low specific activity* (LSA) may be transported in an "essentially" Type A container, in the case of a "nonexclusive use" transport medium. "Essentially" Type A means that the container does not have to satisfy all of the tests of Type A containers. LSA materials transported by conveyances assigned for "exclusive use" may be shipped in packages of less rigorous construction. In this case, there should be an assurance that the package is not going to be loaded or unloaded, except under the direction of the consignee or the consignor. External radiation dose rate standards are specified in 10 CFR 71.47 (Ref. 21):

(a) A package carrying radioactive material and offered for transportation in a non-exclusive vehicle must have a dose rate at any point on its external surface less than 2 mSv/h (200 mrem/h) (see Fig. 10.8) and a transport index (TI; see Section 9.7.2) of less than 10.

(b) If the dose rate exceeds this limit, the package must be transported in an exclusive vehicle and must satisfy the following:

1. Dose rate not more than 2 mSv/h (200 mrem/h) on the external surface of the package; the allowed dose rate will be up to 10 mSv/h (1 rem/h) if the following conditions are met:

(i) Shipment is made in a closed vehicle,

(ii) The package is secured inside the vehicle so that its position does not change during transportation, and

(iii) There are no loading or unloading operations from the beginning to the end of the trip.

2. Dose rate not more than 2 mSv/h (200 mrem/h) on the external surface of the vehicle (including top and underside).

3. Dose rate not more than 0.1 mSv/h (10 mrem/h) at any point 2 m from the outer lateral surfaces of the vehicle (excluding top and underside).

4. Dose rate not more than 0.02 mSv/h (2 mrem/h) in any normally occupied space.

Bibliography

Code of Federal Regulations, Title 10, "Energy," Part 71, "Packaging and Transportation of Radioactive Material," U.S. Nuclear Regulatory Commission (10 CFR 71) (Jan. 2010).

English, M.R., *Siting Low-Level Radioactive Waste Disposal Facilities: The Public Policy Dilemma*, Quorum Books (1992).

Improving the Regulation and Management of Low-Activity Radioactive Waste, National Research Council, National Academies Press (2006).

Kittel, J.H., *Near-Surface Land Disposal (Radioactive Waste Management Handbook)*, Routledge (1989).

Miller, W., *Geological Disposal of Radioactive Waste and Natural Analogues*, Pergamon Press (2005).

Saling, J.H., and Fentiman, A.W., *Radioactive Waste Management*, Taylor and Francis (2001).

Savage, D., *The Scientific and Regulatory Basis for the Geological Disposal of Radioactive Waste*, Wiley (1996).

References

1. Low-Level Radioactive Waste Policy Act, Public Law 96-573 (Dec. 1980); see also Low-Level Radioactive Waste Policy Amendments Act of 1985, Public Law 99-240 (Jan. 1986).

2. *Code of Federal Regulations*, Title 10, "Energy," Part 61, "Licensing Requirements for Land Disposal of Radioactive Wastes," U.S. Nuclear Regulatory Commission (10 CFR 61) (Jan. 2010).

3. Carter, J.T., Jones, R.H., and Luptak, A.J., "US Radioactive Waste Inventory and Characteristics Related to Potential Future Nuclear Energy Systems," FCRD-USED-2011-000058, Rev. 2, Fuel Cycle Research and Development, U.S. Department of Energy, Office of Nuclear Energy (May 2011).

4. Below Regulatory Concern Owners Group, Series of Reports with NP Nos. 5671, 5674, 5676, 5678, 5681, 5683, 5684, and 5685, Electric Power Research Institute (Feb. through Aug. 1989).

5. "Advanced Radioactive Compaction Techniques," EPRI NP-5838, Electric Power Research Institute (Aug. 1988).

6. "Radioactive Waste Volume Reduction and Solidification Systems," EPRI NP-5958, Electric Power Research Institute (Aug. 1988).

7. Rippon, S., "The SFR—Sweden's LLW/ILW Repository," *Nucl. News* (Aug. 1988).

8. *Code of Federal Regulations*, Title 10, "Energy," Part 50, "Domestic Licensing of Production and Utilization Facilities," U.S. Nuclear Regulatory Commission (10 CFR 50) (Jan. 2010).

9. NUREG/CR-0130, "Technology, Safety and Costs of Decommissioning a Reference PWR Power Station," U.S. Nuclear Regulatory Commission (June 1978); see also 0130 Addendum, Pacific Northwest Laboratory for the U.S. Nuclear Regulatory Commission (Aug. 1979).

10. NUREG/CR-0672, "Technology, Safety, and Costs of Decommissioning a Reference BWR Power Station," Pacific Northwest Laboratory for the U.S. Nuclear Regulatory Commission (June 1980).

11. NUREG/CR-5512, "Residual Radioactive Contamination from Decommissioning," Vol. 1 (Oct. 1992).

12. NUREG-0586, "Final Generic Environmental Impact Statement of Decommissioning of Nuclear Facilities," U.S. Nuclear Regulatory Commission (Aug. 1988).

13. NUREG-1500, "Working Draft Regulatory Guide on Release Criteria for Decommissioning: NRC Staff's Draft for Comment," U.S. Nuclear Regulatory Commission (Aug. 1994).

14. "Standard Format and Content of Decommissioning Plans for Licensees under 10 CFR Parts 30, 40, and 70," Reg. Guide 3.65, U.S. Nuclear Regulatory Commission (1994).

15. "Standard Format and Content of Financial Assurance Mechanisms Required for Decommissioning under 10 CFR Parts 30, 40, 70, and 72," Reg. Guide 3.66, U.S. Nuclear Regulatory Commission (1994).

16. "Termination of Operating Licenses for Nuclear Reactors," Reg. Guide 1.86, U.S. Nuclear Regulatory Commission (1994).

17. NUREG/CR-5849, "Manual for Conducting Radiological Surveys in Support of License Termination," U.S. Nuclear Regulatory Commission (1994).

18. "Decommissioning Resource Manual," DOE/EM-0246, U.S. Department of Energy (1995).

19. "A Review of Plant Decontamination Methods—1988 Update," EPRI-NP-6169, Electric Power Research Institute (Jan. 1989).

20. U.S. Nuclear Regulatory Commission Web site, www.nrc.gov (2011).

21. *Code of Federal Regulations*, Title 10, "Energy," Part 71, "Packaging and Transportation of Radioactive Materials," U.S. Nuclear Regulatory Commission (10 CFR 71) (Jan. 2010).

22. *Code of Federal Regulations*, Title 49, "Transportation," Parts 100-177 and 178-199, "A Review of the Department of Transportation Regulations for Transportation of Radioactive Materials," U.S. Nuclear Regulatory Commission (Rev. 2011).

Problems

10.1. A LLW package contains 0.5 Ci/m^3 of ^{137}Cs, 45 Ci/m^3 of ^{60}Co, and 4.0 mg/m^3 of ^3H_2O. Is this a Class A, B, or C package?

10.2. A LLW package contains 3 mCi/m^3 of ^{99}Tc and 2.5 mCi/m^3 of ^{137}Cs. What is the class of this package?

10.3. A LLW package contains 0.9 Ci/m^3 of ^{14}C, 1400 Ci/m^3 of ^{137}Cs, and 180 Ci/m^3 of ^{63}Ni. Is this a Class A, B, C, or GTCC package?

10.4. Classify a package that contains 0.5 Ci/m^3 of ^{99}Tc plus 18 Ci/m^3 of ^{63}Ni.

10.5. Classify a package that contains 0.095 Ci/m^3 of ^{129}I.

10.6. Classify a package that contains 50 Ci/m^3 of ^{59}Ni and 6000 Ci/m^3 of ^{90}Sr.

ELEVEN

NUCLEAR NONPROLIFERATION
AND SAFEGUARDS

11.1 What Is Nuclear Nonproliferation and Safeguards?

The first nation to make a nuclear weapon was the United States (1944–1945). After the end of World War II, four other nations joined the "nuclear" club: Russia (old Soviet Union, 1949), United Kingdom (1952), France (1960), and China (1964). It did not take long for the nations of the world to recognize that it is in their security interests to stop other nations from joining the nuclear club. The term *nonproliferation* refers to this effort, namely, to stop other nations from producing nuclear weapons or any type of nuclear explosive device. The policies, procedures, and controls set up by the International Atomic Energy Agency (see next section) to achieve the nonproliferation goal constitute what is known as *safeguards*.

Nonproliferation should be considered a partial success because, in addition to the five original states, only three others have made and detonated nuclear weapons: India (1976), Pakistan (1998), and North Korea (2005). It has been speculated, but never proven or admitted, that Israel also has nuclear weapons. A few other states started but abandoned such programs: South Africa, Brazil, Iraq, and Libya. As of 2012, the only nation that is believed to be trying to produce nuclear weapons is Iran. In addition to nation-states' attempts, we face the danger of rogue groups or individual terrorists trying to obtain ready-made weapons from the states that have them and to use such weapons to serve their objectives. It is unlikely, although not impossible, that a non-state group or individual will try to make a weapon after acquiring the necessary amount of fissile material.

Safeguards efforts are based on international treaties and on the activities of the International Atomic Energy Agency, which was created in 1957 and is located in Vienna, Austria. The objective of safeguards is to ensure that signatories to nonproliferation treaties comply with the obligations required by that treaty or treaties.

11.2 The Role of the International Atomic Energy Agency

The International Atomic Energy Agency (IAEA) was established in 1957 as an autonomous intergovernmental organization. Although not under direct control of the United Nations (UN), the IAEA reports to both the UN General Assembly and the UN Security Council. The IAEA was set up with the twin mandate of (1) promoting the safe and secure peaceful uses of nuclear science and technology and (2) ensuring that nuclear activities with which the IAEA is associated are not used to further any military purpose. The IAEA has 151 member states. Five departments have been established in order for the IAEA to carry out its mandate[1]:

1. *Nuclear Sciences and Applications:* Helps countries in the use of atomic and nuclear radiation in agriculture, medical programs, water resource management, industrial applications, and marine environment.

2. *Nuclear Energy:* Promotes the efficient and safe application of nuclear power for peaceful uses, primarily for the generation of electricity and the conduct of research; it promotes such nuclear programs and helps nations in planning and executing such activities.

3. *Nuclear Safety and Security:* Established a framework for the protection of people and the environment from the harmful effects of ionizing radiation, globally; developed programs and procedures for emergency preparedness and response to accidents; helps national regulatory bodies in setting up their safety rules; works together with the world transport industry for the safe transportation of nuclear materials.

4. *Technical Cooperation:* Helps nations to improve their scientific and technological capabilities for peaceful applications of nuclear technologies.

5. *Safeguards:* Carries out its responsibilities as the world's inspectorate in the effort to stop the spread of nuclear weapons.

Of these five departments/activities of the IAEA, the last is the topic of this chapter. The IAEA is the only international body with the responsibility of inspecting nuclear facilities in any nation on the planet to verify that such facilities comply with agreements signed by that nation. In addition, the IAEA formulates policies, procedures, and measures to ensure that weapons materials and weapons technology do not illegally become available to non-nuclear weapons nations or rogue groups. The IAEA disseminates such information by publishing reports known as Information Circulars (INFCIRC; see Section 11.3.1).

11.3 The Non-Proliferation Treaty

As explained in Section 11.1, shortly after World War II, there were five nuclear weapons states (NWS). Big and small nations realized that a nuclear war would be disastrous for the planet; also, it was believed that the risk of nuclear war would increase with an increasing number of NWS (the risk would increase due to intentional nuclear conflict, an accidental firing of a nuclear-loaded missile, or unauthorized use). Hence, an international effort was launched to limit the NWS to the five states already having the weapons. The result of that effort was the Non-Proliferation Treaty (NPT), which was ready for signatures in 1968. The original five NWS signed the treaty as did many other nations. Three notable states that never signed are India, Pakistan, and Israel. North Korea signed in 1985 and withdrew in 2003. As of 2012, about 180 member states had signed the NPT.

The NPT consists of 11 articles. The gist of each article is given here; exact wording can be found in Ref. 2:

I. Each NWS party to the NPT agrees not to transfer to any recipient whatsoever nuclear weapons or other nuclear explosive devices or control over such weapons or explosive devices directly or indirectly. In addition, each party agrees not to assist, encourage, or induce in any way any non-nuclear-weapons state (NNWS) in the manufacture or acquisition of nuclear weapons or other nuclear explosive devices or to give control over such weapons or explosive devices.

II. Each NNWS party to the treaty undertakes not to receive the transfer of nuclear weapons or other nuclear explosive devices or take control over such weapons or explosive devices directly or indirectly; not to manufacture or otherwise acquire nuclear weapons or other nuclear explosive devices; and not to seek or receive any assistance in the manufacture of nuclear weapons or other nuclear explosive devices.

III.1. Each NNWS party to the treaty undertakes to accept safeguards, for the exclusive purpose of verification of the fulfillment of its obligations assumed under this treaty with a view toward preventing diversion of nuclear energy from peaceful uses to nuclear weapons or other nuclear explosive devices.

III.2. Each state party to the treaty undertakes not to provide (a) a source or special fissionable material or (b) equipment or material especially designed or prepared for the processing, use, or production of special fissionable material, to any non–nuclear-weapons state for peaceful purposes, unless the source or special fissionable material is subject to the safeguards required by this article.

III.3. The safeguards required by this article shall be implemented in a manner designed to comply with Article IV of this treaty.

III.4. NNWS party to the treaty shall conclude agreements with the IAEA to meet the requirements of this article either individually or together with other states in accordance with the statute of the IAEA.

IV.1. Nothing in this treaty shall be interpreted as affecting the inalienable right of all the parties to the treaty to develop research, production, and use of nuclear energy for peaceful purposes without discrimination and in conformity with Articles I and II of this treaty.

IV.2. All parties to the treaty undertake to facilitate, and have the right to participate in the fullest possible exchange of equipment, materials, and scientific and technological information for the peaceful uses of nuclear energy. Parties to the treaty in a position to do so shall cooperate in contributing alone or together with other states or international organizations to the further development of the applications of nuclear energy for peaceful purposes, especially in the territories of NNWS party to the treaty, with due consideration for the needs of the developing areas of the world.

V. Each party to the treaty undertakes to take appropriate measures to ensure that, in accordance with this treaty, under appropriate international observation and through appropriate international procedures, potential benefits from any peaceful applications of nuclear explosions will be made available to NNWS party to the treaty on a nondiscriminatory basis.

VI. Each of the parties to the treaty undertakes to pursue negotiations in good faith on effective measures relating to cessation of the nuclear arms race at an early date and to nuclear disarmament, and on a treaty on general and complete disarmament under strict and effective international control.

VII. Nothing in this treaty affects the right of any group of states to conclude regional treaties in order to ensure the total absence of nuclear weapons in their respective territories.

VIII.1. Any party to the treaty may propose amendments to it. The text of any proposed amendment shall be submitted to the depositary governments, which shall circulate it to all parties to the treaty. Thereupon, if requested to do so by one-third or more of the parties to the treaty, the depositary governments shall convene a conference, to which they shall invite all the parties to the treaty to consider such an amendment.

VIII.2. Any amendment to this treaty must be approved by a majority of the votes of all parties to the treaty, including the votes of all NWS party to the treaty and all other parties that, on the date the amendment is circulated, are members of the board of governors of the IAEA.

VIII.3. Five years after the entry into force of this treaty, a conference of parties to the treaty shall be held in Geneva, Switzerland, in order to review the operation of this treaty with a view to ensuring that the purposes of the preamble and the provisions of the treaty were being realized. At intervals of 5 years thereafter, a majority of the parties to the treaty may obtain, by submitting a proposal to this effect to the depositary governments, the convening of further conferences with the same objective of reviewing the operation of the treaty.

IX.1. This treaty shall be open to all states for signature. Any state that does not sign the treaty before its entry into force in accordance with paragraph 3 of this article may accede to it at any time.

IX.2. This treaty is subject to ratification by signatory states. Instruments of ratification and instruments of accession shall be deposited with the governments of the United Kingdom, the Union of Soviet Socialist Republics (now Russia), and the United States of America, which are designated the depositary governments.

IX.3. This treaty shall enter into force after its ratification by the states, the governments of which are designated depositaries of the treaty, and 40 other states signatory to this treaty and the deposit of their instruments of ratification. For the purposes of this treaty, a nuclear weapons state is one that has manufactured and exploded a nuclear weapon or other nuclear explosive device prior to January 1, 1967.

IX.4. For states whose instruments of ratification or accession are deposited subsequent to the entry into force of this treaty, it shall enter into force on the date of the deposit of their instruments of ratification or accession.

IX.5. The depositary governments shall promptly inform all signatory and acceding states of the date of each signature, the date of deposit of each instrument of ratification or of accession, the date of the entry into force of this treaty, and the date of receipt of any requests for convening a conference or other notices.

IX.6. This treaty shall be registered by the depositary governments pursuant to Article 102 of the charter of the United Nations.

X.1. Each party shall, in exercising its national sovereignty, have the right to withdraw from the treaty if it decides that extraordinary events, related to the subject matter of this treaty, have jeopardized the supreme interests of its country. It shall give notice of such withdrawal to all other parties to the treaty and to the UN Security Council 3 months in advance.

X.2. Twenty-five years after the entry into force of the treaty, a conference shall be convened to decide whether the treaty shall continue in force indefinitely or be extended for an additional period. This decision will be made by a majority of the parties to the treaty.

XI. English, Russian, French, Spanish, and Chinese texts of this treaty, all equally authentic, shall be deposited in the archives of the depositary governments. Duly certified copies of this treaty shall be transmitted by the depositary governments to the governments of the signatory and acceding states.

Of particular interest are the following declarations of the treaty:

1. The nuclear weapons states promise not only not to provide weapons materials and technology to anybody else, but also commit themselves to disarmament.

2. States with nuclear technology promise to help others that do not have it, with the purpose of every state reaping the peaceful benefits of nuclear energy.

3. The treaty recognizes the inalienable right of any state to utilize nuclear energy for peaceful purposes.

In accordance with Article VIII.3, a conference was convened in 1995 that approved an indefinite extension of the NPT; another review conference in 2010 also reaffirmed the treaty.

11.3.1 Information Circulars

The IAEA disseminates information regarding agreements with the member states by publishing reports known as Information Circulars (INFCIRC). By last count, about 850 INFCIRCs had been issued. The three most important ones directly related to NPT agreements and their enforcement are as follows[1]:

1. INFCIRC/66 (1968): *The Agency's Safeguards System.* This INFCIRC lists the obligations of the IAEA and principles and procedures of safeguards implementation.

2. INFCIRC/153 (1972): *The Structure and Content of Agreements between the Agency and States Required in Connection with the Treaty on the Non-Proliferation of Nuclear Weapons.*

3. INFCIRC/540 (1997): *Model Protocol Additional to the Agreement(s) between State(s) and the IAEA for the Application of Safeguards.* INFCIRC/540 expands the spectrum of information a state must provide to the IAEA. Specific measures to which the states must adhere are (a) provision of information and access to all aspects of a state's nuclear fuel cycle, from uranium mining to disposal of nuclear waste and any other locations where nuclear material is present; (b) provision of information on the manufacture and export of devices using nuclear-related technologies and inspection mechanisms for manufacturing and import locations of such devices; (c) access, after short notice, of inspectors to all buildings on a nuclear site; and (d) collection of environmental samples at times and locations, as deemed necessary by the IAEA.

With the adoption of INFCIRC/540 and the ensuing broader access to information and better use of technology, the IAEA is better equipped to detect and deter the unlawful use of nuclear materials.

11.4 Safeguards

The statute of the IAEA requires the establishment and administration of safeguards to ensure that materials, information, services, and facilities are not used by an agreement state for the construction of nuclear weapons or other nuclear explosives, or for development, possession, and use of fissile materials in violation of such agreement (see Article III.2 description in Section 11.3). Safeguards are policies, procedures, and controls set up by the IAEA, under the NPT agreements between the states and the agency, with the objectives of (1) the timely detection of diversion of nuclear materials from peaceful (civilian) activities to the manufacture of nuclear explosive devices for any purpose, (2) diversion of nuclear materials and relevant information from one state to another or to a nonstate group for making nuclear explosives, and (3) the deterrence of such diversion because of the risk of detection. Achievement of these objectives is based on the independent verification of the national system of accountancy and control of nuclear materials, which a state without nuclear weapons must establish and maintain under the agreement. Verification is accomplished by IAEA inspections, surveillance, and material accountancy (see also Section 11.3.1).

According to the NPT, the nuclear weapons states obey IAEA safeguards on a voluntary basis; that is, these states voluntarily provide a list of facilities that will operate under IAEA safeguards. The status of the nuclear facilities of the nuclear weapons states as of 2012 is as follows:

- United States, United Kingdom, France, India: All civilian facilities under IAEA safeguards

- Russia: Not all civil facilities yet under IAEA safeguards

- China: All imported nuclear facilities under IAEA safeguards

- Pakistan: Civilian reactors under restricted agreement with IAEA

- North Korea: No civilian nuclear power

- Israel: No civilian nuclear power.

Table 11.1 shows type and number of facilities under safeguards agreement as of December 2009.

11.4.1 Compliance with Safeguards

Every state that signed a safeguards agreement with the IAEA, pursuant to the NPT, must be able to show to the agency's satisfaction that it complies with the agreement. One major tool in proving compliance is nuclear material accountability. A state must keep complete records of all nuclear material in its possession at every nuclear facility. At the time of an IAEA inspection, the state must show that the mass of material on its books agrees with the inventory of the material measured at the facility being inspected.

TABLE 11.1

Number of Facilities under Safeguards or Containing Safeguarded
Material on December 31, 2009

Facility Type	Number of Facilities			
	Comprehensive Safeguards Agreements[a]	INFCIRC/66[b] Offer Agreements	Voluntary-Type Agreements	Total
Power reactors	221	7	1	229
Research reactors and critical assemblies	149	3	1	153
Conversion plants	18	0	0	18
Fuel fabrication plants	42	3	1	46
Reprocessing plants	11	1	1	13
Enrichment plants	13	0	3	16
Separate storage facilities	111	2	5	118
Other facilities	76	0	0	76
Total	641	16	12	669

[a]Covering safeguards agreements pursuant to the NPT and/or the Treaty of Tlatelolco and other comprehensive safeguards agreements; includes facilities in Taiwan and China.
[b]Covering facilities in India, Israel, and Pakistan.

The difference between book inventory and the measured (physical) inventory is called *material unaccounted for* (MUF; see also Section 7.4.5). MUF is calculated based on the following formula[3]:

$$MUF = (PB + X - Y) - PE \qquad (11.1)$$

where

PB = the beginning physical inventory

X = the sum of increases to inventory

Y = the sum of decreases from inventory

PE = the ending physical inventory.

Because of statistical uncertainty in any measurement, MUF is not going to be equal to zero. An inspector will be concerned only if the value of MUF is greater than some value not justified by the expected, reasonable measurement uncertainty. Expected measurement uncertainties are given in Table 11.2.

In addition to the value of MUF, assurance of nondiversion of nuclear material is aided by the security of the nuclear site and by containment and surveillance activities.

TABLE 11.2

Expected Measurement Uncertainty σ_E (Relative Standard
Deviation) Associated with Closing a Material Balance

Bulk Handling Facility Type	σ_E
Uranium enrichment	0.002[a]
Uranium fabrication	0.003
Plutonium fabrication	0.005
Uranium reprocessing	0.008
Plutonium reprocessing	0.010
Separate scrap storage	0.04
Separate waste storage	0.25

From Ref. 3.
[a] Read as 0.2%.

11.4.2 Noncompliance with Safeguards

In connection with safeguards, the term *noncompliance* can be found in the statute that created the IAEA; however, no well-defined definition is given. Instead, it is left to the IAEA board to determine whether or not a particular incident constitutes noncompliance. Here are some cases that may constitute noncompliance:

1. The value of MUF is too high and unexplained; in particular if (mass measured) < (book inventory).

2. Nuclear material or nuclear activity has not been declared.

3. Nuclear material is withdrawn from safeguards without notifying IAEA.

4. Use of the nuclear material is not clearly and transparently civil, that is, there is suspicion that its intended use is for military purposes.

5. Nuclear material or information relative to the military use of the nuclear material has been transferred to a third party, either another state or a group.

In the process of deciding whether or not noncompliance has occurred, the following questions are asked:

1. Is there evidence of deliberate falsehoods and concealment efforts, indicating that the actions were intentional and not inadvertent?

2. What material is involved (natural uranium, thorium, fissile material, used nuclear fuel, mixed-oxide fuel)?

3. What are the activities involved? Can they lead to enrichment? Can they produce weapons-grade material?

4. Did the material leave the state?

According to INFCIRC/153, to declare noncompliance, it is sufficient for the IAEA to show that

1. nuclear material or a nuclear activity has not been declared or that nuclear material has been removed from safeguards;

2. the failure is considered to be significant (e.g., because of the nature of the nuclear material or activity); and

3. the purpose of the use of the nuclear material or the nuclear activity is not clearly exclusively peaceful, that it could be military or uncertain, i.e., "unknown."

It is then the state's responsibility to convince the IAEA that there was no intention to use the nuclear material for nonpeaceful purposes. To remedy noncompliance, the state must comply with all the steps outlined in INFCIRC/153 and INFCIRC/540. How to optimize the IAEA safeguards system is presented in Ref. 4.

11.5 Strategic Nuclear Materials—IAEA Definitions

The whole business of safeguards concerns safeguarding materials that may be used to make nuclear weapons. Such materials are thorium, uranium, and plutonium (in general, all of these elements' isotopes, but all isotopes are not equally important, as explained below). Regarding materials under safeguards, the IAEA[3] uses the following definitions:

- *Direct use material:* This is nuclear material that can be utilized to make nuclear explosive devices without further enrichment or transmutation; it includes plutonium containing less than 80% ^{238}Pu, highly enriched uranium, and ^{233}U. Mixed-oxide (MOX) fuel and plutonium in used nuclear fuel (UNF) also belong to this group.

- *Indirect use material:* All nuclear material except direct use material. Examples are natural and low-enriched uranium, depleted uranium, and thorium; these materials need further processing to be transformed into direct use material.

- *Special fissionable material* [essentially the same as the NRC-defined special nuclear material (SNM); see Section 9.7.2]: This includes ^{239}Pu, ^{233}U, uranium enriched in the isotopes 233 or 235, any material containing one or more of the foregoing, and such other fissionable material as the board of governors shall from time to time determine. However, the term *special fissionable material* does not include source material (definition of source material is given in Section 9.7.2).

- *Effective kilogram (ekg):* The ekg indicates the strategic value of nuclear materials. The number of ekg in a given mass is obtained by taking

TABLE 11.3

Significant Quantities

Material	SQ
Direct use nuclear material	
Plutonium[a]	8 kg
^{233}U	8 kg
HEU (^{235}U $\geq$ 20%)	25 kg
Indirect use nuclear material	
Uranium (^{235}U $<$ 20%)[b]	75 kg
	(or 10 t natural U
	or 20 t depleted U)
Thorium	20 t

From Ref. 3.

[a] For plutonium containing less than 80% ^{238}Pu.

[b] Including low-enriched, natural, and depleted uranium.

(1) plutonium, its weight in kilograms; (2) uranium with an enrichment of 0.01 (1%) and above, its weight in kilograms multiplied by the square of its enrichment; (3) uranium with an enrichment below 0.01 (1%) and above 0.005 (0.5%), its weight in kilograms multiplied by 0.0001; (4) depleted uranium with an enrichment of 0.005 (0.5%) or below, and for thorium, its weight in kilograms multiplied by 0.00005. The ekg is used to define the maximum quantity of nuclear materials in a "location outside facilities" (LOF). LOF is any installation or location, which is not a facility, where nuclear materials are used in amounts of 1 ekg or less.

- *Significant quantity (SQ):* The SQ is the approximate amount of nuclear material for which the possibility of manufacturing a nuclear explosive device cannot be excluded. Significant quantities take into account unavoidable losses due to conversion and manufacturing processes and should not be confused with critical masses. SQ values are given in Table 11.3.

In addition to nuclear materials, when safeguards are concerned, the IAEA is also interested in and demands information from the agreement states, in accordance with INFCIRC/66, about materials that are utilized in fission reactors. Examples are nuclear-grade graphite (high purity; <5 parts/million boron, density > 1.5 g/cm^3), deuterium (^{2}H), heavy water (^{2}H$_2$O), and zirconium and zirconium alloys.

11.6 Nuclear Fuel Cycles and Proliferation

No nuclear fuel cycle is 100% proliferation-proof, that is, a cycle that makes it physically impossible to obtain materials that may be used for the construction of nuclear explosives. In any fuel cycle, direct and indirect use materials (see definitions in Section 11.5) are involved at various steps of a nuclear fuel cycle, with various degrees of purity. Given time and resources any state or a nonstate group may transform such materials into "direct use materials." Thus, the question of nuclear fuel cycles and weapons proliferation comes down to this: Which fuel cycle is the most proliferation resistant?

In the 1970s the U.S. government initiated and completed a study called the Nonproliferation Alternative Systems Assessment Program (NASAP)[5] (see also Section 7.2). The main conclusions of NASAP were that (1) no fuel cycle is 100% proliferation-proof and (2) the once-through fuel cycle is the most proliferation resistant because weapons-grade material is never separated during the various steps of the cycle.

In view of these facts, nonproliferation and safeguards rely on institutional controls (agreements) and better detection capabilities of nuclear materials.

11.7 Detection of Nuclear Materials

The ability to detect and identify nuclear materials is, perhaps, the most important tool in nuclear safeguards. Detection may be required under various circumstances at many locations. Some examples are (1) screening at border crossings (identifying nuclear materials and stopping them from being smuggled into a country); screening is required of cargo containers and carriers; (2) screening of materials in transit (highways, waterways, railroads, airplanes); (3) searching for and finding nuclear materials at locations where there is suspicion that such threatening materials may be hidden; and (4) actions required after a radiological weapon has been detonated; this includes determination of quantity and type of radioactive material dispersed, extent of contamination, and decontamination and recovery processes.

Methods for detection of nuclear materials may be chemistry based (radiochemistry and mass spectrometry) or radiation based (detection of ionizing radiation). Detection methods are also defined as destructive or nondestructive. Nondestructive methods are preferred because they do not alter the identity of the sample mass. A third way of categorizing detection methods is active and passive. In active methods, external radiation (neutrons, predominantly) irradiates the sample and produces detectable radiations. In passive methods, radiations emanating from the sample are detected. What follows is a brief description of each method.

11.7.1 Passive Detection Methods

Passive detection methods may detect (1) neutrons from spontaneous fission and from (α, n) reactions in the sample or (2) X-rays emitted by the decaying fissile isotopes.

TABLE 11.4
Spontaneous Fission Neutron Yields*

Isotope	Atomic Number Z	Half Life (yr) (Total)	Spontaneous Fission Neutron Yield (n/s·g)
^{232}Th	90	1.41×10^{10}	$<1.6 \times 10^{-7}$
^{233}U	92	1.59×10^{5}	8.6×10^{-4}
^{235}U	92	7.04×10^{8}	3.0×10^{-4}
^{238}U	92	4.47×10^{9}	1.5×10^{-2}
^{237}Np	93	2.14×10^{6}	1.1×10^{-4}
^{239}Pu	94	2.41×10^{4}	2.2×10^{-2}
^{240}Pu	94	6.56×10^{3}	1.02×10^{3}
^{241}Pu	94	14.4	1.02×10^{3}
^{244}Cm	96	18.1	1.1×10^{7}
^{252}Cf	98	2.646	2.3×10^{12}

*Some numbers calculated by the author based on reported half lives; some taken from Ref. 6.

All of the isotopes of interest in safeguards undergo spontaneous fission as one mode of decay albeit at different rates, of course (see Table 11.4). The predominant decay mode is alpha decay. The alphas produce neutrons by means of the (α, n) reaction. Two such reactions are:

$$^{18}O + {}^{4}He \rightarrow {}^{21}Ne + {}^{1}n \quad \text{and} \quad {}^{19}F + {}^{4}He \rightarrow {}^{22}Na + {}^{1}n$$

The neutron detector used is primarily a ^{3}He counter.

All isotopes of interest in safeguards also emit X-rays that are used as identity markers for each isotope. Table 11.5 lists the predominant radiations emitted. The detector used is a high-purity Ge crystal. The Ge detector has the best energy resolution and, therefore, offers the best chance to identify individual X-ray energies.

Passive methods present difficulties because the neutron emission rate is relatively low and the emitted X-rays are relatively soft; hence, any shielding of the material will absorb most of them.

11.7.2 Active Detection Methods

Active detection methods (also called interrogation methods) are based on the following principle: External incident radiation (neutrons or gammas) bombards the material and causes fissions in the fissile material. The presence of radiation that results from fission indicates the presence of fissile material.[7,8]

Neutrons may come from two sources. One source is 14-MeV neutrons produced by a neutron generator based on the reaction $^{2}H + {}^{3}H \rightarrow {}^{4}He + {}^{1}n$; the other is neutrons from a ^{252}Cf source generating fast neutrons from spontaneous fission of that isotope. If a neutron generator is used, the sample

TABLE 11.5

The Major Gamma-Ray Signatures of Nuclear Materials

Isotope	Half Life (yr)	Energy (keV)	Specific Activity (Bq/g)	Remarks
^{233}U	1.592×10^5	291.3	5.8×10^4	From ^{232}U contamination
		317.2	8.3×10^4	
		2614	$\sim 1 \times 10^5$	
^{235}U	7.038×10^8	185.7	4.32×10^4	
		143.8	8.81×10^3	
^{238}U	4.468×10^9	766.4	3.74×10^1	From ^{234m}Pa
		1001	7.48×10^1	From ^{234m}Pa
^{237}Np	2.14×10^6	312.2	$\sim 1 \times 10^7$	
^{239}Pu	2.415×10^4	129.3	1.15×10^5	
		413.7	2.76×10^4	
^{240}Pu	6568	160.3	3.37×10^4	
^{241}Pu	14.35	148.6	7.15×10^6	
		208	2.04×10^7	From ^{237}U
^{241}Am	432.7	59.5	4.57×10^{10}	
		125.3	6.36×10^6	
^{243}Am	7370	75	4.96×10^9	
		117.6	4.22×10^7	
		142	8.51×10^6	

must be transported to the generator; a ^{252}Cf source can be moved to the sample.

Photons with energy greater than 6 MeV, the approximate photofission threshold of the isotopes under investigation, are used to initiate photofission reactions, that is, the reaction (γ, fission) in the fissile material. The photons are produced as bremsstrahlung with an electron accelerator. (Electrons are accelerated, then they hit a target and all their kinetic energy is radiated as bremsstrahlung; this is the same technique used in the production of medical X-rays.)

After fissions take place, the presence of fissile material is indicated by the detection of fission neutrons and gammas. The detected neutrons are prompt fission neutrons (primarily; some delayed neutrons may also be detected). In addition, the shape of the fission fast neutron energy spectrum produced may serve to identify the isotope that fissioned.

The gammas are emitted by certain fission products with short half lives; usually, gammas with energy greater than 3 MeV are measured.

11.8 Proliferation Resistance and Physical Protection

As explained in Section 11.6, there is no way to conduct nuclear activities that are 100% proliferation-proof. The international community understands this fact and realizes that in order to improve (to harden, if you will) proliferation resistance it has to rely on both intrinsic (technological) and extrinsic (institutional) measures. According to the IAEA, intrinsic proliferation-resistant features "are those features that result from the technical design of nuclear energy systems, including those that facilitate the implementation of the extrinsic measures."[9] Extrinsic "are those features that result from the decisions and undertakings of States related to nuclear energy systems."[9] An international effort is under way, led by the GEN-IV International Forum working group (GEN-IV reactors are discussed in Section 1.3), to develop a methodology for proliferation resistance and physical protection (PR&PP) of nuclear materials for all GEN-IV nuclear energy systems.

Proliferation resistance is defined as that characteristic of a nuclear energy system that impedes the diversion or undeclared production of nuclear materials, or misuse of technology, by the host state in order to acquire nuclear weapons or other nuclear explosive devices. Physical protection is defined as that characteristic of a nuclear energy system that impedes the theft of materials suitable for nuclear explosives or radiation dispersal devices and the sabotage of facilities and transportation by subnational entities and other non-host-state adversaries.

Any PR&PP methodology must consider the threats by potential agents (states or substate groups). Regarding proliferation resistance (PR), threats include the following:

1. Concealed diversion/acquisition of material from a declared facility

2. Concealed production of material in a declared facility

3. Misuse of declared materials and facilities

4. Production of material in undeclared hidden facilities.

Measures in support of PR are extrinsic. They include the state's nonproliferation commitments (NPT agreement), control and verification procedures, surveillance, and IAEA inspections.

Regarding physical protection (PP), threats include these:

1. Theft of nuclear material or information that can be used to make nuclear explosives

2. Sabotage of nuclear facilities and transportation of nuclear materials by nonauthorized agents (terrorists, other substate groups).

The barriers against theft are based on the special characteristics of the materials themselves (radioactivity, mass size) and on the physical barriers presented by the locations where the materials are kept (vaults, hot cells, water pools, air-cooled vaults). In addition, there are surveillance systems and security guards.

The goal of the research and development activities of the GEN-IV International Forum (GIF) is for the design of all GEN-IV nuclear energy systems to be such that these systems constitute a very unattractive path for diversion or theft of materials that may be used for construction of nuclear explosives; in addition, the physical protection will be enhanced against acts of terrorism. GIF is also studying the concept of *safeguards by design*, which refers to the incorporation into the design of a plant traits that will facilitate safeguards measures and activities when the plant is operating, without impeding operations.

A comprehensive view of PR&PP, with detailed case studies, is presented in Ref. 10.

11.9 Concluding Remarks

The destructive power of nuclear weapons is so huge that it is possible, if such weapons are used, to destroy life on earth. With this thought in mind, it is not surprising that both weapons and non-weapons states agree that nuclear safeguards are necessary and must be effective; that is, they must stop the proliferation of all nuclear explosives. The business of nonproliferation is a global effort that must succeed for the benefit of all mankind.

We have reasons to be optimistic. After the original five nuclear weapons states, only three additional ones have declared possession of nuclear weapons; this is definitely an encouraging sign. The creation of the NPT and the fact that 180 states have signed it is a great achievement. The IAEA, the international agency that has assumed the task of ensuring compliance with the NPT, is an effective organization, respected by the international community.

We should not, however, disregard the potential actions of the nonsignatories to the NPT, especially substate groups and terrorists. Although the risk that a rogue group may come into possession of a ready-made weapon or of nuclear materials can never become zero, it can definitely become acceptably small. The current PR&PP measures that are in place and the improved ones envisioned for the GEN-IV energy systems minimize such risks.

In the long run nonproliferation of nuclear weapons will succeed through adherence to the NPT, by using ever-improving technology for effective inspections, and, most important, by persuading any country that decides to develop nuclear weapons that it is not in their interest to do so.

Bibliography

Howlett, D.A., *Euratom and Nuclear Safeguards*, Palgram Macmillan (1990).

Joy, D.R., *An Introduction to the Nuclear Fuel Cycle and Nuclear Safeguards*, JAI Corporation (1999).

Knief, R.A., *Nuclear Engineering. Theory and Technology of Commercial Nuclear Power*, 2nd ed., American Nuclear Society (1992).

Nuclear Safeguards Analysis: Nondestructive and Analytical Chemical Techniques, ACS Symposium Series Vol. 79, ACS Publications (1978).

Nuclear Safeguards, Security, and Nonproliferation, J.E. Doyle, Ed., Elsevier (2008).

Tsoulfanidis, N., and Landsberger, S., *Measurement and Detection of Radiation*, 3rd ed., CRC Press (2010).

References

1. International Atomic Energy Agency Web page, www.iaea.org (2011).

2. "Treaty on the Non-Proliferation of Nuclear Weapons," IAEA/INFCIRC/ 140, International Atomic Energy Agency (1970).

3. "Safeguards Glossary," ed. 2001, International Atomic Energy Agency (2002).

4. Drobysz, S., and Sitt, B., "Optimizing the IAEA Safeguards," Centre d'Etudes de Securite Internationale et de Maitrise des Armaments (CESIM) (2011); www.cesim.org.

5. Spiewak, I., and Barkenbush, J.N., "Nuclear Proliferation and Nuclear Power: A Review of the NASAP and INFEC Studies," *Nucl. Safety*, **21**, 6, 691 (1980).

6. Shultis, J.K., and Faw, R.E., *Fundamentals of Nuclear Science and Engineering*, 2nd ed., Table 6.2, CRC Press, Taylor-Francis (2008).

7. Slaughter, D., et al., "Detection of SNM in Cargo Containers Using Neutron Interrogation," UCRL-ID-155315, Lawrence Livermore National Laboratory (Aug. 2003).

8. Jones, J.L., et al., "Photonuclear-Based Nuclear Material Detection System for Cargo Containers," *Nucl. Instrum. Methods Phys. Res. B*, **241**, 1–4, 7706 (Dec. 2005).

9. "Proliferation Resistance Fundamentals for Future Nuclear Energy Systems," STR-332, International Atomic Energy Agency (Dec. 2002).

10. Safeguards Special Issue, *Nucl. Technol.*, **179** (Sep. 2012).

TWELVE

ENVIRONMENTAL EFFECTS FROM THE GENERATION OF ELECTRICITY

12.1 Introduction

If one looks back through the history of the human race, it becomes obvious that man has improved life on this planet by engaging in activities that changed his environment to some degree. Examples of such activities are the use of fire, the development of agriculture, the construction of buildings, the mining of materials, the construction of canals and dams, and the operation of factories. Whereas it is generally accepted that no human endeavor occurs without some effect or some risk to the environment, it is also clear that, on the whole, man has improved his lot by engaging in these activities and creating, as a result of them, the industrialized technological society in which we live today. In general, use of energy (total, not just electricity) in the world keeps increasing (Figs. 12.1 and 12.2) because it is energy use in its various forms that improves the standard of living.

Until the 1960s, mankind did not give much thought to environmental effects. Perhaps the reason for such an attitude was the apparent continuous, until that time, improvement of the standard of living, and the not so apparent continuous deterioration of the environment, as judged primarily by the quality of air and water.

In the 1960s, the environmental movement started and raised society's concerns about the changes caused in our biosphere by human activities. It became clear that business as usual could not and should not continue. In many cases, certain activities had to stop, and did stop. For example, certain dams were not built; use of some pesticides (e.g., DDT) is prohibited. In other cases, standards had to be established to protect the quality of air and water and, by implication, to protect people; every industry had to comply with those new procedures and standards. To ensure that the necessary changes would be implemented by industry, by state and federal institutions, and by

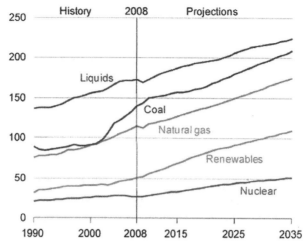

FIGURE 12.1 World energy consumption by fuel (energy unit is quads, 1 quad = 10^{15} BTU). (Data from U.S. Energy Information Administration, www.eia.gov.)

individuals, the U.S. Congress passed the National Environmental Policy Act (NEPA, 1969), the Clean Air and Water Act (1970 and 1972), and also created the Environmental Protection Agency (1970).

The goal of NEPA is expressed very well in its preamble:

> To declare national policy which will encourage productive and enjoyable harmony between man and his environment; to promote efforts which will prevent or eliminate damage to the environment and biosphere and

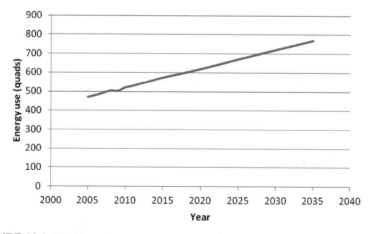

FIGURE 12.2 World total energy consumption. (Data from U.S. Energy Information Administration, www.eia.gov.)

stimulate the health and welfare of man; to enrich the understanding of the ecological systems and natural resources important to the Nation. . . .

NEPA contains three main sections:

1. Declaration of national environmental policies and goals

2. Establishment of action-forcing provisions for federal agencies to enforce those policies and goals

3. Establishment of a Council on Environmental Quality (CEQ) in the Executive Office of the President.

In practical terms, NEPA makes its presence known in the form of its requirement that an environmental impact statement (EIS) be prepared for any project that will be constructed. The EIS constitutes a very detailed assessment of the environmental effects of any project. Federal agencies are not excluded from NEPA's EIS requirement. For example, if DOE is going to build a repository for the disposal of nuclear waste, it must prepare and provide to the licensing agency (NRC) an EIS. Any electric utility that decides to build an electricity generation plant, of any type, must also prepare an EIS.

The Clean Air and Water Act was passed by Congress in two parts in 1970 (air) and 1972 (water); many amendments followed. The full text, with amendments as of 2008, can be found in 42 CFR 85. The objective was, and still is, to enhance the public health and welfare by keeping the nation's air and water clean. Research and development activities were established to achieve prevention and control of pollution. Provisions were made for assistance to state and local governments to help them with prevention and control of pollution.

The Environmental Protection Agency (EPA) was created in 1970 with the objective of consolidating in one agency essentially all activities of the federal government related to environmental protection (standards setting and enforcement, research, monitoring, set of consequences for noncompliance). There is no doubt that the creation of the EPA had a positive effect for the environment. The EPA is the enforcing agency for both NEPA and the Clean Air and Water Act.

The generation of electricity is indispensable to our daily lives. There is no doubt that the use of electricity has benefited man and improved life tremendously. From lighting to heat, from communications to music, from industrial tools to medical instruments, electricity permeates every aspect and every second of our lives—and is making those lives better. But, like any other human activity, the generation of electricity produces some undesirable effects. The abandonment of electricity in order to avoid the detrimental environmental effects resulting from its production is not a viable alternative. Everybody, either directly involved in this enterprise or indirectly reaping the benefits of it, should be concerned about possible detrimental environmental results. Our society, like an individual, should not accept any harmful activity that does not lead to a benefit believed to be worth more than its harm. Once a decision is made to proceed with the production of a product or a service, the process chosen should be the most environmentally benign, other factors being equal.

This chapter discusses the environmental effects caused by the various methods of producing electricity. In every case, the effects for the total cycle of the process are considered. For example, the effects from an oil-fired plant include not only those from the direct burning of the oil, but also the effects of pumping the oil from the ground. The effects from the manufacturing of materials used in the generation of electricity (metals, concrete, etc.) are also taken into account. By presenting the effects from all methods used for the generation of electricity, the reader will be able to put all of the risks into the proper perspective.

Discussion of the various methods of generating electricity and their corresponding environmental effects will make it clear that no method is 100% environmentally benign. For this reason, the electrical needs of a country (or of the world) should be satisfied by choosing methods of electricity generation that are environmentally acceptable (despite their detrimental effects) but also satisfy two other very important factors. One is economics, the other is assurance of fuel supply (which is related to a country's energy independence). Because these two factors play a role in the decision-making process of every country when choosing a means of electricity generation, they are mentioned for cases to which they apply.

What follows is a detailed presentation of the effects on the environment caused by the generation of electricity, both direct and indirect (or external; see Section 12.3) from all the methods used in this endeavor. Because this book is about nuclear energy, particular attention is paid to the environmental effects that accrue from the use of fission reactors.

12.2 The Various Types of Electricity Generating Systems and Their Environmental Effects

The following systems are currently used for the generation of electricity:

1. Coal-fired plant

2. Natural gas–fired plant

3. Oil-fired plants

4. Nuclear plants

5. Hydroelectric plants

6. Geothermal plants

7. Solar plants

8. Windmills

9. Solid waste–fueled plants

10. Other (biomass, tidal, ocean waves, ocean thermal, etc.).

We can divide the list into renewables and nonrenewables. The term *renewable* means that the fuel is renewable. In this sense, renewables are considered to be hydro, solar, wind, biomass,[a] tidal, and ocean waves; the others are considered to be nonrenewables. As the following discussion will show, using renewables does not mean that there are no environmental effects.

12.3 External Costs of Energy Production

The "obvious" or "direct" costs of energy production include land acquisition, plant construction, cost of fuel, operation and management costs, cost of regulation, taxes, and insurance costs. In addition to these costs, however, it has been recognized recently that energy production includes some "hidden" or "external" costs that must be taken into account when the total lifetime cost of an energy system is evaluated (see the Bibliography entry "External Costs of Energy"). External costs are not passed on to the customers; that is, they are not included in the energy price (until now anyway). Examples of external costs include effects of air emissions, water use and water discharges during operation of the plant, land use, depletion of natural resources, disposal of the wastes generated, and public subsidies.[1] Also, both direct and indirect costs have an effect on people. Direct effects are employment opportunities, injury and death of workers and members of the public, and sickness caused by breathing or being exposed to pollutants. Indirect effects include alteration of the landscape in the vicinity of the location where the fuel is extracted and in the vicinity of the plant, and delayed health effects to people (e.g., lung disease from breathing pollutants or exposure to radiation, latent cancer from exposure to radiation).

12.4 Fossil-Fueled Plants

Fossil fuels are coal, oil, and natural gas. Fossil fuels are burned to heat water in a boiler to produce steam. The steam drives a turbine, which rotates the electrical generator, thus producing electricity, as shown in Fig. 12.3. The major environmental effects resulting from the use of fossil fuels are the release, during the burning process, of substances such as fly ash, CO_2, nitrogen oxides, sulfur dioxides, and traces of heavy metals (lead, mercury, arsenic, nickel, cadmium, and beryllium). Table 12.1 presents amounts of gas emissions from fossil fuels.[2]

[a] Biomass is questionable as renewable because fertilizer and water are needed for the growth of the plants.

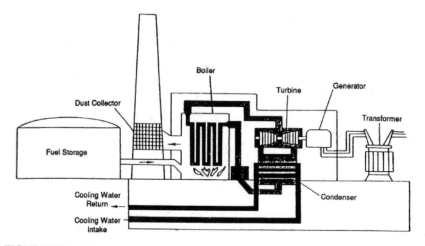

FIGURE 12.3 Schematic of a fossil-fueled power station. Fossil fuel—oil, coal, or natural gas—is burned in a boiler. Water circulating through the boiler absorbs the heat and changes to steam. The pressure of the steam against the turbine blades spins the shaft and turns the generator. Used steam cooled by the condenser is changed back into water and pumped back to the boiler. The cool water that condenses the steam is drawn from a river, lake, or the sea and is discharged back at a slightly higher temperature.

Coal contains uranium and thorium and their daughters in trace amounts (it also contains ^{40}K, another long-lived radioisotope). When coal is burned, the concentration of these metals increases by as much as a factor of 10 (Ref. 3). In 2010 the United States consumed 955.6×10^6 t of coal (data from www.eia.gov). Using the average uranium and thorium concentrations in coal of 1.3 and 3.2 ppm, respectively, this means that the use of coal released to the environment 1243 t of uranium and 3058 t of thorium. People living next to a coal-fired plant receive a measurable dose of radiation. Immediate potential health hazards, because of this exposure, are negligible; far more serious hazards result from emissions in the atmosphere. However,

TABLE 12.1
Amount of Gases Emitted by Fossil-Fueled Power Plants

Pollutant	Hard Coal	Brown Coal	Oil	Nat. Gas
CO_2 (g/GJ)	94,660	101,000	77,400	56,100
SO_2 (g/GJ)	765	1,361	1,350	0.68
NO_x (g/GJ)	292	183	195	93.3
CO (g/GJ)	89.1	89.1	15.7	14.5
Particulates (g/GJ)	1,203	3,254	16	0.1

From Ref. 2.

because of the very long half lives involved, the amount of uranium and thorium in coal fly ash does not disappear; it accumulates and it may cause adverse ecological effects in the future. Uranium from fly ash may seep into the soil and water, thus affecting food and water. The dose from uranium and thorium in fly ash is estimated at a few millirems per year (definitely less than 10 mrem/yr; compare this to ~300 mrem/yr from the background radiation).

As a result of the emissions from fossil fuels, particularly coal and oil, two major problems have been created. One is the greenhouse effect and the other, acid rain. Persons directly involved with the extraction of the fuel from the ground are also affected. Finally, adverse effects result from the production of the materials used for the extraction, transportation, and storage of the fuel, as well as for the construction of the plant itself. Extensive tables giving numerical estimates of the effects have been presented by many authors, among then Inhaber.[4] Table 12.2, taken from Ref. 4, is reproduced here to provide an idea of the value of the numbers involved.

12.4.1 The Greenhouse Effect and Climate Change

The term *greenhouse effect* is used to describe the potential change of the earth's temperature as a result of changes in the composition of the atmosphere. The atmosphere is a gaseous sheet of finite thickness surrounding the planet. When sunlight reaches the atmosphere, some of it is reflected back to space but most of it reaches the earth's surface and makes it warmer. The heated earth's surface reradiates part of the heat upward as infrared radiation; some of this radiation escapes but most of it is absorbed by the "greenhouse" gases, primarily CO_2, CH_4, and water vapor, and is directed back to earth, keeping it warm.[5-11] Other greenhouse gases, with minor effect, are nitrogen oxides (NO_x) and two chlorofluorocarbons ($CFCl_3$ and CF_2Cl_2). It is estimated that CO_2 is responsible for about half of the greenhouse effect.[12] The chlorofluorocarbons are responsible for depletion of the ozone layer.

A basic radiation heat balance is expressed as follows. Let

R = radius of the earth

A = albedo of the earth (reflection probability)

S = solar radiation flux (W/m^2)

σ = Stefan-Boltzmann constant = 5.67×10^{-8} W/m^2K^4

T = temperature of the earth (K).

One can write the energy balance:

$$\begin{pmatrix} Solar\ energy\ reaching \\ the\ earth \end{pmatrix} = \begin{pmatrix} energy\ radiated \\ back\ to\ space \end{pmatrix}$$

$$\pi R^2 (1 - A)S = 4\pi R^2 \sigma T^4 \tag{12.1}$$

TABLE 12.2

Risks Resulting from the Operation of a Coal-Fired Power Plant*

Risks	Gathering and Handling Fuel	Transportation	Electricity Production	Total
Occupational:				
Accident				
Death	$(0.7 \text{ to } 1.5) \times 10^{-3}$	$(1.6 \text{ to } 5.0) \times 10^{-3}$	$(1.3 \text{ to } 9.0) \times 10^{-5}$	$(2.5 \text{ to } 6.7) \times 10^{-3}$
Injury	0.04 to 0.07	$(1.3 \text{ to } 4.8) \times 10^{-2}$	$(1.6 \text{ to } 8.5) \times 10^{-3}$	0.056 to 0.083
Man-days lost	8 to 16	10 to 32	0.16 to 0.97	20 to 51
Disease				
Death	$(0 \text{ to } 7.5) \times 10^{-4}$	—	—	$(0.75) \times 10^{-4}$
Disability	$(4.2 \text{ to } 8.4) \times 10^{-3}$	—	—	$(4.2 \text{ to } 8.4) \times 10^{-3}$
Man-days lost	0.2 to 5.0	—	—	0.2 to 5.0
Public:				
Accidental				
Death	—	$(0.8 \text{ to } 1.9) \times 10^{-3}$	—	$(0.8 \text{ to } 1.9) \times 10^{-3}$
Injury	—	1.6×10^{-3}	—	1.6×10^{-3}
Man-days lost	—	5 to 11.6	—	5 to 11.6
Disease				
Death	$(1.4 \text{ to } 14) \times 10^{-3}$	—	0.016 to 0.047	0.017 to 0.061
Disability	—	—	94 to 280	94 to 280
Man-days lost	8.4 to 84	—	580 to 1750	590 to 1830

*From Ref. 4; per MWe-year; 70% capacity factor assumed.

If one assumes that $A = 0.3$ and $S = 1367$ W/m^2, then $T = 256$ K. Since the mean measured temperature of the earth is ~288 K, this increase of 33 K is attributed to a greenhouse effect operating during a few hundred thousands of years and keeping the temperature of our planet at the comfortable average value of 288 K = 15°C = 59°F. By contrast, Venus is surrounded by too much CO_2 and its temperature is 450°C = 840°F, and Mars has too little CO_2 and a surface temperature of -63°C = -82°F.

Until about 200 years ago, when the Industrial Revolution started, the planet and life on it thrived under this thermal equilibrium. After that, machines started replacing human labor (steam engines, trains, cars, planes, industrial machinery) and their exhausts introduced considerable amounts of gases into the atmosphere. Table 12.3 shows the increase in concentration for three greenhouse gases during the past 200 years (Ref. 11). Figure 12.4 was produced by the National Oceanic and Atmospheric Administration Mauna Loa Observatory, Hawaii,[11,13] and shows the increase of CO_2 in the atmosphere since 1960. Seasonal variations (the dips and spikes in the figure) are the result of CO_2 in the Northern Hemisphere being removed from the atmosphere during the growing season and then released during the autumn and winter. Analyses of air trapped in ice cores in Antarctica indicate that there was little, if any, change in carbon dioxide for many centuries before the 19th century and the Industrial Revolution. More than one-quarter of the previously mentioned increase in CO_2 in the atmosphere has occurred in the past 10 years.

A segment of the scientific community has been aware of the CO_2 problem for many years. The chemist Arrhenius had recognized the potential seriousness of the problem early in the last century. His calculations, in 1896, and predictions of the increase in the average of the earth's temperature due to this effect, although a bit higher, are surprisingly in agreement with today's estimates. Intensified scientific activity has been stimulated by the precise measurements of Keeling,[14] a scientist at Scripps Institution of Oceanography. A rise in the earth's temperature, a phenomenon also called *global warming*, may lead to climate change. Global observations and measurements show some undesirable trends: global and ocean temperature increases, polar ice melting, and rising sea levels. Do these trends provide proof that the greenhouse effect or global warming is already here or are

TABLE 12.3
Increase of Greenhouse Gases Concentration, 1800–2000

Gas	1800	1900	2000
CO_2 (ppm)	260	280	375
CH_4 (ppb)	750	800	1750
NO_x (ppb)	270	280	315

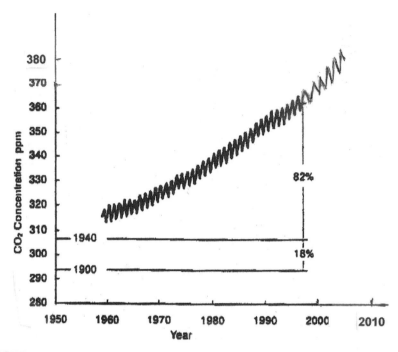

FIGURE 12.4 Atmospheric CO_2 concentrations since 1950 at Mauna Loa, Hawaii. (Data combined from Refs. 11 and 13.)

they seasonal variations? Although a large majority of the scientific community believes that global warming has already started and is due, primarily, to human activities, there is always some uncertainty. Leaving the uncertainty aside, one can make the following argument against air pollution of any sort and in favor of actions that will reduce the emissions of any pollutants in the atmosphere.

The earth's atmosphere is finite in volume and mass. If the activities of the human race continue to add to it quantities of CO_2, CH_4, NO_x, etc., eventually the composition of the atmosphere will change and the present "thermal equilibrium" will be disturbed. As a result, the earth's heat balance may change. Which way? Will the new temperature be higher or lower? Will that mean climate change? Climatologists point out that a temperature change will almost certainly cause global changes in rain patterns, winds, and ocean currents. Few believe that any such changes will be beneficial to mankind or to the biological space. More than that, once the trend becomes real, it will not be possible to reverse it quickly; it will take time and a substantial global effort to return to the previous state. Therefore, the prudent approach is to reduce the pollutants that go into the atmosphere by (1) curtailing the activities that generate the pollutants and (2) replacing the

TABLE 12.4
Amount of CO_2, per Capita, in Several Countries

Country	Amount (t/person-yr)	Country	Amount (t/person-yr)
Australia	10.75	Japan	9.7
Belgium	10.0	North Korea	2.6
Brazil	1.8	South Korea	10.1
Canada	17.4	Mexico	4.1
China	4.6	Qatar	58.0
Egypt	2.2	Russia	11.2
France	5.8	South Africa	7.3
Germany	9.7	Sweden	5.1
Greece	8.7	Switzerland	5.6
Haiti	0.2	Turkey	3.4
India	1.2	United Kingdom	8.6
Italy	7.4	United States	19.1

From International Energy Agency, www.iea.org, 2007.

polluting industrial activities with others that are environmentally benign. All nations contribute, to various degrees, to CO_2 emissions as Table 12.4 clearly shows. (Table 12.4 does not list all countries, but provides a representative sample of underdeveloped, under development, and developed countries.)

Fortunately the world, especially the developed countries, have recognized the potential problem, and organized activities are under way to increase substantially the contribution of the so-called "green technologies" for energy production, thus reducing the use of polluting fuels. Of course, such transformation (from today's fuels to "green" ones) cannot happen overnight. This gradual transformation of the energy portfolio has been recognized by international conferences held on climate change. The first such conference was held in 1992, in Rio de Janeiro, Brazil; the second, resulted in the *Kyoto protocol*. The Kyoto protocol was the result of a meeting in Japan in 1995; it became effective in 2005 and it was scheduled to expire at the end of 2012. But, in November 2011, in another conference held in Durban, South Africa, a decision was made to continue the Kyoto protocol. International agreements are not easy to create, but these conferences show that the world is moving, albeit slowly, in the right direction.

12.4.2 Acid Rain

Acid rain is the term[15] used to describe the transformation of sulfur dioxide (SO_2) and nitrogen oxides (NO_x) in the atmosphere into sulfuric (H_2SO_4) and nitric (HNO_3) acids, respectively. In addition to the acid, nitrogen oxides contribute to the production of ozone. These sulfuric and nitric oxides are emitted during the combustion of fossil fuels, primarily coal and oil. They can be carried very far by the wind and rise very high in the atmosphere, and they are also relatively easily dissolved in water.

The sulfuric and nitric acids formed by the sulfur and nitrogen oxides fall back on the earth with precipitation (rain and snow) at considerable distances away from their source. Thus, this form of pollution affects not only the population close to the location where the fuels are burned, but also may affect people farther away. Acid rain crosses state as well as national boundaries.

The acids falling on the earth, either on the ground or on trees or in water, cause deleterious effects. Acid rain may change the acidity (the pH) of water, resulting in harmful effects for aquatic life. Acid rain falling on trees may cause loss of leaves and damage to bark and may impede tree growth. (The effects on trees have been clearly observed in many parts of the world, most notably in Eastern Europe.) Acid rain going into the soil may disrupt soil nutrients; it also causes respiratory problems. Finally, in a different domain, acid rain definitely produces corrosion in buildings (thus ruining architectural wonders), steel bridges, railroad tracks, metal pipes above and below ground, and planes and automobiles.

In view of these detrimental effects, governments (especially in the developed world) have taken steps to curtail emission of sulfur and nitrogen oxides by requiring electric utility companies to use scrubbers that trap the pollutants at the source before they reach the atmosphere. In cars, catalytic converters reduce emissions. In addition, as already mentioned in the previous section, serious efforts are being made by countries throughout the world to replace fossil fuels with alternatives that are, essentially, environmentally benign (green/renewable).

All of the developed countries in the world have passed legislation to reduce acid rain. The U.S. government set up specific emission standards in the Clean Air Act (the full text of the act can be found in 42 CFR 85). As a result of this legislation, the effect of acid rain in the United States is almost nonexistent. Regions of the country in the industrial Midwest and Northeast that were showing the devastating effects of acid rain in aquatic and plant life during the early 1970s are thriving today.

12.5 Hydroelectric Power Plants

A hydroelectric power plant generates electricity by utilizing the potential energy of water falling down over a certain height (or depth), and that energy is used to turn a turbogenerator to produce electricity. The available power depends on the difference in height between the source of the water and the location of the turbine and on the volume of the water. The source of the water is usually river water collected behind a dam, which allows the water to descend down a tunnel to the turbine.

A variation of this process is *pumped storage*. In this method, water is pumped from a lower elevation to a higher elevation reservoir during times of off-peak electric demand. During periods of high demand, the stored water is allowed to flow downward and run the turbine to generate electricity. Despite the cost of pumping the water, pumped storage is a net revenue producer for the company running the plant, because electricity sold at peak demand brings in more revenues than the off-peak electricity cost used to pump the water.

At first glance, hydroelectric power looks very attractive. It is renewable, generates no emissions during operation, has low operational costs, and is relatively inexpensive. The reservoir of water behind the dam offers a recreational value (swimming, fishing, and boating), and provides an excellent habitat for fish and water fowl. Water reservoirs may also be used for flood control.

Despite these benefits, hydroelectric power is not viewed as completely benign anymore. Three environmental/ecological effects make it unattractive, especially in developed countries like the United States: (1) ecological changes in the locality where the dam is built, (2) effects from the production of the large amount of materials needed for the construction of the dam (concrete, steel, etc.), and (3) effects resulting from "catastrophic dam failures" that have occurred and still occur in various parts of the world. Table 12.5 presents a sample of dam failures.

With the construction of a dam, the local habitat is completely changed, from that of a river to that of a lake. A relatively large amount of acreage is flooded with the ensuing destruction of homes of preexisting wildlife and river fish. In addition, in some cases, the dam blocks the upstream and down-

TABLE 12.5
A Sample of Dam Failures and Resulting Fatalities

Year	Place	Fatalities
2010	Kyzyl-Agash, Kazakhstan	43
2009	Sayano-Shushenskaya, Russia	75
2009	Situ Gintung, Indonesia	99
2009	Algodoes, Brazil	7–10
2005	Shakidor, Pakistan	70
1979	Morvi, India	3,000
1977	Teton, USA	9–11
1975	Banqiao, China	26,000
1967	Koyna, India	180
1963	Vajont, Italy	~3,000
1961	Babi Yar, Ukraine	145
1960	Oros, Brazil	~1,000
1959	Frejus, France	421
1959	Vega de Tera, Spain	123–150

Source: Internet search for "world dam failures/wikipedia."

stream movement of fish, for example, salmon. For these reasons, construction of future dams in the United States, even small recreational ones, is highly unlikely.

About 7% of U.S. electricity was being produced by hydro in 2012. Because the amount of generating capacity is increasing, but no new hydropower is being added, this percentage will decrease continuously. According to the U.S. Energy Information Administration (www.eia.gov), the installed hydroelectric capacity in the United States in 2010 was 78,204 MW conventional and 20,538 MW pumped storage; the total hydro capacity amounts to ~9% of the U.S. total.

12.6 Geothermal Power Plants

Geothermal energy, from heat deep inside the earth, is found in many forms such as dry steam, hot water, and hot dry rock. This heat is emanating from the extremely hot core of our planet, where it is generated by radioactive decay. This energy source can be used with varying efficiency and economics to generate electricity, as well as for other applications such as space heating, industrial processes, and desalination. In 2010, the world geothermal installed electric capacity was 10,715 MW, of which 3,498 MW was in the United States (28 GW was used for nonelectricity applications). Electricity is generated by using the hot water pumped from the earth's interior to drive a turbogenerator. Apart from the source of heat, a geothermal power plant is constructed and operates like a fossil-fueled plant.

The use of geothermal heat amounts to a renewable, reliable, economic method to produce electricity; the method has limitations, however, because geothermal heat is not found everywhere. The development to its full potential depends on factors such as technology, depth of the geothermal field (the deeper it is, the more expensive it becomes), subsidies, cost of money, and energy prices. Geothermal heat is considered to be environmentally benign.[16] It definitely produces a smaller amount of greenhouse gases, per megawatt, than the other fossil fuels. However, it has its own adverse environmental effects.

The hot fluid pumped from the earth's depths carries gases such as CO_2, CH_4, H_2S, and NH_3 that contribute to the greenhouse effect and also produce noxious odors if released into the air. In addition to these gases, the pumped fluid sometimes contains toxic substances such as mercury, arsenic, boron, and antimony, which can cause environmental problems if released.

Certainly on a local level, geothermal power is not benign. There is noise and air pollution from the effluents already mentioned (H_2S is especially nasty; it smells like rotten eggs). Pollution of surface or groundwater may result from the release of liquid effluents. Finally, there is the problem of possible land subsidence—the withdrawal of fluids may cause the ground to subside and form huge cracks and craters (sink holes) on the surface.

In the United States, the total geothermal installed in 2010 was 3,498 MW, which amounts to ~0.3% of the total U.S. capacity.

12.7 Solar Power Plants

Solar energy (sunlight) can potentially heat and cool buildings as well as generate electricity. Solar heating and cooling of buildings has reached the commercial stage and is economical in many areas of the world. In the United States, these areas are predominantly located in the southwestern part of the country. The rest of this section will be limited to a discussion of electricity generation using sunlight.

Using sunlight as the source (fuel) of energy, electricity may be produced by one of the following two methods: photovoltaics (PV) or concentrated heat (CH). Using PV, electricity is produced by direct conversion of the sunlight into electricity using the photoelectric effect. The preferred base material is silicon (Si). Using CH, the sunlight is concentrated using lenses and mirrors; the heat thus collected is used to produce steam that drives a turbogenerator. Both systems have advantages and disadvantages.

The use of solar energy to produce electricity continues to increase. At present, the cost of solar electricity is higher than that of the predominant methods that use fossil fuels or uranium, but the cost is coming down consistently. Governments offer subsidies to make solar financially attractive. In the United States, both federal and state governments offer tax and other incentives in support of solar power. The reasons for this support are (1) solar power belongs to the class of renewables (fuel guaranteed) and (2) there are no harmful emissions. The "no harmful emissions" statement does not mean that the use of solar power has no adverse environmental effects. Here are the two major ones:

1. Adverse ecological effects may be caused by the very large areas that need to be covered by solar collectors. It has been estimated that a 1000-MWe plant would require from 16 to 20 square miles of land, about one-third the area of the District of Columbia.

2. Adverse effects may result from the production of the needed materials. For example, solar collectors need large amounts of silicon; production of silicon is a very energy-intensive (electricity) process and waste products from the production of solar collectors may yield adverse effects.

Since there is no sunlight at night, to provide solar electricity without interruptions, a method must be found to store the electricity produced when the sun shines and use it when it does not (the same holds true for wind power; see next section). Many methods have been proposed for energy storage including batteries and molten salts; cost is the main criterion for the method finally selected.[17]

In the United States, the total solar power installed in 2010 was 987 MW, which amounts to ~0.09% of the total capacity.

12.8 Wind Power Plants (Wind Farms)

Wind power is based on conversion of the kinetic energy of wind into some useful form of energy such as mechanical (windmills, sailing ships, pumping of water) or electrical. It is the generation of electricity by wind that will be discussed further in this section. Modern wind machines that generate electricity consist of a tower at the top of which are blades that rotate with wind action. The wind acts in a way similar to the action of air on the wings of an airplane (the blades have an aerodynamic structure similar to that of airplane wings), but instead of creating a lift, the wind speed rotates the blades. The blades are placed on top of a tower for two reasons: The first is to allow free flow of the wind through the blades and the second is because the wind speed increases with height. Towers have a height of 60 to 100 m; they are made of steel and are placed on a platform made of concrete. The blades must be made of durable, noncorrosive material and must be immune to lightning. Several types of materials have been used for their construction, but the preferred ones are composites that make the blades durable yet not too heavy. The blade span may be up to 100 m in diameter. The blades are connected to a shaft that drives a turbogenerator that generates electricity.

The power that is generated and the factors on which it depends are estimated as follows (see Ref. 18 for derivations or the Bibliography). The kinetic energy of a given mass of air increases with the square of the wind speed; the mass flow rate increases linearly with speed; hence, the energy rate (power) available depends on wind speed to the third power. The mass flow rate itself is proportional to the density of air and to the area swept by the air stream, which is defined by the span of the blades. The operation of this "engine" depends on a lower and upper limit of wind speed. At speeds of 4 m/s or less, the machine is on standby; as soon as the speed passes that limit, the blades start rotating and electricity is produced. If the wind speed exceeds ~25 m/s, the aerodynamic stresses become so high that the current turbines are designed to automatically shut down to avoid damage. Betz[18] was the first to calculate that the maximum efficiency of a wind engine (efficiency defined as the ratio of utilized wind energy divided by the incident wind energy) is 59.3%.

The output of a wind turbine is not constant, because wind speed is not constant and the output depends so strongly on that speed. As a result, the capacity factor of a wind turbine is at best ~35%, a relatively low number compared to that for nuclear or fossil plants (>80%). What this means is that a wind turbine with a rated (design) power of 10 MW will produce energy, on average, as if its power was ~3 MW.

The power of a single wind turbine may be up to 10 MW. It is standard practice to locate many turbines in one location, forming a wind power plant called a "wind farm." A large wind farm may consist of hundreds of individual wind turbines; all the turbines are connected to the electric grid. Wind farms located offshore are attractive because of higher wind speeds, relative to land, and reduced objections in terms of the aesthetics of the landscape.

Wind power has zero emissions during operation and it is definitely renewable. However, wind farms produce certain environmental/ecological effects:

1. Noise "pollution"; noise can be controlled, but not eliminated.

2. Wildlife impact; a considerable number of birds are killed by the rotating blades.

3. Aesthetic/visual impact; since wind turbines are placed on high ground, they can be seen from a long distance, thus producing an undesirable aesthetic effect.

4. The manufacturing of the turbines and construction of the concrete platforms, on which the turbine tower is placed, generate emissions. The footprint of these emissions, per megawatt, is considerable (see Section 12.11).

Deaths occur as a result of wind turbine operation. Causes of death include being struck by blades that blow away or fall from a wind tower or struck by ice missiles (ice forms on the blades and is hurled at tremendous speed when operation starts). Fire is also a hazard because once a fire starts on a wind tower, there is little firefighters can do to extinguish it. For the United States, about 41 worker deaths and 16 deaths of members of the public were reported for 2008.[19] The number of deaths per megawatt-electric is greater from wind turbines than from nuclear plants.

In the United States, the total wind power installed in 2010 was 39,516 MW, which amounts to ~3.5% of the total U.S. capacity.

12.9 Less Developed Electric Power Plants

Other less developed electric power sources include ocean tides and ocean waves, wood, biomass (municipal and other waste, agricultural by-products), batteries, and hydrogen fuel cells. Of these, only tidal and wave power will be discussed further because the others do not represent new technologies; they just use the materials listed as a fuel in fossil-type power plants.

Tidal power or *tidal energy* is the term used to describe the conversion of the energy of the ocean's tides into useful electrical energy. The ocean's tides—the back-and-forth motion of the seawater—are the result of the periodic variation in gravitational forces between the earth and the moon, primarily, and the sun, secondarily. Three general methods are used to harness tidal energy[20]:

1. *Tidal stream generator:* The kinetic energy of the water in the tides is used directly to turn a turbogenerator. (In a sense, this technology is similar to that of a wind turbine).

2. *Tidal barrage:* A "barrage" is essentially a dam built across the full width of an estuary. Use is made of the potential energy of the water due to the height difference between high and low tides; hence, the tidal barrage is like having a hydroelectric plant placed on the water.

3. *Dynamic tidal power:* This is a new, untested method. Theoretically, this method would utilize the interaction between potential and kinetic energy of the water in tidal flows. Dynamic tidal power would require the construction of a very long dam (30 to 50 km), straight out from the coast to the sea, with a perpendicular barrier at the end, thus forming a large T. Oscillating tidal currents favorable for this method are found along the coasts of the United Kingdom, Korea, and China.

Tidal power plants have the potential to produce large amounts of electricity, but they have some severe limitations:

1. They are expensive compared to the established methods of generating electricity.

2. They provide low power per individual generator. Because of the relatively low water head, individual generators are limited to 25 to 50 MW; therefore, many units would be needed to produce significant amounts of electricity.

3. They involve local dependence. Few coastal regions offer the right tides (i.e., difference between high and low tides).

4. They have a low capacity factor. Because of ebb and flow, the capacity factor of such plants is less than ~40%.

5. They have environmental/ecological detrimental effects, locally.

Wave power captures the energy of the waves and converts it into electricity. One way to achieve this conversion is to use the rise and fall of the waves to compress air, which is subsequently used to drive a turbine. Unfortunately, suitable waves cannot be found in every coast. Wave power may be exploited along the coast of Scotland, Canada (north), Africa (south), Australia, and the United States (northeastern).

Advantages of tidal and wave power are that they are renewable and have zero emissions. As of 2012 there were no such plants operating in the United States. The first tidal plant started operating in France at La Range in 1966 with a capacity of 240 MW. In North America, there is only one such plant operating; it is the Annapolis Royal Generating Station at the inlet of the Bay of Fundy, Canada; its capacity is 20 MW. In 2011, the South Korean Sihwa Lake Tidal Power Plant started operating with a capacity of 254 MW. There are some other plants with power of less than 10 MW, and many more are under construction or under development in many parts of the world, notably in Scotland and China.

12.10 Nuclear Power Plants and Their Environmental Effects

Generation of electricity by nuclear fission reactors started in the 1950s. As of 2012 there were 441 nuclear plants operating in the world (104 in the United States) and 66 under construction (2 in the United States) (see also Chapter 1). These plants provide about 6% of the world's energy needs (about 14% of its electricity; 19% in the United States). During almost 60 years of operation, nuclear fission has proven to be a highly stable, entirely predictable, and well-understood complex engineering process. The performance of nuclear power plants is continuously improving as shown by the ever increasing capacity factor, which is now ~90%, and by the fact, in the United States at least, that all the plants that applied to the NRC for life extension received it. Approval of life extension shows confidence on the part of the regulatory agency that a plant that has operated in a safe manner during its initial lifetime design will continue to do so for additional years (typical life extension is 10 to 20 years).

Despite the generally proven successful operation of nuclear power plants, there seems to be a public perception that nuclear power poses a great threat to the environment. But, in fact, it is quite possible that, had circumstances permitted the discovery of nuclear fission prior to the extensive use of coal and oil to produce electricity, most of our electrical needs would now be satisfied with nuclear power. The use of power plants fueled with coal and oil might have been prohibited since they would not have been able to satisfy stringent air quality standards to match the standards demanded of nuclear plants. Probably the biggest advantage of using a nuclear power plant for the generation of electricity is the lack of emissions of greenhouse gases.[b] Table 12.6 shows the amounts of the three main greenhouse gases not released in the atmosphere due to the operation of the 104 nuclear plants in the United States. All of this mass of gases, shown in Table 12.6, would have been released in the air if fossil-fueled plants, instead of nuclear plants, had generated the electricity.

The environmental/detrimental effects from the construction and operation of nuclear power plants fall into the following categories:

---

[b] A relatively small amount of greenhouse gases is emitted at various stages of the nuclear fuel cycle; no greenhouse gases are emitted during the operation of a nuclear power plant.

TABLE 12.6

Greenhouse Gas Emissions Avoided as a Result of the
Use of Nuclear Power, 2000–2010 (Millions of Tons)

Year	SO_2	NO_x	CO_2
2000	3.27	1.40	677.20
2001	3.10	1.30	664.00
2002	3.07	1.26	694.80
2003	3.05	1.13	679.80
2004	3.12	1.02	696.60
2005	3.02	0.96	681.92
2006	2.84	0.90	681.18
2007	2.76	0.89	692.71
2008	2.41	0.83	688.72
2009	1.99	0.51	647.22
2010	1.45	0.51	642.09
TOTAL	29.90	10.70	7,446.24

From Nuclear Energy Institute, www.nei.org.

1. Effects associated with materials used for the construction of the plant (concrete, steel, etc.)

2. Effects associated with the nuclear fuel (from mining of uranium to disposal of radioactive wastes)

3. Radiation exposure to workers and the public during normal operation of the plant

4. Potential radiation exposure during an accident that may result in the release of radioactive fission products to the environment.

The first concern is no different for nuclear plants than it is for any other type of plant. In fact, on a per-megawatt-electric basis, nuclear is not the most material-intensive construction (see next section). The second concern is specific to nuclear because the fuel, especially used nuclear fuel (UNF), does not disappear after being burned and is radioactive. All available evidence indicates that the effect of the nuclear fuel cycle on the environment (whether air, water, vegetation, or people) is less than that from many other activities including the use of coal and oil (see next section). The third concern arises because some radioactive releases take place during the normal operation of nuclear power plants. The best way to estimate the effect of these releases is to compare them with those from other sources. Such a comparison is presented in Fig. 12.5. Table 12.7 summarizes all of the risks from a nuclear power plant.

The fourth concern is the most controversial one because it involves the probability of a reactor accident. The probability of a reactor accident that may release radioactive products to the environment has been the subject of

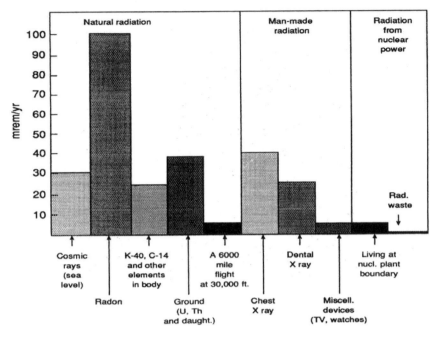

FIGURE 12.5 Average radiation dose to the population from natural and man-made sources. (From G. Greenhalgh, *The Necessity for Nuclear Power*, Graham and Trotman, Ltd., London, 1980.)

many studies. Two major studies instigated by the NRC are WASH-1400, known as the Rasmussen report,[21] and NUREG-1150.[22] The best estimate for core damage is about 10^{-5} to 10^{-6} per reactor year (for GEN-IV reactors this probability is estimated to be 10^{-6} to 10^{-7}). According to NUREG-1150 results:

- Average probability of an individual early fatality per reactor-year:
  - Typical PWR: 2×10^{-8}
  - Typical BWR: 5×10^{-11}
  - NRC safety goal: 5×10^{-7}

- Average probability of an individual latent cancer death per reactor-year:
  - Typical PWR: 2×10^{-9}
  - Typical BWR: 4×10^{-10}
  - NRC safety goal: 2×10^{-6}

TABLE 12.7

Risks Resulting from the Operation of a Nuclear Power Plant*

Risks	Gathering and Handling Fuel	Emissions (Sulfur Oxides)	Transportation	Electricity Production	Waste Management	Total
Occupational:						
Accidental						
Death	$(1.2 \text{ to } 5.7) \times 10^{-4}$		$(2.7 \text{ to } 12) \times 10^{-6}$	$(13 \text{ to } 17) \times 10^{-6}$	5×10^{-6}	$(3.0 \text{ to } 7.6) \times 10^{-4}$
Injury	$(3.4 \text{ to } 16) \times 10^{-3}$		$(6.0 \text{ to } 20) \times 10^{-5}$	1.7×10^{-3}	2.7×10^{-4}	$(16 \text{ to } 29) \times 10^{-3}$
Man-days lost	0.9 to 4.2		$(1.9 \text{ to } 8.2) \times 10^{-2}$	0.16 to 0.19	0.04	2.5 to 6.0
Disease						
Death	$(2.2 \text{ to } 60) \times 10^{-5}$		$(0.3 \text{ to } 40) \times 10^{-7}$	13×10^{-5}	7.4×10^{-5}	$(2.4 \text{ to } 8.1) \times 10^{-4}$
Disability	$(1.1 \text{ to } 1.6) \times 10^{-5}$		$(0.6 \text{ to } 80) \times 10^{-7}$	$(6 \text{ to } 22) \times 10^{-5}$	1.5×10^{-4}	$(2.2 \text{ to } 3.9) \times 10^{-4}$
Man-days lost	0.1 to 3.6		$(0.2 \text{ to } 25) \times 10^{-3}$	0.8	0.46	1.6 to 4.9
Public:						
Accidental						
Death	—		1.2×10^{-5}	—	—	1.2×10^{-5}
Injury	—		1.1×10^{-4}	—	—	1.1×10^{-4}
Man-days lost	—		0.08	—	—	0.08
Disease						
Death	31×10^{-6}	$(3.6 \text{ to } 10) \times 10^{-6}$	13×10^{-7}	$(3 \text{ to } 23) \times 10^{-5}$	$(0.5 \text{ to } 25) \times 10^{-5}$	$(7.0 \text{ to } 52) \times 10^{-5}$
Disability		0.020 to 0.063	44×10^{-8}	$(7 \text{ to } 260) \times 10^{-7}$	2.5×10^{-4}	0.020 to 0.063
Man-days lost	0.19	0.13 to 0.41	7.8×10^{-3}	0.18 to 1.4	0.03 to 1.5	0.5 to 3.5

*From Ref. 21. Risk per MWe-year, with a 70% capacity factor.

Consider the 104 nuclear plants operating in the United States and assume that all of them are PWRs; also assume a 60-year life per plant. The total probability of adverse events over a 60-year plant life are

Probability of an early fatality: $2 \times 10^{-8} * 104 * 60$

$$= 1.25 \times 10^{-4} \ (\sim 0.01\%)$$

Probability of a latent cancer death: $2 \times 10^{-9} * 104 * 60$

$$= 1.25 \times 10^{-5} \ (\sim 0.001\%)$$

These numbers mean very little standing alone, but they obtain significance if they are compared to the frequency of other accidents, some of them accepted routinely (Figs. 12.6 and 12.7). Comparison of the frequency of accidents from the use of various fuels is also shown in Fig. 12.8. Notice how much smaller the frequency of nuclear accidents is relative to the other methods of generating electricity. The NRC conducted a study on the consequences of reactor accidents and the draft report[23] came out in January 2012.

The safety record of the nuclear industry during the past 55 years is outstanding. Just three accidents have happened. Measuring the importance of an accident on the basis of persons injured or killed and on the effects to the environment, here is a brief accounting of these events.

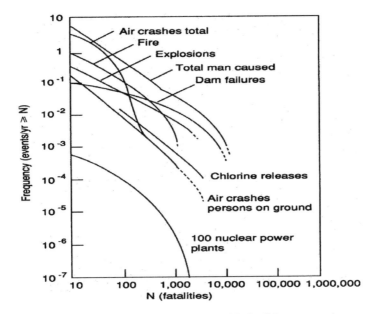

FIGURE 12.6 Frequency of man-caused events with fatalities greater than a number N (Ref. 21).

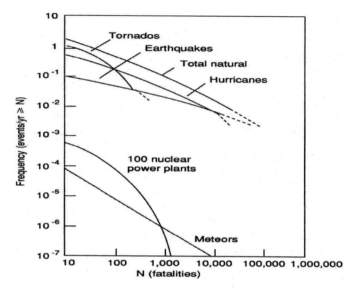

FIGURE 12.7 Frequency of natural events with fatalities greater than N compared to estimated fatalities from the operation of 100 nuclear power plants (Ref. 21).

The first one was the Three Mile Island accident in the United States in 1979. As a result of that mishap, a reactor was destroyed. No person in or out of the plant was injured or exposed to ionizing radiation that might have caused any health effects; no land was contaminated.

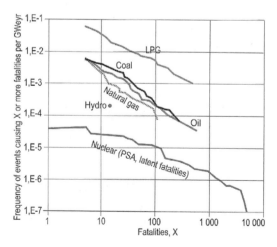

FIGURE 12.8 Frequency of accidents and consequences from the use various fuels for the generation of electricity. Data is for OECD countries for 1969–2000 (Ref. 24).

The second accident was that at Chernobyl in the Ukraine in 1986. First, it must be stated that a reactor of that type would never have been licensed in the West and today no such reactor operates anywhere in the world. The immediate death toll from the accident was 33 persons, mostly firefighters; there was radiation exposure to people not only in the area surrounding the plant, but also in other countries. Based on the *linear non-threshold hypothesis*, on which radiation protection standards are based, some cancers will develop from that exposure, but the number will be difficult to determine since the exposure was not much higher than the background radiation. Land was contaminated around the plant and a whole village was evacuated; reports as of 2012 say that life, in terms of plants, animals, and birds, is slowly returning to normal.

The third event occurred in March 2011 at Fukushima Daiichi, Japan. (What happened at Fukushima was not really a "nuclear accident"; a natural phenomenon, an earthquake, initiated a series of events, including a tsunami, that resulted in plant structural and reactor core damage.)

There are six reactors at the Fukushima site; all six are BWRs designed in the early 1970s. At the time of the earthquake, two reactors were shut down. When the earthquake struck, the operating reactors shut down immediately, as per design. Emergency power from diesel generators started to circulate the water and keep the cores cool. However, about an hour later, an unprecedented tsunami hit the site. The force of this water swept away the generators and their fuel supply, and cooling of the cores stopped. Because heat continued to be generated from the fission products in the core (see Chapter 9), some core meltdown has occurred. In addition, hydrogen explosions resulted from the generation of hydrogen from a zirconium–water reaction. Radioactive material was released and contamination of the land around the site exposed people to radiation. Two workers were killed, being swept away by the tsunami. (The tsunami also killed ~20,000 people, an event completely unrelated to the nuclear reactors.) As in Chernobyl, some cancers may develop as a result of exposure to radiation. However, similar to Chernobyl, it will be difficult to quantify cancers occurring as a result of exposure to radiation from this event. The accident at Fukushima is still being analyzed.

These three events do not contradict the accident probabilities given earlier in this section.

12.11 Comparison of the Various Energy Systems

Comparison of the various energy systems used for the generation of electricity and their environmental effects is very difficult and no matter who does the study and what the results are, a certain degree of controversy will always materialize. The reasons for the difficulty and the controversy are as follows, but note that this list is not all inclusive:

1. A comparison must be based on a life cycle assessment (LCA) of each plant; that is, it must consider all of the effects from the total plant life.

2. The LCA must include all activities related to a plant (fuel acquisition, transportation, and use; operation of the plant; decommissioning).

3. The LCA must account for all materials involved in construction and operation of a plant.

4. Both direct and indirect (external) effects must be included (see also Sections 8.6 and 12.3). Direct effects are those to workers and people at the locality (emissions to air and water, land occupation, thermal releases, odors, noise). External effects include diseases caused by the materials used and the emissions of the plant, as well as ecological effects of the emissions far away from the plants and far into the future.

5. How close will the final numbers of the comparison represent the total cost? It is not easy or feasible, sometimes, to quantify monetarily all of the effects mentioned above.

To summarize, comparison of the various energy systems must address their impact to occupational health, public health, and global effects (immediate and future ones).

Despite these difficulties, studies have been made and should be made because they offer information for the overall cost of a technology, albeit they may never be complete. In Chapter 8, Fig. 8.5 shows production costs for the major methods of generating electricity. Table 12.8 presents greenhouse gas emissions for various systems used in the generation of electricity; these data come from European plants, but with respect to these emissions, plants anywhere in the world are about the same. Finally, Tables 12.9, 12.10, and 12.11 present various data for fossil and nuclear plants.

Regarding costs, the most recent relevant study is one by OECD/IEA/NEA.[27] The study considered plants that will be commissioned by 2015 and obtained costs based on a levelized average lifetime cost, using the discounted cash flow method. The study reached two important conclusions:

1. For cases of low discount rate (cost of money 5%), "more capital-intensive, low-carbon technologies such as nuclear energy are the most competitive solution compared with coal-fired plants without carbon capture[c] and natural gas-fired combined cycle plants for baseload generation." However, a very low coal price may make coal plants competitive with or without carbon capture.

[c] The term *carbon capture* or *carbon capture and sequestration* is an attempt to capture CO_2 at its source (power plant stack) and thus prevent it from being released to the atmosphere. The captured CO_2 will be stored; concepts for storage are still under development.

TABLE 12.8

Direct and Indirect Greenhouse Gas Emissions for Various
Electricity Generation Systems

System	Direct (t CO_2 eq./GWh)	Indirect (t CO_2 eq./GWh)
Lignite, with FGD, high	1320	50
with FGD, low	1020	30
Coal, with FGD, high	1010	10
with FGD, low	70	50
with CCS	180	20
Oil, low NO_x	700	80
combined cycle	600	50
Natural gas, CC, high	380	80
low	350	50
with SCR	380	120
with CCS	180	40
Photovoltaic, high		100
low		10
Hydro, high		90
low		1
Biomass, high		40
low		10
Wind, offshore, high		15
offshore, low		2
onshore, high		10
onshore, low		2
Nuclear, high		40

From Ref. 25.
Key: FGD, flue gas desulfurization; CC, combined cycle; CCS, combined capture and storage;
SCR, selective catalytic reduction.

2. For high discount rates (10%), "coal without carbon capture, followed by coal with carbon capture equipment, and gas-fired combined cycle turbines are the cheapest sources of electricity." Results of the study are summarized in Table 12.12. Note the differences for the three regions shown and also the large uncertainties in the cost.

12.12 Summary and Conclusions

As of 2012, the major methods of generating electricity are by burning coal, natural gas, or uranium or by using hydro power. Wind power has started to make an impact and solar is just starting to appear in the charts (Table 12.13). Similar data for the world are not too different.

The effluents of the various types of fuels used to generate electricity have been considered; the data presented in the previous sections indicate the following:

TABLE 12.9

Estimated Annual Occupational Health Consequences Resulting from Fuel Used by 1000-MWe Power Plants Operating at a 75% Capacity Factor*

	Coal				Oil		Nuclear		
	Accidental Deaths	Accidental Injuries[a]	Pneumoconiosis Deaths[b]	Pneumoconiosis Cases[b]	Accidental Deaths	Accidental Injuries[a]	Accidental Deaths	Accidental Injuries[a]	Cancer (cases/deaths)
HSC Report	1.05	—[c]	~7	—	0.23	—	0.075	—	—
Norwegian	2.13	125	—	—	0.17	4.7	0.05 to 0.2	1.0 to 10.0	—
Swedish	1.6	394 (4 to 20) 219 (21 to 56) 73 (56 or more)	2.0	44	0.22	26	0.051	16.2	0.06 to 0.09[d]
Inhaber (REV-1 & REV-3)	0.53 to 1.13	30 to 52.5 (93)	0 to 2.6	0.41 to 0.62	0.11 to 1.28	11.3 to 90 (55)	0.06 to 0.43	2.55 to 12 (50)	0.16 to 0.45
WASH 1224	0.98	40.5 (60)	—	0.6	0.11	10.5	0.095	5.1	—
Comar & Sagan[e]	0.4 to 1.03	24.6 to 52	0 to 3.5	0.6 to 48	0.1 to 1.21	10.5 to 83	0.053 to 0.4	2.4 to 11.5	0.015 to 0.43
Fagnani & Maccia	1.05	1039	—	0 to 1.6	0.08	11.4	0.12	27	0.07
Hamilton	0.75	52	0.02 to 0.46[f]	0.58 to 1.15[f]	—	—	0.36	15.3	0.11
Hamilton	0.64	33 (50)	0 to 7	20.5 to 27	1.12	74	0.25	10.6	0.14
US/NRC[g]	0.1 to 0.66	4 to 40							
Black & Niehaus	0.50 to 0.55	2300 days	0.07	—	0.29	1980 days	0.07[h]	143 days[h]	0.003 to 0.014
Ramsay[i]	0.33 to 0.99	66 to 132	3.3	—	0.07 to 0.23	—	0.07 to 0.23	13 to 23	0.07 to 0.13
Range	0.33 to 2.13	24.6 to 1039	0 to 7	0.41 to 48	0.1 to 1.28	4.7 to 90	0.05 to 0.43	1 to 27	0.015 to 0.45

*From Ref. 26.

[a]The average number of days lost per injury is given in parentheses. Swedish coal figures based on Western German data.

[b]Some U.S. figures refer to "miner's illnesses" or to "black lung disease." "Cases" sometimes exclude fatal cases of list projections rather than current experience.

[c]A blank in the table does not mean there is considered to be no risk, but either no attempt has been made to estimate the risk, or the estimates given in the reports cannot be broken down into the risks for each stage of the energy cycle.

[d]Includes subsequent genetic effects.

[e]Reference quotes studies with load factors mostly at or near 75%.

[f]Referred to as occupational "disease."

[g]Lower and upper limits are for open-cast and deep underground extraction. A 50% ma was assumed in calculating risks.

[h]Black and Niehaus's nuclear accidental deaths and injuries include reprocessing. Cancer figures for mining only.

[i]Includes occupational deaths and accidents at all stages of the fuel cycle. Coal extraction assumed to be 40 to 75% open-cast.

TABLE 12.10

Estimated Annual Deaths and Injuries Resulting from Transport of Fuel for 1000-MWe Power Plants Operating at a 75% Capacity Factor*

	Coal				Oil[a]		Nuclear			
	Deaths		Injuries[b]		Deaths	Injuries[b]	Deaths		Injuries[b]	
	Occupational	Public	Occupational	Public	Occupational	Occupational	Occupational	Public	Occupational	Public
HSC Report	0.15	—[c]	—	—	—	—	—	—	—	—
Revised UK estimate	0.03	0.20	—	—	—	—	—	—	—	—
Inhaber	1.2 to 3.75	0.6 to 1.43	9.75 to 36	12	0.03 to 0.11	1.2 to 9.75	0.002 to 0.009	0.009	0.045 to 0.15	0.083
(REV-1 & REV-3)			(93)	(93)		(55)			(50)	(70)
Norwegian	0.19	0.3	4	—	0.11	2.2	0	0.01	0.05 to 0.14	0.08
Swedish	0.8		236		0.34	17	0.002		0.045	0.08
WASH 1224	0.055	0.55	5.1	1.17	0.03	1.1	0.002	0.009	0.045	0.08
			(47)	(171)		(36)			(25)	(75)
Comar & Sagan[d]	0.055 to 0.4	0.55 to 1.3	0.33 to 23	—	0.03	1.1 to 9	0.002	0.009	0.045 to 0.14	—
Fagnani & Maccia	0.07		1.3		0.12	2.1	0.007		1.6	—
Hamilton		0.3 to 1.5	1.4 to 6.8		—	—	0.011	~0.001	0.11	~0.001
Hamilton		1 to 3	10 to 30		0.1	9	—	—	—	—
US/NRC[e]		1.9	—	21						
Black & Niehaus	0.26 to 0.29	0.43 to 1.04	533 to 660 days	458 to 555 days	0.051[f]	353 days[f]	0.0015	0.0023 to 0.0045	5.3 days	4.5 days
Range	0.055 to 3.75	0.3 to 1.9	0.33 to 236	1.17 to 21	0.03 to 0.34	1.1 to 17	0 to 0.011	0.001 to 0.01	0.045 to 1.6	0.001 to 0.08

*From Ref. 26. Wide variations due to national practices must be expected.

[a]None of the studies estimated risks to the public from transport of oil for power stations.

[b]The average number of days lost per injury is given in parentheses, if known.

[c]A blank in the table does not mean there is considered to be no risk, but that no attempt has been made to estimate it.

[d]Reference quotes studies with load factors mostly at or near 75%.

[e]Level-crossing accidents. U.S. conditions.

[f]Public oil deaths and accidents are quoted at approximately 1% of occupational levels.

TABLE 12.11

Estimated Annual Occupational Health Consequences Resulting from the Operation of 1000-MWe Power Plants Operating at a 75% Capacity Factor*

	Coal		Oil		Nuclear (including reprocessing)		
	Accidental Deaths	Accidental Injuries[a]	Accidental Deaths	Accidental Injuries[a]	Accidental Deaths	Accidental Injuries[a]	Cancer (cases/deaths)
HSC Report	0.15	—[b]	—	—	0.11	—	—
Inhaber (REV-1 & REV-3)	0.0098 to 0.068	1.2 to 6.4 (93)	0.0098 to 0.038	0.68 to 1.5 (55)	0.01 to 0.013	1.37 (50)	0.081
Norwegian	0.01	4	0.01	3.6	0.1 to 0.2	0.7 to 2.8	—
Swedish	0.05	4	0.03	4	0.03	11.1	
WASH-1224	0.03	1.2 (142)	0.037	1.5 (85)	0.012	1.42 (37)	0.14 to 0.21[c]
Comar & Sagan[d]	0.01 to 0.03	0.9 to 1.5	0.01 to 0.037	0.6 to 1.5	0.01	1.3	0.024
Fagnani & Maccia	0.017	2.9	0.017	4.3	0.013	4.9	0.09
Hamilton	0.12	3.8	—	—	0.015	1.3	0.08
Hamilton	0.01	1.2	0.01	1.2	0.01	1.3	—
Black & Niehaus[e]	0.012	160 days	0.0098	98 days	0.011	105 days	0.098 to 0.135
Range	0.01 to 0.15	0.9 to 6.4	0.01 to 0.038	0.6 to 4.3	0.01 to 0.2	0.7 to 11.1	0.024 to 0.21

*From Ref. 26.

[a]The average number of days lost per injury is given in parentheses, if known.

[b]A blank in the table does not mean there is considered to be no risk, but either no attempt has been made to estimate the risk, or the estimates given in the reports cannot be broken down into the risks for each stage of the energy cycle.

[c]Includes subsequent genetic effects.

[d]Reference quotes studies with load factors mostly at or near 75%.

[e]Nuclear effects exclude reprocessing. Cancer figures also include all subsequent genetic effects.

TABLE 12.12
Levelized Cost of Electricity for Nuclear, Coal, Gas, and Wind Power Plants

	Plant Type	5% Discount Rate Cost ($/MWh)	10% Discount Rate Cost ($/MWh)
North America	Nuclear	50	76
	Coal	73	90
	Gas	76–92	87–93
	Wind, onshore	50–100	70–140
Europe	Nuclear	50–80	82–138
	Coal	62–120	80–141
	Gas	80–120	86–122
	Wind, onshore	85–163	122–235
Asia Pacific	Nuclear	30–50	42–76
	Coal	55–88	68–108
	Gas	68–110	78–120
	Wind, onshore	80	115

From Ref. 27.

TABLE 12.13
Sources of Electricity Generation in the United States in 1988, 1998, and 2010

Source	1988 ($\times 10^9$ kWh)	1998 ($\times 10^9$ kWh)	2010 ($\times 10^9$ kWh)
Coal	1,538 (57%)	1,808 (56%)	1,545 (43%)
Nuclear	527 (20%)	674 (21%)	671 (19%)
Gas	253 (9%)	309 (10%)	850 (24%)
Hydro	223 (8%)	304 (10%)	217 (6%)
Oil	149 (6%)	110 (3%)	31 (0.4%)
Geothermal			13 (0.4%)
Wind			76 (2%)
Solar			1 (<1%)
Other	12 (<1%)	7 (~0.2%)	177 (5%)
TOTAL	2,702	3,212	3,581

From U.S. Energy Information Administration, www.eia.gov.

1. No method of generating electricity exists that is without risk or without any adverse environmental effects.

2. Fossil fuels release effluents that may cause global warming and acid rain.

3. Nuclear fission reactors used for the generation of electricity do not pose a greater threat, either to people or to the environment, than the other methods employed for the same activity. In fact, the existing data (Tables 12.9, 12.10, and 12.11) show that overall risks from nuclear power compare favorably with the other methods and fuels.

It is fitting to conclude this chapter with a quote from Dr. Sigvard Eklund, a former director of the International Atomic Energy Agency: "If there is a danger to mankind from nuclear energy it does not lie in the use of nuclear energy to generate electric power. It lies in the armaments and in the risk of proliferation; it could lie in the political tensions which may follow the failure to develop nuclear power and other resources as replacements to declining petroleum resources."

Bibliography

Boxwell, M., *Solar Electricity Handbook: A Simple Practical Guide to Solar Energy: Designing and Installing Photovoltaic Solar Electric Systems*, Greenstream Publishing (2011).

Dibble, Bradley J., *Comprehending the Climate Crisis: Everything You Need to Know About Global Warming and How to Stop It* (Oct. 21, 2011).

Environmental Effects of Electricity Generation, Organisation for Economic Co-operation and Development (1985).

Environmental Engineering, 4th ed., R. Weiner and R. Matthews, Eds., Butterworth-Heinemann (2003).

"External Costs of Energy (ExternE)," European Study, 1991–2005, www.externe.info.

Fremlin, J.H., *Power Production: What Are the Risks?* Oxford University Press (1987).

Gipe, P., *Wind Power: Renewable Energy for Home, Farm, and Business*, Chelsea Publishing Co. (2004).

Global Warming, M. Anderson, Ed., Britannica Educational Publishing (2011).

Greenhalgh, G., *The Necessity for Nuclear Power*, Graham and Trotman, Ltd., London (1980).

Hohmeyer, O., *Social Costs of Energy Consumption: External Effects of Electricity Generation in the Federal Republic of Germany*, Springer (1989).

Hore-Lacy, I., Tarlton, S., Praznik, B., and Damiens, R., *Nuclear Energy in the 21st Century: World Nuclear University Primer*, World Nuclear University Press (2010).

Inhaber, H., *Energy Risk Assessment*, Gordon & Breach (1982).

Mathez, E.A., *Climate Change: The Science of Global Warming and Our Energy Future*, Columbia University Press (2009).

Patel, M.R., *Wind and Solar Power Systems: Design, Analysis, and Operation*, 2nd ed., Taylor and Francis (2005).

Ramsay, W., *Unpaid Costs of Electrical Energy: Resources for the Future*, Johns Hopkins University Press (1979).

Sincero, A.P., and Sincero, G.A., *Environmental Engineering*, Prentice Hall (1996).

Wind Power in Power Systems, T. Ackerman, Ed., Wiley (2005).

Wind Power Plants: Fundamentals, Design, Construction and Operation, R. Gasch and J. Twele, Eds., Springer (2011).

References

1. Hohmeyer, O., *Social Costs of Energy Consumption: External Effects of Electricity Generation in the Federal Republic of Germany*, Springer (1989).

2. "Air Pollution from Electricity-Generating Large Combustion Plants," European Environmental Agency (2008).

3. Hvistendahl, M, "Coal Ash Is More Radioactive Than Nuclear Waste," *Sci. Am.* (Dec. 2007)

4. Inhaber, H., *Energy Risk Assessment*, Gordon & Breach (1982).

5. *EPRI J.* (July/Aug. 1978).

6. Liss, P.S., and Crane A.J., *Man-Made Carbon-Dioxide and Climatic Change: A Review of Scientific Problems*, Geo Books, Norwich, CT (1983).

7. *The Long-Term Impacts of Increasing Atmospheric Carbon Dioxide Levels*, G. MacDonald, Jr., Ed., Ballinger Publishing Co. (1982).

8. Wigley, T.M.L., "The Pre-Industrial Carbon Dioxide Level," *Climatic Change*, **5**, 315 (1983).

9. Rotty, R.M., "Data for Global CO_2 Production from Fossil Fuels and Cement," *Scope*, **16**, 124 (1981).

10. Hansen, J., et al., "Climate Impact of Increasing Atmospheric Carbon Dioxide," *Science*, **213**, 957 (1981).

11. *Global Warming*, M. Anderson, Ed., Britannica Educational Publishing (2011).

12. "Energy and the Greenhouse Effect: Background and Perspective," Science Concepts, Inc., for U.S. Council for Energy Awareness (1989).

13. Robinson, A.B., Baliumas, S.L., Soon, W., and Robinson Z.W., "Environmental Effects of Increased Atmospheric Carbon Dioxide," *Med. Sentinel*, No. 5, 171 (1998).

14. Gammon, R., Thorning, K., Keeling, D.C., and Moss, D., "Comparison of the Atmospheric CO_2 Measurement Program of GMCC/NOAA," Final Report, National Oceanic and Atmospheric Administration (May 1984).

15. *Acid Rain Information Book*, 2nd ed., D.V. Bubenick, Ed., Noyes Publications (1984).

16. Glassley, W.E., *Geothermal Energy: Renewable Energy and the Environment*, CRC Press (2010).

17. Oloyede, I.O., Forsberg, C.W., and Driscoll, M.J., "GW Electricity Storage Requirements for Nuclear and Renewable Power Production," *ANS Trans.*, **103**, 567 (2010).

18. Betz, A., *Introduction to the Theory of Flow Machines*, D.G. Randall, trans., Pergamon Press (1966).

19. Fatality data culled from an Internet search under "windpower fatalities." For more authoritative data see Gipe, P., *Wind Power: Renewable Energy for Home, Farm, and Business*, Chelsea Publishing Co. (2004).

20. Hulsbergen, K., Steijn, R., van Banning, G., and Klopman, G., "Dynamic Tidal Power: A New Approach to Exploit Tides," 2nd Int. Conf. on Ocean Energy, Brest, France, 2008.

21. "Reactor Safety Study: An Assessment of Accident Risks in U.S. Commercial Nuclear Power Plants," WASH-1400, U.S. Nuclear Regulatory Commission (1975).

22. NUREG-1150, "Severe Accident Risks: An Assessment of Accident Risks in U.S. Commercial Nuclear Power Plants," Vols. 1 and 2, U.S. Nuclear Regulatory Commission (June 1989).

23. NUREG-1935, "State-of-the-Art Reactor Consequence Analyses (SOARCA) Project," Draft, U.S. Nuclear Regulatory Commission (Jan. 2012).

24. "Risks and Benefits of Nuclear Energy," Organisation for Economic Co-operation and Development, Nuclear Energy Agency (2007).

25. "Nuclear Energy in Perspective: Nuclear Energy and Addressing Climate Change," Organisation for Economic Co-operation and Development, Nuclear Energy Agency (Dec. 2009).

26. Cohen, A.V., and Pritchard, D.K., "Comparative Risks of Electricity Production Systems: A Critical Review of Literature," Health and Safety Executive Research Paper 11, reported by S. Rippon, *Nucl. News*, p. 58 (Feb. 1981).

27. "Projected Costs of Generating Electricity," Organisation for Economic Co-operation and Development, Nuclear Energy Agency (2010).

INDEX

ABOUT THE AUTHOR

 **Dr. Nicholas Tsoulfanidis** received a bachelor's degree in physics from the University of Athens, Greece, and a master's and a doctorate degree in nuclear engineering from the University of Illinois. In 1968 he joined the faculty of the nuclear engineering program at the University of Missouri–Rolla, where he served as a faculty member until 2004. He was chairman of the Nuclear Engineering Department, interim vice chancellor for academic affairs (one year), and associate dean of the School of Mines and Metallurgy for Graduate Studies and Research for more than 10 years. From July 1, 2005, to July 31, 2007, he served as interim chair of the Chemical and Metallurgical Engineering Department at the University of Nevada–Reno (UNR). He is now an adjunct professor at UNR.

In addition to his teaching and administrative duties, Dr. Tsoulfanidis performed research in the area of radiation transport, radiation protection/health physics, and the nuclear fuel cycle. He has written numerous technical papers and is the primary author of the text *Measurement and Detection of Radiation*, 3rd edition (2011). He has received many awards, the most prominent being the Glenn Murphy Award (1995) given by the American Society for Engineering Education for "Outstanding Contributions in the Profession and Teaching of Nuclear Engineering."

Since June 1997, Dr. Tsoulfanidis has served as editor of *Nuclear Technology*, an international technical journal published by the American Nuclear Society. He is also a Fellow of the American Nuclear Society.